WITHDRAWN

CLIMATES OF THE PAST

An Introduction to Paleoclimatology

THE UNIVERSITY SERIES IN GEOLOGY

Edited by

RHODES W. FAIRBRIDGE

Professor of Geology, Columbia University

Additional titles will be listed and announced as published

Martin Schwarzbach
Professor of Geology, University of Cologne

Climates of
An Introduction to

the Past
Paleoclimatology

Translated and edited by
RICHARD O. MUIR

*Lecturer in Geology, Chelsea College
of Science and Technology, London*

D. VAN NOSTRAND COMPANY, LTD.
LONDON . PRINCETON, NEW JERSEY . NEW YORK . TORONTO

D. VAN NOSTRAND COMPANY, LTD.
358 Kensington High Street, London, W.14

D. VAN NOSTRAND COMPANY INC.
120 Alexander Street, Princeton, New Jersey
24 West 40 Street, New York 18, New York

D. VAN NOSTRAND COMPANY (Canada) LTD.
25 Hollinger Road, Toronto 16

Translated from the second completely revised and enlarged German edition
entitled *Das Klima der Vorzeit* and published by
Ferdinand Enke Verlag, Stuttgart

Printed in Great Britain by Hazell Watson & Viney Ltd, Aylesbury, Bucks

Dedicated to
MY MOTHER
and the memory of
MY FATHER

Preface

This book deals with the earth's climatic history over the last thousand million years. The translation follows closely the second German edition, in which the text had been completely revised and rewritten, most of the figures replaced by new ones, and their number increased from 70 to 134. Thus, the result is, virtually, a completely new book.

The alterations were due partly to my desire to present the large volume of material relevant to Paleoclimatology more clearly than before, and—partly to the enormous advances which have been made in the science in the past decade or so. During this period, there have appeared techniques for temperature determination using oxygen isotopes, and the application of paleomagnetism to paleoclimatology—both opening up undreamt-of vistas. Deep-sea research and C^{14} dating have been developed during this time to play a paramount role in the investigation of the climates of the past. It is still true, however, that we cannot put forward a completely satisfactory explanation of the development of paleoclimates, and though some of the new climatic hypotheses are indeed interesting, and though their number is still increasing, the emphasis in this book rests more on the facts (or more correctly, on what the geologist regards as such); in short, on climatic indicators.

I wish to compliment Dr. Richard O. Muir on his success in translating faithfully, but not pedantically, my original ideas concerning this exceedingly complex field of science. Dr. Muir, himself an able and thoughtful geologist, has enhanced the value of this first English edition by introducing some slight additions and amendments based on the findings of recent conferences and publications. The bibliography has been somewhat enlarged to include these recent papers, and its format has been altered to conform with standard American practise. The Russian translation of the first edition of this work was criticized for containing relatively little reference to new Russian discoveries. A determined effort has now been made to overcome this weakness, thanks in part to helpful personal contacts, though it must be admitted that formidable difficulties still remain. These stem partly from the linguistic barrier, and partly from the difficulty of obtaining the original publications.

Finally I would like to thank D. Van Nostrand Company (in particular, their Senior Editor, Mr. D. J. Carpenter) for their speed, efficiency and unfailing courtesy in producing this English language edition, and especially Prof. Rhodes W. Fairbridge, who suggested the translation and made valuable recommendations. I hope it will serve the needs for advanced students and researchers in America, Britain and the English-speaking world, who are faced by the ever-swelling mass of literature at home and the additional language problem abroad. The work is therefore dedicated to all whose researches may provide answers to some of the questions here raised.

MARTIN SCHWARZBACH

Cologne, 20 August, 1962

Contents

Part 1

GENERAL PALEOCLIMATOLOGY

I

Definition and Historical Development of Paleoclimatology

> Les cieux même ont varié, et toutes les choses de
> l'univers physique sont comme celles du monde moral,
> dans un mouvement continuel de variations successifes.
> BUFFON, Époques de la Nature, 1778

DEFINITION AND SIGNIFICANCE

Paleoclimatology, the study of climates of the past, is closely related to geology, to climatology, and to meteorology, and it touches upon many branches of the natural sciences.

The climatic evidence afforded by fossil plants, animals, and sediments is of particular importance for the reconstruction of paleoclimates; recently, however, physical methods have also been devised. It is worth pointing out that the basic data have mainly been derived from geology (together with paleobotany in particular), i.e. from an "inexact" natural science, while the often highly speculative attempts at explanation have come very largely from the "exact" sciences of astronomy, physics, geophysics, and meteorology. Neither of the two most consistent and most frequently quoted earlier descriptions of paleoclimates, namely the texts by Köppen-Wegener and by Brooks, was written by a geologist.

Paleoclimatology helps us to reconstruct the earth's surface features in times past (paleogeography) and throws light on the problem of polar wandering—for which a particularly close relationship with paleomagnetism has recently emerged. It also relates to the geology of economic deposits, and to the question of evolutionary development, and is fundamentally important in regard to cosmogenic hypotheses.

HISTORY

As early as the seventeenth century, it was suggested that the climate had been warmer at times than it is today. Around 1800, it was discovered that existing glaciers were formerly much more extensive and, soon after this, that there had been an Ice Age. In the latter half of the nineteenth century,

the multiple nature of the Quaternary Ice Age, and the existence of glaciations going back in time to the pre-Quaternary and, in fact, to the Precambrian Era were recognized.

The following are a few of the more important dates in the development
of paleoclimatology (many of them taken from Zittel's *History of Geology
and Paleontology*, 1901):

1686 The distinguished English physicist, ROBERT HOOKE, concluded from
the presence of fossil turtles and large ammonites at Portland Bill,
that the climate had once been warmer. He considered that this
climatic change was due to variations in the inclination of the earth's
axis.

1778 BUFFON (Paris) described the cooling of the earth in "Époques de la
Nature". At first, life could exist even at the poles. Remains of
elephants, rhinoceroses, etc., had been found in the northern parts of
Europe, Asia, and North America; later, these creatures withdrew
toward the equator.

1799 ALEXANDER VON HUMBOLDT thought that the once warmer climate
was the result of heat released by the crystallization of beds of rock.
(As a "Neptunist", he considered at that time that even granite and
other igneous rocks originated in water.) Later, in 1823, HUMBOLDT
also related climate to vulcanicity (see Chapter 24).

1802 JOHN PLAYFAIR considered that erratic blocks were transported by
glaciers. (Similar suggestions had already been made in the Swiss
Alps toward the close of the eighteenth century).

1817 Swiss Natural Science Society's competition on the greater extension
of the Alpine glaciers.

1822 Fundamental lecture by the Swiss engineer IGNATZ VENETZ on this
topic (published 1833). JENS ESMARK came to similar conclusions
about the Norwegian glaciers in 1824.

1823 W. BUCKLAND interpreted the Quaternary deposits as sediments of
the Flood and, for them, he coined the term "Diluvium".

1829 The controversy regarding theories of the Ice Age appeared for the
first time in literature in GOETHE's novel *Wilhelm Meisters Wander-
jahre* (Part 2, Chapter 10). This section was missing from the first
edition of 1821. (See R. Phillipson's study 1927.)

1830–33 CHARLES LYELL's *Principles of Geology* appeared (fig. 1). Here and
in later editions (12th edition 1875), there are numerous references
to the climate of the past (warmer climate of the Tertiary Period,
spreading of Mesozoic reef corals as far north as our latitudes, and of
coal-forming plants even into the polar region). LYELL considered that
the cause of climatic variation lay in the distribution of land, sea, and
ocean currents, etc.—a very modern concept. In a letter to Mantell,
he wrote, "I will give you a formula which will permit tree ferns to

flourish at the poles, or, when it pleases me, spruce at the equator". In maps, he showed how, by a different arrangement of the continents, a very warm or extremely cold climate can originate either at the equator, or in the polar area. LYELL explained erratic blocks as due to drifting ice floes. (The swan song of this "Drift Theory" was V.v. Scheffel's humorous ditty of the "erratischen Block", 1867—see quotation at the beginning of Chapter 5.)

FIG. 1. CHARLES LYELL (1797–1875)
Founder of the Principle of Uniformitarianism; he explained paleoclimates on the basis of varying paleogeography.

1832 Professor REINHARD BERNHARDI (School of Forestry, Dreissigacker near Meiningen) explained the erratics of North Germany by glacier transport.

1837 The German botanist K. F. SCHIMPER coined the term "Eiszeit" (Ice Age), in his ode to Galileo's birthday.
In the same year, F. A. QUENSTEDT gave his inaugural lecture on "Das Klima der Vorzeit", and the French physicist and mathematician POISSON assumed that the earth had at times moved through cold regions in space.

1840 L. AGASSIZ, Neuchâtel (Later "Harvard's most famous professor"), *Études sur les glaciers.*

1841 J. DE CHARPENTIER, *Essai sur les glaciers.*

1842 J. F. ADHÉMAR (Paris) cited variations in the earth's orbit as the cause of the Ice Age. (First discussion of this problem by JOHN HERSCHEL, 1830.)

1844 B. COTTA (Freiberg in Saxony) regarded the striation on porphyries near Leipzig as due to the action of glaciers. In fact, he remarked that he "froze" at the thought, as such ideas usually encountered harsh criticism in north Germany because of the great influence of L. v. BUCH. The latter considered that the erratic blocks were transported by mud flows "Rollsteinfluten" (1815), and, in 1850, called the glacial theory "a strange aberration of the human mind" (in a letter to Carl Naumann—see *Geologie*, 2, p. 114, 1853). SARTORIUS V. WALTERHAUSEN likewise spoke in 1846 of "the fairy tale of a so-called Ice Age".

1847 F. ROEMER (later of Breslau) investigated the Cretaceous rocks of Texas, and recognized Cretaceous climatic belts and a Cretaceous Gulf Stream.

1855–59 O. HEER (Zurich) *Flora tertiaria Helvetiae*, with numerous fundamental paleoclimatic conclusions (fig. 2).

1855 A. C. Ramsay (Quart. J. Geol. Soc.) considered (incorrectly) that the Permian sediments of England were glacial.

1856 W. T. Blanford discovered the Upper Paleozoic moraines in India, and thereby initiated the investigation of pre-Quaternary Ice Ages.

1863 Escher v.d. Linth & E. Desor regarded a diluvial "Sahara Sea" as the cause of glaciation in the Northern Hemisphere.

Fig. 2. Oswald Heer (1809–1883) Investigator of the Tertiary flora and its climatic significance. (Reproduced by kind permission of Geol. Inst. Zurich.)

Fig. 3. Albrecht Penck (1858–1945) Eminent worker on Alpine glaciology. (From Verh. III Internat. Quat. Congr., Vienna 1938.)

1866–83 O. Heer *Flora fossilis arctica*, the first thorough investigation of the polar flora, and its paleoclimatic significance.

1875 3rd November: Otto Torell (Stockholm) spoke to the Geological Society of Germany in Berlin on the glacial striae of Rüdersdorf near Berlin, and finally established the notion that the Scandinavian Ice extended as far as North Germany.

1875 James Croll *Climate and Time in their Geological Relations*—a major extension of Adhémar's hypothesis.

1901–09 A. Penck (fig. 3) & E. Brückner *Die Alpen im Eiszeitalter*; a milestone in the history of investigation of the Ice Age, occasioned by a competition held by the Breslau section of the Deutsch–Österreichischen Alpenvereins. The names Günz, Mindel, Riss, and Würm, Glaciations were put forward.

1906 A. Penck coined the term "tillite" for an old moraine.

1924 W. Köppen (fig. 4) and A. Wegener (fig. 5) "Die Klimate der Vorzeit";

foundation of the hypothesis of continental drift on a paleoclimatic basis; interpretation of Milankovitch's (1920) radiation curves.

1926 A. P. COLEMAN (Toronto) "Ice Ages, recent and ancient", a detailed summary of pre-Quaternary glaciations.

1926 C. E. P. BROOKS "Climate through the Ages" (2nd Edition, 1949). Important summary of the meteorological aspects of paleoclimatology.

FIG. 4. VLADIMIR KÖPPEN (1846–1940) AT THE AGE OF 78
Famous climatologist; collaborator and father-in-law of A. Wegener. (Photograph kindly placed at my disposal by Prof. Kuhlbrodt, Hamburg.)

FIG. 5. ALFRED WEGENER (1880–1930)
Celebrated for his research work in Greenland and founder of the theory of continental drift; produced with V. Köppen, "Die Klimate der Vorzeit". (From Meteorol. Zeitschr. 1931.)

1930 F. KERNER-MARILAUN (Vienna) "Paläoklimatologie". Original and cautious theoretical approach.

1950 HAROLD C. UREY effected the first temperature determinations using the O^{18}/O^{16} method.

The more recent developments in the investigation of the Quaternary Period have not been reviewed. In particular, there have been some outstanding synopses of the Quaternary Ice Age (Chapter 19), which still represents the most important starting point for all paleoclimatic studies. Its investigation has long been cultivated in particular scientific societies and journals. A "Geognostic Association" has existed in Lübeck for more than 100 years—as E. Boll records in his "Geognosie der deutschen Ostsee-

länder zwischen Eider und Oder", in 1846—which has attempted to establish
"the native country of our boulders or rolled stones", by geological investigations in the Baltic lands. The same work was continued on a wider scale
by the "Gesellschaft für Geschiebeforschung". Quaternary research workers
are at present combined to form the International Quaternary Association
(INQUA).

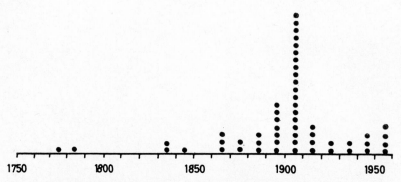

FIG. 6. TIME DISTRIBUTION OF THE MORE IMPORTANT GLACIAL THEORIES (AND
SEVERAL OTHER CLIMATIC HYPOTHESES)

Each dot represents a hypothesis. Notice the large number at the turn of the
century.

Throughout the history of paleoclimatology, there has never been a
proper balance between observation and hypothesis. E. BRÜCKNER aptly
remarked in 1890 that there are "probably few fields in which speculation
is so far in advance of established facts as it is in this". The ten years
around 1900 were endowed with an unusually high number of theories
about the Ice Age (fig. 6). None of them has hitherto provided a plausible
and valid explanation of climatic variation throughout the history of the
earth.

At the turn of the century, people were facing the problems of paleoclimates hopefully, but now we are again rather resigned to having to
concern ourselves with basic research. This may be more prosaic but is
more important than the erection of daring theories which, in words of
the most literal significance, "float in the clouds". In further investigations
of paleoclimates, we must try above all to find new climatic indicators, and
to investigate, more closely, areas and periods whose paleoclimatology is
hitherto known only superficially. Then the way will be paved for more
exact syntheses than we can put forward at present.

Further reading: ARLDT, 1922; ECKHARDT, 1921; WOIKOFF, 1895

2

The Present Climate, and Its Significance for Paleoclimatology

Here winter has so little significance, and Kew Gardens and Richmond Great Park are so studded with laurels and other evergreens, with so many birds singing and fluttering under them, that I am hardly aware that now, in Göttingen (almost in the same latitude), people are riding about in sleighs.

G. C. LICHTENBERG, in a letter from London to Prof. Baldinger, dated 10th January 1775.

GENERAL REMARKS

The present climate of the earth is dependent upon a number of factors, among which the following are of particular significance:

(a) Solar radiation,
(b) The astronomical situation of the earth (orbit, inclination of the axis etc.),
(c) The atmosphere,
(d) The topography of the earth's surface, and the distribution of land and sea.

On the other hand, the internal heat of the earth has very little effect.

In the course of the earth's history, these factors have altered, sometimes fundamentally. It is, therefore, important to know how each of them influences our present climate. Hence we shall consider some of the essential facts of present-day climatology.

Solar Radiation

2 cal./cm²./min. of solar radiation are received at the upper limit of the atmosphere. This value, the solar constant, has varied only by a very small amount in the last decade. Before that, we have no exact data.

Inclination of the earth's axis

The inclination of the axis (obliquity of the ecliptic), amounts at present to $23\frac{1}{2}°$. It is responsible for the different seasons, and for the temperature drop between the equator and the poles. Table 1 shows how these would vary with change of the axial inclination.

TABLE 1

INCLINATION OF THE EARTH'S AXIS AND CLIMATE

INCLINATION OF THE AXIS	SEASONS	TEMPERATURE DIFFERENCE BETWEEN POLE AND EQUATOR
0°	Absent	Very great
90°	Maximum difference between summer and winter	Minimum difference between pole and equator

Distribution of Land and Sea

The very unequal distribution of land and sea exerts a considerable influence on temperature conditions throughout the world.

Land masses intensify the extremes of climate (continental climate); thus in Asia and North America, the isotherms bend far to the south in winter (fig. 7), far to the north in July. In northern Asia, the extreme mean

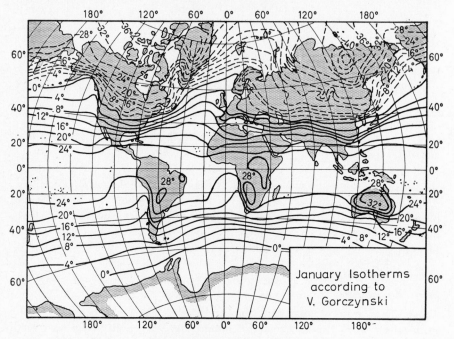

Fig. 7. Map of the January Isotherms (after V. Gorczynski, from Conrad, 1936)

monthly temperatures differ by more than 60° C (fig. 8). The greatest diurnal temperature variation also occurs in deserts in the hearts of continents (up to about 50° C). The highest and lowest recorded temperatures are:

Over 50° C (Death Valley, California).
Minus 71° C (Oimekon, northeast Siberia).
Minus 88° C (Russian station Vostok, Antarctica).

Temperature varies greatly in mountain areas. The mean temperature decreases by 0·5–0·6° C for every 100 m. increase in height.

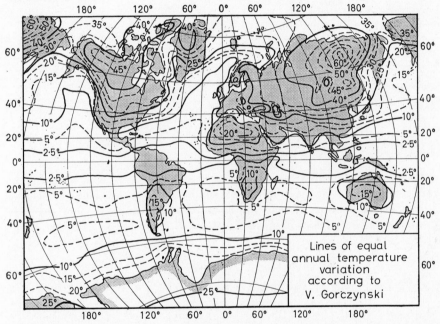

FIG. 8. MEAN ANNUAL RANGE OF TEMPERATURE (after V. Gorczynski, from Conrad, 1936)

Oceans, on the other hand, reduce temperature variation (maritime climate). The difference between summer and winter temperatures in equatorial oceans is only 2½° C. The variation remains less than 5° C over three-quarters of the surface of the oceans. Only in smaller enclosed seas, can the variation be considerable (up to 17° C in the Baltic, up to 27° C in the inner part of the Yellow Sea). The Persian Gulf and the Red Sea are the warmest marine areas. There the summer temperature reaches 36° C. Over 35% of the oceans' surface, the temperature never drops below 25° C. In the ocean deeps, on the other hand, the prevailing temperature remains exceedingly uniform between 0° C and 2° C (the land-locked seas are exceptional; e.g. the Mediterranean has a temperature of 13° C at depths of up to 4000 m.). Ocean currents also regulate temperatures in seas and adjacent continents (see p. 14).

The difference between maritime and continental climates becomes clear when one compares localities at the same latitude but at different distances from the ocean (Table 2).

TABLE 2

COMPARISON OF TEMPERATURES AT DIFFERENT
LOCALITIES IN EURASIA, AT LAT. 52°N (°C)

	VALENTIA (IRELAND)	MÜNSTER (GERMANY)	WARSAW	ORENBURG* (URAL)	IRKUTSK	NORTCHINSK
Longitude	10°W	8°E	21°E	55°E	105°E	117°E
January Temperature	7·3	1·3	−4·3	−15·3	−20·8	−33·6
July Temperature	15·1	17·3	18·7	21·6	18·4	18·2
Annual Variation	7·8	16·0	23·0	36·9	39·2	51·8

*(Chaklov)

Likewise, the mean temperatures at a given latitude, and their annual range, are quite different in the northern and southern hemispheres because of the preponderance of land in the northern hemisphere, and the high proportion of oceans in the southern (Table 3). The distribution of land and

TABLE 3

MEAN TEMPERATURE AT DIFFERENT LATITUDES (°C)
(AFTER MEINARDUS)

LATITUDE	JANUARY (JULY IN S)	JULY (JAN. IN S)	ANNUAL MEAN	ANNUAL VARIATION
60°N	−16·1	14·1	−1·1	30·2
30°N	14·5	27·3	20·4	12·8
0°	26·4	25·6	26·2	0·8
30°S	14·7	21·9	18·4	6·9
60°S	−10·3	1·2	−4·1	11·5

sea must therefore have a greater influence on temperature distribution than any astronomical factors, because the latter are almost identical in both hemispheres.

Wind

Pressure distribution—hence wind direction—is largely under "planetary" control (i.e. particularly dependent on the earth's rotation; fig. 9), but is also affected by the distribution of land and sea.

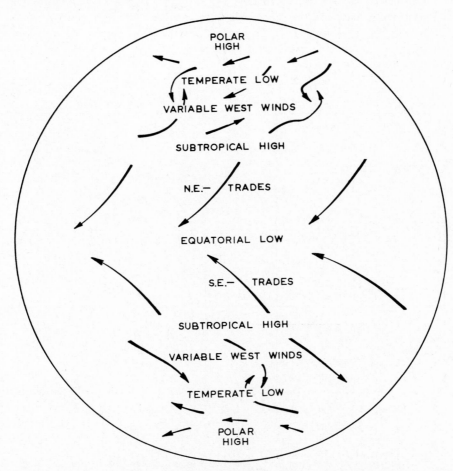

FIG. 9. DIAGRAM OF THE PRESSURE BELTS OF A HOMOGENEOUS GLOBE (after Kendrew, 1957)

In the *equatorial zone*, low pressures result from ascending air currents; the winds often fail (calms, doldrums, etc.). At greater altitude, poleward moving air deflected by the earth's rotation forms the antitrades.

In the *horse latitudes* (between 20° and 30°) descending air streams cause high-pressure areas (Azores High etc.). Winds blowing from here toward the equator produce the trade winds (N.E. in the northern hemisphere; S.E. in the southern).

In *temperate latitudes*, there is a fluctuation between eastward-drifting high- and low-pressure areas (anticyclones and depressions). This pressure variation causes frequent changes in the speed and direction of the wind, though westerlies prevail. Over the continents, stable low-pressure areas tend to form in summer, anticyclones in winter.

Monsoons are seasonally variable winds within the sphere of influence of continental land masses. They originate because the equatorial low-pressure belt moves poleward in summer. In India, for example, the summer monsoons are the rain-laden southwesterlies; the drier winter monsoons blow from the northeast (fig. 10).

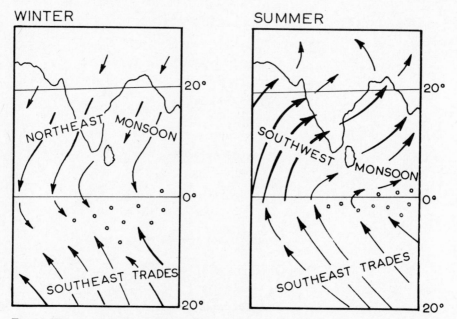

FIG. 10. WINTER AND SUMMER MONSOONS IN INDIA. oo = DOLDRUMS (From *Dierckes Atlas*)

Ocean Currents

The major wind systems give rise to ocean currents flowing in the same direction (fig. 11). Warm or cold currents are produced depending on whether the water flows from the equator or from the poles. Cold currents also develop where currents of polar water (which covers all of the ocean floor) rise from the depths.

The more important warm currents are the Gulf Stream in the North Atlantic, the Kuro-Schio in the North Pacific, the Brazil Current off the coast of that country, and the Agulhas Current off southeast Africa. The Gulf Stream is unusually warm because, thanks to the configuration of the coast line of Brazil, it is also fed by part of the South Equatorial Current.

The major cold currents are the Labrador Current off the east coast of

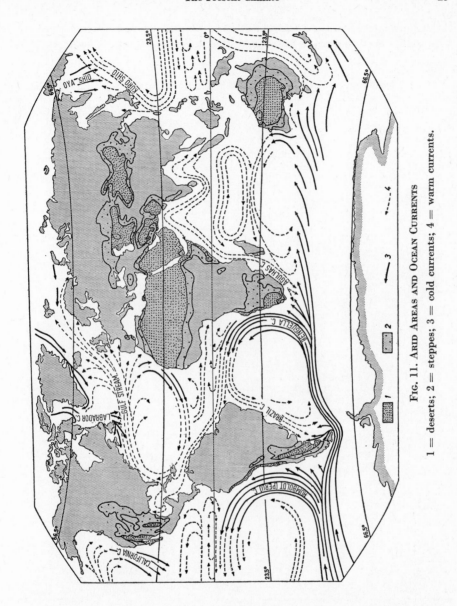

FIG. 11. ARID AREAS AND OCEAN CURRENTS

1 = deserts; 2 = steppes; 3 = cold currents; 4 = warm currents.

Canada, the Californian Current off the west coast of North America, the Humboldt (Peru) Current in the southeast Pacific, and the Benguela Current in the southeast Atlantic.

The influence of currents on temperature is often very considerable (fig. 12); this shows up most clearly along the course of the Gulf Stream. On the Norwegian coast, the January temperature is about 25° C warmer than it should be at that latitude.

In high latitudes, the eastern sectors of oceans, i.e. the western coasts of continents are favored; in lower latitudes the reverse is true (Table 4).

TABLE 4

INFLUENCE OF OCEAN CURRENTS ON ANNUAL MEAN
TEMPERATURE (°C)

LATITUDE	AMERICA WEST COAST	AMERICA EAST COAST	EURASIA WEST COAST
57°N	—	Nain, Labrador: −6·8	Aberdeen, Scotland: 8·2
41°N	—	New York 10·6	Naples: 16·5
22-23°S	Antofagasta: 17·2	Rio de Janeiro: 23·2	—

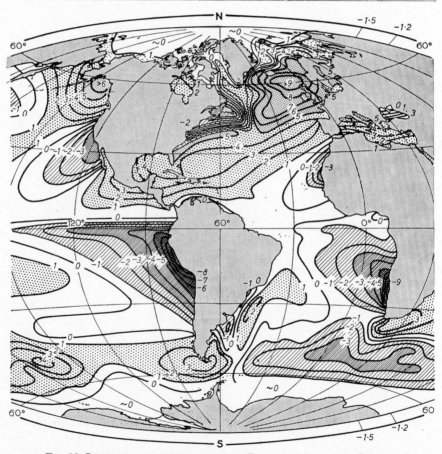

FIG. 12. INFLUENCE OF CURRENTS ON THE TEMPERATURE OF THE OCEANS

The differences shown are those between the surface temperature and the normal temperature of a water-covered globe (in °C). Unshaded = normal; dotted = above normal; shaded = below normal. (From G. Dietrich, 1957.)

Distribution of Rain and Snow

Rainfall distribution depends on a number of factors.

The planetary wind systems.—The equatorial zone with its ascending, and thus cooling, air masses has an abundant rainfall; the horse latitudes, with descending currents, are rain deficient, and the world's desert belts form there.

Distribution of land and sea.—Coasts with a prevailing onshore wind have a heavy rainfall, but the further one goes into the heart of the continent, the less becomes the precipitation, and so the greater becomes the proportion of deserts (fig. 11).

In the west-wind belt, the west coasts of the continents have most rain; where the trade winds blow, the east coasts are wetter. Those monsoon winds that blow from the sea bring rain, e.g. the summer monsoon in India; but when they blow from the continent, they are dry.

Ocean currents.—Ascending cold currents create aridity. For this reason deserts have formed on the west coasts of North Africa, South West Africa, Peru, and southern California.

Mountains.—In so far as they force the clouds to rise, and thereby create cooling and condensation, mountains function as rain traps; the windward sides receive abundant rainfall, the lee sides are rainfall deficient (Table 5).

TABLE 5
ANNUAL MEAN RAINFALL ON KAUAI ISLAND, HAWAII

Mount Waialeale	Windward (N.E. trades) 480 inches.
Waiawa	Lee (N.E. trades) 260 inches.

Combined Effects of Rainfall and Temperature

Weathering, plant growth etc., depend not so much on the absolute amount of rainfall as on the relationship between rainfall and temperature; temperature decides whether areas with a low rainfall are arid or humid (Table 6). Attempts have been made to represent this mutual relationship by means of a rain factor (R. Lang).

TABLE 6
IMPORTANCE OF TEMPERATURE IN DETERMINING EFFECT OF RAINFALL

LOCALITY	ANNUAL RAINFALL (inches)	ANNUAL MEAN TEMPERATURE	CLIMATIC TYPES
Suakin (Red Sea)	8·7	28°C	Desert
Jakobshavn, Greenland	8·7	−6°C	Continental glaciated

$$\text{Rain factor} = \frac{\text{annual rainfall in mm.}}{\text{mean annual temperature in }°C}.$$

This, however, does not take into account the fact that the seasonal distribution of rainfall also plays a major role.

Meridional and Zonal Circulation

At present, the general atmospheric circulation, particularly in the northern hemisphere, shows sometimes meridional, sometimes zonal tendencies. The West Wind Drift is favored by zonal circulation but weakened by meridional circulation. High-level cyclones of cold polar air extend far toward the equator, and are compensated by a drift of warm tropical air toward the poles (Comprehensive review by Flohn).

Further reading: ALISSOV, 1954; ALISSOV, DROSDOV & RUBINSTEIN, 1956; CONRAD, 1936; DIETRICH, 1957; FLEMING, 1957; GENTILLI, 1958; HANN & KNOCH, 1932; KENDREW, 1957; KÖPPEN, 1931; MILLER & STOMMEL, 1958; VISHER, 1924, 1945; LAMB, 1961.

3

The Reconstruction of Paleoclimates

To those men the marks were what cigarette ash was to
Sherlock Holmes in reconstructing a crime and finding
the criminal, the sureness of deduction rivaling that of
Holmes himself.

R. A. DALY, The Changing World of the Ice Age, 1934.

PALEOCLIMATOLOGY AND NEOCLIMATOLOGY

The aim of the paleoclimatologist is in many respects similar to that of
the climatologist studying modern climates. He would attempt to reconstruct the climatic picture of a definite epoch in the earth's history and, at
the same time, try to explain that picture in terms of the geography of the
time. One difference is that the paleoclimatologist must reckon, not only
with a variable geography, but also with the possibility that solar radiation
and other factors may have altered. The main dissimilarity, however, lies
in the methods employed. Thermometer and barometer do not exist for the
paleoclimatologist; he must acquire all his meteorological and climatic data
in an indirect, roundabout fashion. He has available three main sources of
information.

Climatic indicators, i.e. geological phenomena which are partly dependent
on climate (weathering, fossils, etc.). These may be compared with present-
day phenomena, and from modern climatic conditions those of the past may
be deduced.

Mathematical considerations.

Physical methods with the aid of oxygen isotopes, etc.

Of the above methods, mathematical techniques are the most uncertain;
they have virtually only theoretical and historical significance. Physical
methods include the most modern techniques, which may also, in theory,
be the most exact. However, there are considerable limits to their application. Climatic indicators have by far the greatest significance; hence much
more space is intentionally devoted to them.

Uncertainty of Climatic Indicators

There are many climatic indicators and imaginative geologists are always finding new ones. Unfortunately, however, most of them are extraordinarily indefinite. In this respect they resemble legal evidence, and F. Kerner-Marilaun once said with some justification of climatic evidence that, "There is no doubt that an examining magistrate would consider such a body of evidence quite insufficient to elucidate a very intricate case."

The causes of this uncertainty are as follows:

(*a*) Many fossils have been only very approximately evaluated, and many have been misinterpreted altogether. This applies in great measure to the leaves of plants, to which group, at least in the Tertiary and Quaternary Periods, the most common and most climatically comparable fossils belong. For example, the otherwise reliable O. Heer describes fossil palm leaves from Greenland, which in reality are groups of parallel-veined leaves of quite different origin. One is even an inorganic structure.

(*b*) Fossilization is selective, and the original floral or faunal assemblage may sometimes have been quite different. False conclusions are thereby drawn—e.g. in fallen trees the wood is overrepresented and thin leaves are less easily preserved than thick ones.

(*c*) Fossils (e.g. pollen) may be derived. Unless this is realized they indicate climatic conditions which in fact belong to an earlier Period.

(*d*) The climatic requirements of a plant or an animal may vary in the course of time. Extinct species may have been adapted to a climate quite different from that in which their modern counterparts live. The classic example is the Mammoth. Since it was, at first, regarded as a warmth-loving animal like the present-day elephant, warm climates were proposed for Siberia in "Mammoth times". Nowadays, by contrast, we regard Mammoth as an important indicator of a very cold climate.

(*e*) Completely different geological processes can result in the same rock type. An example of this is afforded by unbedded, unsorted boulder beds. These may represent moraines (i.e. may have been caused by glaciers), but they can also be scree deposits, slumped masses, or other rocks not dependent on climate. Many "glaciations" are based on such false "moraines".

(*f*) In the same way, different causes can produce the same effect in organisms. While a meagre coral fauna may be the result of too low a temperature, it can also be brought about by other nonclimatic factors, such as too low a salinity.

(*g*) Under certain conditions, a climatic indicator may only denote meteorological conditions over a short period of time. These need not necessarily correspond with mean conditions, i.e. with climate. This applies, for example, to many statements about wind direction. When trees are uprooted by a tornado, they may be preserved in this position throughout geological time and so the wind direction may be definitely established. It need not, however, correspond to the prevailing wind direction of the area.

CLASSIFICATION OF CLIMATIC EVIDENCE

In the following chapters, the arrangement of climatic evidence is based on what it shows (temperature, rainfall etc.), irrespective of its geological character, to provide a meteorological classification. It is also possible to draw up a geological classification on the following lines:

Biological evidence of climate.—1. Fossils having a close systematic relationship with modern species. Most common in the recent past, e.g. reindeer and musk ox in the Quaternary, palms in the Tertiary, pollen analysis.

2. Fossils having particular ecological or physiological peculiarities (e.g. size and coloring of organisms, drip-points on leaves, reef formation, annual rings).

Lithogenetic evidence of climate.—1. Weathering processes (laterite, silicification).

2. Mineralogy and petrology of sediments (limestone, salt deposits, moraines).

3. Particular sedimentation phenomena (bedding, ripple marks, distribution of loess).

Morphological evidence of climate.—Inselbergs, river terraces, corries, eskers, etc.

Further reading: ARLDT, 1922; COLBERT, 1953; CLOUD, 1959; DEEVEY, 1953; DUNBAR & ROGERS, 1957; JOLEAUD, 1939; KRUMBEIN & SLOSS, 1951; KUBIENA, 1953; LOUIS, 1960; MARKOV, 1960; NAIRN, 1961; PETTIJOHN, 1949; ROBINSON, 1949; RUCHIN, 1958; SHOKALSKAYA, 1953; TWENHOFEL, 1926; J. WALTHER, 1894.

4

Evidence
of
Hot Climates

It is unlikely that the bones of antediluvian beasts could
have been drifted into our northern latitudes from
tropic lands. They were all indigenous, though the
conditions which gave rise to tropical vegetation and
faunas here are yet quite unknown, yet shrouded in
darkness.

C. G. HALLMANN, Archiv für die neuesten
Entdeckungen der Urwelt, 1820.

RED WEATHERING PRODUCTS AND SOILS

In warm areas, the course of weathering varies greatly, depending on
whether the climate is wet or dry. The corresponding weathering products,
therefore, often bear witness to several of the distinctive characteristics of
the climate.

Red coloration of sediments is a case in point. It is absent from areas of

TABLE 7
SOILS FORMED FROM SILICATE ROCKS IN DIFFERENT
LATITUDES (AFTER KUBIENA)

CLIMATIC ZONE	VEGETATION	SOIL TYPE
Arctic zone	Cold wastes, vegetation very scarce Woodless tundra	Unweathered soil Tundra type
Temperate zone	Cool temperate, coniferous forest Central European deciduous woodland Mediterranean xerophytic woodland	Primary iron podsol Central European brown earth Meridional brown earth
Subtropic zone	Subtropical rain forest Subtropical savanna	Subtropical brown loam Subtropical red loam
Tropical zone	Tropical savanna Tropical rain forest	Tropical red loam (tendency for formation of laterite and red earth) Tropical brown loam (tendency for formation of laterite)

excessive rainfall where brown iron hydroxides form instead or where, especially in cold climates, the presence of humic acids leads to leaching of the iron with consequent formation of podsols (Table 7). On the other hand, contrary to widely held belief, red beds are characteristic not of desert areas but rather of regions where the climate is hot and the rainfall seasonal. Krynine considers that red coloration denotes a mean annual temperature in excess of 16° C, and a rainfall of over 40 inches in areas of silicate rocks, or over 25 inches where carbonates are stained. These conditions are found as far from the equator as in parts of the Mediterranean area but are most

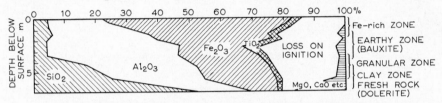

FIG. 13. CHEMICAL COMPOSITION OF A LATERITE PROFILE IN TASMANIA

Downward increase in silica and decrease in alumina and iron oxide. Source rock; dolerite (after Owen, 1954).

extensively developed in the tropical savannas, the region of greatest development of laterites. *Laterite* is derived from the Latin, later=brick, because the deposits, when air dried, were used for building purposes. Their chemical composition is compared with that of other soils in Table 8 and fig. 13, which show that there is enrichment of Al_2O_3, and Fe_2O_3 and a loss of SiO_2. The weathering, by Harrassowitz's definition is "alitic" (i.e. a high proportion of aluminum results), and not "sialitic" (high concentration of silica and of aluminum). Such aluminum hydrates as hydrargillite and diaspore are formed. Only in the deeper parts of tropical soil profiles are the

FIG. 14. LATERITE PROFILE IN THE MOUNTAINS OF SURINAM, SOUTH AMERICA

Note vertical passage from unweathered rock to kaolin and bauxite (after van Kersen, 1956).

silicate clay minerals, e.g. kaolin, developed (fig. 14). The cause of the leaching of silica is to be found in the absence of the humic acids, which would fix the colloidal SiO_2, because, in these areas, humus decomposes too quickly. Redeposition of silica often takes the form of silicification.

TABLE 8

CHEMICAL COMPOSITION OF SOILS (AFTER BRINKMANN)

	BASALT SOURCE ROCK	BROWN EARTH ENGLAND	RED EARTH PALESTINE	RED LOAM E. AFRICA	LATERITE INDIA
SiO_2	49	47	41·2	33·6	0·7
Al_2O_3	15	18·5	13·4	26·5	50·5
Fe_2O_3	4	14·6	11·3	13·8	23·4
H_2O	2	7·2	13·3	17·5	15·4

Lateritic weathering often extends down to considerable depths (up to 50 m.); on the whole, hot, humid regions bear a very thick mantle of weathering products and the rate of chemical alteration is high.

Laterites are particularly widely developed throughout the savanna belts of India, Africa (fig. 15), Australia (fig. 16), and South America. There is considerable dispute as to whether they are fossil soils. H. Erhart holds that the primary lateritic soils developed in tropical rain forests that were later converted into savanna by destruction of the trees. This drastic process he called biorhexistasis. Others consider that lateritization is related to a cycle of arid and semiarid climates. (W. Brückner). It can probably be assumed that laterites originated, in most cases, between the tropical rain forests and the savanna lands.

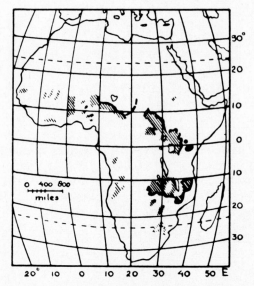

FIG. 15. DISTRIBUTION OF LATERITE IN AFRICA (after Prescott and Pendleton, from Mohr and van Baren, 1954)

Red loams are typical of subtropical savannas, while brown loams originate in the rain forests, and brown earths in temperate woodlands.

Fossil red beds are widely distributed and individual formations are named on this basis (Old Red, Rotliegendes, Buntsandstein, etc.). It is possible that the red coloration is secondary, and that lateritic weathering prevailed not in the area where the beds are now found, but in an adjacent region whence the superficial red soils were swept into the basin of sedimentation (Dunham, v. Houten, Krynine). This, however, is too slight a difference to matter greatly in paleoclimatology. Bauxite, a very important ore of aluminum, may be regarded as a fossil laterite. The name is derived from Les Baux, in Provence. Silicate- and calc-bauxites can be distinguished, though naturally the latter are derived at least partly from silicate rocks. Most European examples are to be found in the Cretaceous System (de Weisse, Valeton), while those of Arkansas belong to the Lower Tertiary (Gordon).

Similar weathering products, mostly of slightly younger age, are the pea- or bean-sized concretions of limonite (Bohnerze) that have accumulated in the Swiss and Swabian Jura. In some sections, it can be seen that the red beds occupy pockets in the substratum and have been covered by younger sediments (fig. 97). A famous example of lateritic weathering may be observed between the Tertiary basalt flows of the Giant's Causeway in Northern Ireland. Here the laterite zone is as much as 30 m. thick (Eyles, 1952).

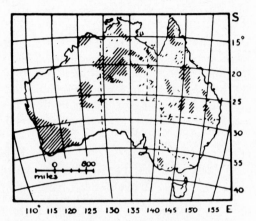

Fig. 16. Distribution of Laterite in Australia (after Prescott and Pendleton, *ibid.*)

Kaolin is developed in the deeper parts of the laterite profile (v. Kersen). It still remains to be seen whether all kaolin originates from lateritic weathering, but it does at least seem to be indicative of a fairly hot, wet climate.

Further reading: MOHR & v. BAREN, 1954.

CAVE DEPOSITS

G. M. Moore (1956) made some notable observations in caves in North America. He found that there, lime is depositing either as aragonite or as calcite, depending on whether the cave is located south or north of the 15·6° C isotherm (aragonite forming in the warmer areas). Near to the boundary, aragonite is often present under a surface layer of calcite. This, Moore has explained by assuming that the mean annual temperature was once 8° C higher than it is now. It is improbable that such a rise in temperature could be equated with the postglacial Climatic Optimum, since it has been shown that the increase at that time was much less. Research in the Rhineland (Holz, 1960), indicates that the chemistry of the cave rocks is an important factor and that aragonite will form on dolomite at temperatures well below 15·6° C. This had already been known to occur in caves in the eastern Alps.

MARINE ORGANISMS AND LIMESTONE DEPOSITION

Solution and deposition of calcite are largely dependent on the CO_2 content of water. At low temperatures, water contains more dissolved CO_2 and, therefore, can also carry more $CaCO_3$ in solution. Hence most thick, extensive deposits of limestone develop in the shallower parts of warm seas. There, the smallest mineral grains are constantly being stirred up, and may serve as nuclei of crystallization for the calcite with which the water is supersaturated. Sedimentation of calcareous muds, oolites, etc. may result. On the other hand, in the polar regions, in areas swept by cold currents, and in the great ocean deeps, calcite tends to be dissolved; the sediments of these areas tend to be lime-deficient, or lime-free. This does not prevent calcareous

TABLE 9
WATER TEMPERATURE AND LIME CONTENT OF MARINE CLAYS (AFTER GRIPP)

	TEMPERATURE IN °C		LIME CONTENT OF MUDS IN %
	FEBRUARY	SUMMER	
Baltic and North Sea	2–6	14–17	0–15
Western Mediterranean: North coast South coast (Libya)	9–11 16·2	20–22 24	25–28 Greater than 90
Red Sea	18·8–25·5	25–31	Greater than 90

muds with Globigerinids, etc., from depositing at many localities in the deeper parts of the ocean, but their calcite content is low. Table 9 and fig. 17 clearly show how lime content is dependent on temperature. Wiseman has demonstrated that the curves showing $CaCO_3$ content and paleotemperature of a deep-sea core follow parallel courses (fig. 18). Yalkovski, however. has pointed out that there are cases in which this relationship is not so clear.

We must assume then that the thick limestone formations of our mountain ranges also formed in warm seas. In western Europe these are present in the Lower Cambrian of the Sudetenland, the Middle Devonian of the Rhineland, the Carboniferous Limestone of Belgium and England, the Alpine Trias, the Muschelkalk, and the Middle and Upper Jurassic. They are composed, in part, of reef limestones, which we shall discuss later.

Bradshaw has shown by experiments on Recent forams that the formation of marine organic limestones is also clearly dependent on temperature. *Streblus beccarii var. tepida* develops at 20° C only a quarter as fast as it does at 25–30° C. The rate of formation of calcareous tests is correspondingly lower. Moreover, the rock-forming larger foraminifera—Fusulinids and Schwagerinids in the Permo-Carboniferous, Nummulites, etc., in the Older Tertiary—are regarded as having been the inhabitants of the warmer parts of the oceans. Raup's work on the sea urchin *Dendraster* has shown, however, that the relation between growth and temperature is sometimes rather complicated.

We still cannot say to what extent the magnesium and strontium content of calcareous shells indicates the temperature of the sea water in which they formed; other factors involved, e.g. salinity, make interpretation complicated. Research by Pilkey and Hower (1960) has revealed that with in-

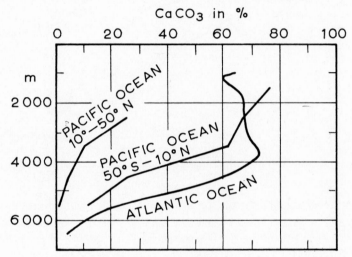

FIG. 17. RELATIONSHIP BETWEEN CaCO$_3$-CONTENT AND DEPTH IN ABYSSAL SEDIMENTS

Pacific, after Revelle, Atlantic (after Pia; from Dietrich, 1957).

creasing temperature, there is an apparent increase in magnesium content and a decrease in the Sr/Mg ratio of Recent *Dendraster* tests.

It is worth pointing out though, that there is also an upper limit to the temperature that any organism can tolerate, which in the case of the previously mentioned foram is about 30–35° C. The optimum temperature for modern reef corals lies in the range 25–30° C.

The inhabitants of well-lit tropical seas are often notably gaily colored. It is true that the color patterning of the shell is rarely retained in fossils— Schwarzbach (1942) records just over 150 pre-Tertiary examples—but nevertheless a third of all known occurrences belong to the marine beds of the Upper Carboniferous of North America and Europe; areas which on other grounds are assumed to have enjoyed a hot climate.

The Cypraeidae (Schilder), *Lingula* (Schwarzbach, 1942) and *Nautilus*

(Durham, 1950) may all be mentioned as specific examples of modern warmth-loving marine organisms which probably denote similar conditions where they are found as fossils.

From the beginning of the Tertiary Period onward, when modern genera become abundant, it is possible to make certain climatic deductions from the nature of the fish faunas. This is clearly demonstrated by Weiler's work on

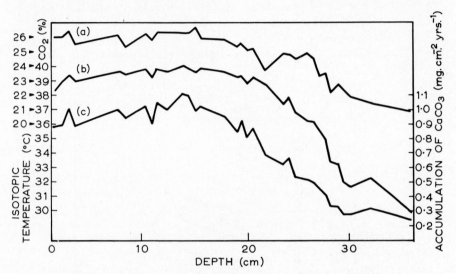

FIG. 18. LIME CONTENT OF ABYSSAL SEDIMENTS, AND ISOTOPIC TEMPERATURE

Core about 35 cm. long, from the equatorial Atlantic. a = O^{18}/O^{16} temperature calculated from *Globigerinoides sacculifera*; b = CO_2 content (%); c = the rate of accumulation of $CaCO_3$ (after Wiseman, 1959).

Tertiary otoliths in West Germany; there the proportion of tropical genera decreases constantly from the Lower Oligocene to the Upper Miocene (fig. 99). Nevertheless, the discovery of the catfish, *Heterobranchus* in the Vienna Basin indicates that the Pliocene climate in Central Europe was still warmer than today's; *Heterobranchus* is now confined to the tropical areas of Africa and Asia (Thenius).

Further reading: CAILLEUX, 1950; GUNTER, 1957; REVELLE & FAIRBRIDGE, 1957; RODGERS, 1957; WIELAND, 1942.

REEF FORMATION

Because of their great significance, a separate section must be devoted to reefs, which in the past have been built not only by corals, but also by archaeocyathids, sponges, bryozoa, thick-shelled pelecypods (rudistids), and calcareous algae. Coral reefs are, however, most important, at least at the present time. Fossil reef deposits are described as bioherms (Cumings & Shrock, 1928; Cumings, 1932).

Modern reef corals generally inhabit warm seas, though Teichert has again recently pointed out that coral banks extend quite far toward the poles. They are to be found off the coast of Japan (lat. 35° N) where the sea temperature in February is only 12° C (Yabe & Sugiyamo), off Western Australia, as far south as lat. 32° S (Fairbridge) and off the shores of Norway (69° N) in depths of 350–500 m. (Broch). These isolated occurrences cannot, however, be compared with the really thick reefs of the tropics. Most reef corals require a minimum temperature of at least 21° C (as well as clear aerated shallow water of normal salinity and depths of not more than 20–50 m.). Therefore true coral reefs are confined to the littoral zone between latitudes 30° N and 30° S (fig. 19) [for a more accurate map see J. W. Wells, 1957].

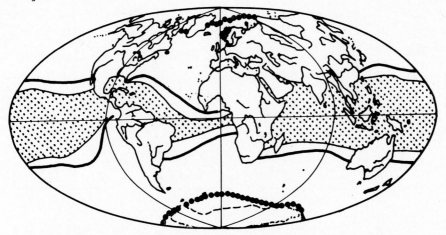

FIG. 19. PRESENT DISTRIBUTION OF ROCK-FORMING CORALS (MADREPORIA)

Dotted = abundant development of coral reefs; thick line = poleward limit of reefs (corresponding to a mean annual surface temperature of 25.5° C; * = individual coral banks . . . . = limit of solitary Madreporia (also limit of sea anemones) (after Pax, 1925). The influence of cold currents can be seen *e.g.* in Eastern Atlantic.

Fossil reef limestones are often distinguished by the fact that they are massive and give rise to squat hill masses. Their organic remains are often largely destroyed as a result of such diagenetic processes as dolomitization. Well-known and intensely studied examples include the Silurian reefs of Gothland (Hadding *et al.*) and North America (Lowenstam), the Middle Devonian reefs of the Rhenish Schiefergebirge (Jux) and the Ardennes (Lecompte), the Capitan reef of the Guadeloupe Mountains (Newell *et al.*), and the Triassic reefs of the South Tyrol Dolomites (fundamental research by F. v. Richthofen and Mojsisovicz more than 100 years ago). Jurassic reef limestones are shown in fig. 94. Fossil atolls are also known (fig. 20).

Whether or not we may ascribe the same climatological requirements to those reefs as to modern reef corals cannot be determined—at least not for pre-Tertiary forms—on the grounds of their natural affinities. We may undoubtedly assume for other reasons, especially because of the considerable lime formation, that the extensive reefs of earlier periods are indicative of relatively warm water conditions. This is in complete agreement with other paleoclimatic evidence for, with the progressive cooling of the climate since the Mesozoic and early Tertiary, as revealed by plants, etc., there has been

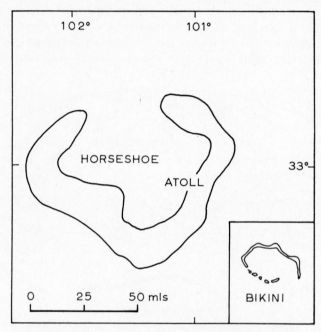

FIG. 20. HORSESHOE ATOLL, TEXAS; UPPER CARBONIFEROUS—
LOWER PERMIAN

Reconstructed from borehole data (after Stafford, 1959).
Present Bikini Atoll on same scale for comparison.

a gradual southward withdrawal of reef corals from Europe, North America, and Asia. In Paleozoic times, reefs flourished as far north as the present polar region; in the Mesozoic, they reached as far as 54° N in Europe, in the Oligocene, $51\frac{1}{2}$° N, in the Miocene, they no longer extended beyond 50° N, and now their poleward limit is 32° N (see figs. 122, 123).

At present, as in the past, *the number of species of reef dwellers* varies zonally as indicated in Table 10. Because of the incomplete nature of our knowledge of numbers of species in fossil reefs, we cannot be too exact about their regional variation, but comparison with present conditions is very instructive.

According to Gerth, the Older Tertiary coral fauna of the Mediterranean area comprised some 62 genera, compared with 26 in the present eastern

TABLE 10
RELATIONSHIP BETWEEN NUMBER OF SPECIES AND
TEMPERATURE IN MODERN AND FOSSIL REEFS

	VERY HOT AREAS	NO. OF SPECIES	LESS WARM AREAS	NO. OF SPECIES	AUTHOR
Madreporites in modern reefs	Torres Str. Moluccas Red Sea Philippines	63 70 71 180	Bahamas Bermudas	35 10	Pax, 1925, in Kükenthal's Hdb. of Zool.
No. of species in Jurassic reefs, in Europe	Lat. 49°N Lat. 47°N	126 184	50·5°N 54·5°N	17 6	Arkell, 1935

and western Atlantic. This indication of very warm Older Tertiary seas agrees completely with other climatic evidence.

The growth of individual corals too is controlled by climate, though it also depends to a considerable degree on other factors. The amount of annual growth of rock-forming corals is revealed by their rejuvenescence

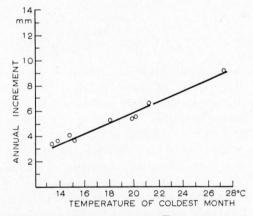

FIG. 21. DEVONIAN REEF CORAL
SHOWING ANNUAL GROWTH
STAGES

Cyathophyllum (M. Devonian), Eifel. Approximately natural size.

FIG. 22. RELATION BETWEEN TEMPERATURE OF
THE SEA AND RATE OF GROWTH OF THE RECENT
REEF CORAL *Favia speciosa* (after Ma, 1934).

which gives rise to a structure like annual rings (fig. 21). Ma has represented diagramatically the results of his work on the modern *Favia speciosa* (fig. 22); he has applied the same technique to fossils, but, since we can never be sure that the same species are being compared, and since nonclimatic factors cannot be eliminated, this method, interesting as it is, rests on very insecure foundations.

Further reading: STUBBLEFIELD, 1960.

LAND ANIMALS

The *mammals* are adaptable. Mammoth and woolly rhinoceros, now with tropical affinities, once dwelt in the cold steppes of the Ice Age. Mammals are therefore of little use for paleoclimatic comparisons, because fossil species do not necessarily denote the same environment as their modern equivalents unless they are identical with them (e.g. musk ox).

Bergmann discovered in 1847 that, in general, the size of mammals tends to increase toward the poles. Rensch has suggested that the gradual increase in size of Tertiary mammals may be explained on the basis of this "Bergmann's Rule", as there was a gradual climatic deterioration during this era. Contrariwise, general evolutionary tendencies may have played a greater part than climate in this size increase. This is probably also true of the decreasing maximum size of *insects*. Handlirsch obtained the following mean values for the span of the anterior wings.

Recent — Central Europe ..	7 mm
Recent — Tropics	16 mm
Upper Jurassic (Malm).. ..	20 mm
Lower Jurassic (Lias)	11 mm
Triassic	14 mm
Permian	17 mm
Late Pennsylvanian	20 mm
Early Pennsylvanian	51 mm

The unusually large size of the present tropical insects compared with those of temperate latitudes, indicates that climate, as well as evolution, does help to determine size, and may have done so in the Carboniferous and the Malm, though the tremendous size of some of the Carboniferous insects can hardly have been due entirely to climatic factors.

Cold-blooded land animals are of great climatological importance. For them, life under polar conditions would have been very difficult, and for the larger representatives, e.g. Reptiles, even the temperate zone was an unsuitable habitat, because they could not avoid the cold of winter by burrowing. According to Rensch, cold-blooded animals attain their maximum size where the environment is most favorable to them, i.e. in hot humid climates. For this reason, the largest beetles, locusts, myriapods, spiders, etc., are to be found in the tropics and subtropics. The same relation between size of insects and temperature has already been discussed. For individual species of reptiles, the mean size clearly increases toward the equator; and so does the number of species. According to Hesse, there are 64 species in Europe, 221 in Indochina and Siam, and 536 in India, Burma, and Ceylon. Over 140 species of snakes have been recorded in the Mediterranean area, but only 2 as far north as Leningrad; there are 12 species in Germany, 122 in the much smaller area of Java. Only very occasionally, as with the New Zealand tuatara (*Sphenodon*, Mertens) may reptiles be relatively tolerant in their temperature requirements. We must also bear in mind that some reptiles, e.g. the flying reptiles, may have been warm-blooded (Broili, Schuh). On the whole, however, the large reptiles of the past, such as the giant Jurassic and Cretaceous saurians, are indicative of warm climates (Schuchert, Yakovlev, Audova *et al.*). Audova may, of course, be wrong in explaining the extinction of the large Mesozoic reptiles on the basis of climatic deterioration. In cold phases, they could easily have retreated, as they did at other times, to warmer parts of the earth.

PLANTS

It must first of all be pointed out that the floras of tropical areas contain many more species than do those of cooler latitudes. The tropical rain forests of the Cameroons contain 800 species, of which between 500 and 600 are trees: there are only 10–15 kinds of trees in central European woodlands (Eidmann, 1942). When Heer showed that there were 136 different woody plants in the Miocene marls of Oeningen on Lake Constance, compared with 91 in the Zurich canton of the present time, this certainly favored the hypothesis that temperatures were higher during the Miocene Period; the more so since as a rule only a part, indeed often only a small part of the flora is preserved as fossils. For this reason, no conclusion may be drawn from beds which are deficient in fossil species.

Tropical rain forests are characterized above all else by an abundance of climbing plants, a feature which Chesters also found in the Miocene Flora of Rusinga Island, Lake Victoria.

In North America, in particular, a great many investigators (Sinnot, Bailey, Berry, Chaney, Sanborn, Becker, *et al.*) have tried to determine statistically the occurrence of certain features such as size and shape of leaf, drip-points, etc., among Recent floras (Table 11). The difference between tropical and cooler climates emerges very clearly.

TABLE 11

PROPORTION OF ENTIRE MARGINED LEAVES IN RECENT FLORAS (DICOTYLEDONOUS WOODY PLANTS)

Panama, lowland	88%	California, Redwood	23%
Florida	83%	Italy	50%
Simla, mountains	58%	England	32%
Upper Ganges plain	71%	Northeast Germany	21%
Hawaii, mountains	56%	North Japan	8%
Hawaii, lowland	76%		

Among the rich Eocene floras of North America, the Wilcox flora contains 87% of entire margined leaves (Berry), the Goshen flora 61% (Chaney and Sanborn). They evidently represent tropical rain forests. Table 12 does, however, indicate that it is not always so easy to deduce climatic conditions. The proportion of leaves with entire margins did not decrease throughout the Tertiary as regularly as would theoretically be expected. Therefore in statistical studies, the results should not be interpreted too rigidly, especially when based on insufficient material.

TABLE 12
PROPORTION OF ENTIRE MARGINED LEAVES IN TERTIARY FLORAS (DICOTYLEDONOUS) OF GERMANY (AFTER SCHWARZBACH, 1946)

	NO. OF COMPARABLE SPECIES	ENTIRE-MARGINED SPECIES IN %
Eocene, Geiseltal – – – – – – –	27	75
Eocene, Bornstedt near Eisleben . . .	31	50
Eocene, Eisleben	31	15
U. Oligocene, Düren	100	45
L. Miocene, Mainz	47	70
Miocene, Eichelskopf near Homberg . .	46	65
Miocene, Senftenberg near Neiderlausitz .	48	10
Pliocene, Frankfurt	39	30

The "tropical character" of the Carboniferous coal forests has been vigorously advocated, especially by H. Potonié (1920), on the basis of more general characteristics. His main evidence lay in the occurrence of tree ferns, in the axillary position of the fructifications of such plants as *Sigillaria,* in the aphlebia (i.e. large, heavily modified pinnules) of certain large ferns—particularly the Pecopterids, and in the absence of annual growth rings. Axillary fructifications are now to be found on such plants as the cocoa tree; aphlebia in the Gleicheniacicae and other forms; both appear predominantly in hot areas. Their significance is not yet known; their occurrence among the Sigillariaceae is now questioned. Tree ferns may not be cited in this context, as now they are much more characteristic of wet than of warm climates, and can even withstand snow. We should not, therefore, automatically ascribe the Carboniferous coal forests to tropical, but rather to warm (i.e. to tropical or subtropical), and above all to wet climates.

Systematic affinities between fossil plants and Recent species can only be used to provide paleoclimatic evidence from Tertiary times onward. O. Heer must qualify as the pioneer of such comparisons for, by comparing the Tertiary palms, *Liquidambar, Cinnamomum, Laurus, Liriodendron,* etc., with their modern representatives, he was able to estimate the Tertiary temperatures of Switzerland. His results were based, not on specific plants, but on the whole flora.

Some common Tertiary plants may be mentioned briefly, *Sequoia* and

Taxodium are relict plants now confined to California and the Gulf Coast respectively. Their distribution does not correspond to the total area in which they could flourish, but they are nevertheless of some paleoclimatic value (fig. 23); the same may be said of *Glyptostrobus* of southeast China.

Palms afford striking examples of trees which thrive in warm climates today, and are common in fossil floras. Even wood, roots and fruit have been found, though many have been incorrectly identified (Chapter 3). Their present poleward limits run through North Carolina (35° N), Japan (36° N) and New Zealand (44° S), but their areal distribution was much more extensive in Tertiary times.

Today, *Cinnamomum* (e.g. Cinnamon and Camphor trees) flourishes mainly in the tropics, though some species are to be found in Florida and southern Japan.

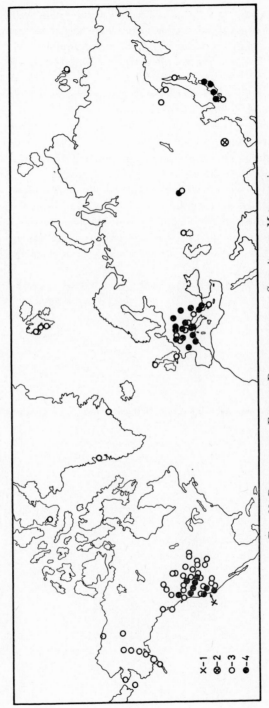

FIG. 23. PRESENT AND FORMER DISTRIBUTION OF *Sequoia* AND *Metasequoia*

1 = Present occurrence of *Sequoia*; 2 = present occurrence of *Metasequoia*; 3 and 4 = Tertiary occurrences of *Sequoia* and *Metasequoia* respectively. From two maps by Schloemer-Jäger, 1958.

Heer points out that *Cinnamomum camphora* still blooms in Florence and Pisa though it no longer bears fruit there. He compares this with *Cinnamomum polymorphum* which occurs frequently in the Tertiary (Siebengebirge, Cologne, etc.), and thereby estimates a mean annual temperature of 15° C.

The fruits of *Mastixiodea* and *Symplocacea* are often found in the Tertiary lignites of Germany (Kirchheimer). Their modern counterparts are *Mastix* (Cornaceae), one of the stately trees of the thinly wooded mountains of southern Asia, and *Symplocus*, whose 300 species are mostly scattered throughout the same mountains and those of the tropical zone of Central and South America.

Lastly, we must mention the calcareous algae, which achieved great importance as rock formers, e.g. in the Triassic reefs of the Alps. Such fluctuations in the distribution of the Dasycladaceae as the Rhaeto-Liassic retreat in Europe (Table 13), were probably controlled by climate.

TABLE 13

DISTRIBUTION OF DASYCLADACEANS IN THE MESOZOIC OF EUROPE (AFTER PIA)

	MIDDLE TRIAS	UPPER TRIAS	LOWER JURASSIC	MIDDLE JURASSIC	UPPER JURASSIC
Northern limit	51°N	48°N	46°N	52°N	54°N
No. of species	42	3	3	3	20

Further reading: GOTHAN & WEYLAND, 1954; MAHABALE, 1954; SEWARD, 1931.

5

Evidence of Cold Climates

Einst ziert ich, den Äther durchspähend, als Spitze
des Urgebirgs Stock; Ruhm, Hoheit und Stellung
verschmähend, ward ich zum erratischen Block.

J. V. v. SCHEFFEL, 1867.

GLACIERS AND MORAINES

Glaciers constitute easily the most outstanding feature of areas with a cold climate. Small isolated glaciers can, it is true, exist in the tropics wherever the mountains are high enough. Thus Mount Kenya, Kilimanjaro, and Ruwenzori in equatorial Africa all bear a number of corrie- and hanging-glaciers. On Ruwenzori they extend down to 1400 m. When dealing with

FIG. 24. PLEISTOCENE GROUND MORAINE LEFT BY THE SCANDINAVIAN ICE SHEET.

Hermsdorf, Germany (about 600 miles from the Scandinavian mountains). Scale given by hammer. (Photograph: M. Schwarzbach, 1941.)

C.P.—4

TABLE 14—CHARACTERISTICS OF

	MORAINES (TILLITE)	GLACIO-MARINE DEPOSITS; IN PART TILLITE	SLUMPED	
			SUBAERIAL	
Cause	Glaciers	Icebergs	Gravity, often + earthquakes (land-slides); thixotropic and periglacial processes	
Bedding	Absent (but boulders mostly oriented)	Present	Absent	
Sorting	Absent	Absent	Absent	
Shape of blocks	Rounded and facetted boulders often present	As for moraines	Mostly angular; rounded boulders possible.[1]	
Striated blocks	Normally present	Present	Rare (short, curved striae)	
Striated pavements	Occasionally present	Possible in a few cases	Rare	
Contortion of the bedrock	Not uncommon	Possible in a few cases		
Type of blocks	Polymict	Polymict	Often monomict	
Source of blocks	Often distant (100 mls. +)	Mostly distant	Local	
Initial dip	Almost horizontal	Horizontal	Shallow dip	
Peculiarities	Often unusually extensive distribution. Matrix clay or loam, usually more abundant than blocks	Associated marine fossils; matrix usually clay		

[1] Already formed boulders may be caught up in slumped mass.

former glaciers it is, therefore, important to prove either that they form part of a really widespread mountain or continental glaciation, or else that they lay near sea level. The latter may be perceived where beds containing marine fossils are interstratified with the moraines. In maritime climates, glaciers and luxuriant vegetation can coexist, as Darwin so dramatically realized on his journey round the world (Chapter 11). Glaciers flow into the Gulf of Penas on the coast of Chile "within less than 9° from where palms grow, within $4\frac{1}{2}$° of a region where the jaguar and puma range over the plains, less than $2\frac{1}{2}$° from arborescent grasses, and (looking westward in the same hemisphere) less than 2° from orchidaceous parasites and within a single degree of tree ferns!". On the whole, the snouts of glaciers tend to lie far below the snow line.

MORAINES AND PSEUDOMORAINES

MASSES / SUBAQUEOUS	FANGLOMERATE	VOLCANIC BRECCIAS	TECTONIC BRECCIAS
	PSEUDOMORAINES IN PART		
Gravity usually + earthquakes	Flowing water in arid regions	Volcanic processes (fissure filling, pyroclastics)	Tectonic processes
Absent or present	Often indistinct	Absent or present	Absent
Absent or present	Often indistinct	Absent or present	Absent
Mostly angular (possibly rounded boulders[1])	Often poorly rounded	Angular	Angular
Rare	Absent	Possible	Rare
Rare	Absent	Possible with pyroclastics; slickensides	Slickensides possible
Occasionally present	Absent	Absent	Possible
Monomict or polymict	Usually polymict	Always include blocks of volcanic rocks	Usually few types
Local or fairly distant	Mostly fairly local	Sometimes from great depth	Mostly local
Shallow dip	Almost horizontal	Vertical, inclined or horizontal	Steep or shallow
Often with slumped balls and limnic or marine fossils	Little matrix		Often in narrow zone

The former presence of glaciers can be proved by their deposits—*ground moraines*—and by the typical land forms they produce—e.g., *end-moraines*. Ground moraines are unbedded and unsorted, and they contain large and small rock fragments, often with rounded corners, set in apparently haphazard fashion in a matrix of loam or marl. We speak of the deposits as boulder clay or till (fig. 24), or, where they are older and completely consolidated, as tillite (figs. 76–78, 83, 103). Penck first coined this term for the Dwyka moraines of South Africa in 1906. Since it is very difficult to distinguish between moraines and pseudomoraines, I would recommend that the term tillite be applied not only to undoubted moraines but to all moraine-like sediments of probable or possible glacial or glacio-marine origin. Those later shown to be pseudomoraines of nonglacial origin, may then, more properly, be called pseudotillites.

The boulders are often polished and striated (figs. 76, 79); so is the rock pavement (figs. 25, 26). The glacial striae on the Muschelkalk sediments near Berlin are characteristic, and their study by Torell in 1875 initiated the modern development of glaciology. Such striated pavements were also

FIG. 25. GLACIALLY STRIATED PAVEMENT WITH FLATTER "STOSS" SIDE AND STEEPER LEE SIDE

The glacier came from the right. Piedmont of the Solheima Glacier, Iceland. (Photograph: M. Schwarzbach.)

formed during the pre-Quaternary glaciations (figs. 77, 89). The frequency of striation depends on the rock type; in Illinois, R. C. Anderson found that basic lavas were most abundantly striated, followed by limestone and dolomite.

Further reading: GRIPP, 1929; C. D. HOLMES, 1960; PORTMANN, 1956; H. SMITH, 1948.

Pseudomoraines

Unfortunately, moraine-like deposits can also form by quite different mechanisms, e.g., slumping. These pseudomoraines (pseudotillites) may also contain striated blocks. Slumped masses (fig. 27), fanglomerates, volcanic breccias, and tectonic breccias can all be confused with moraines. Examples of submarine slumping in the Culm (Carboniferous greywacke association) of the Rhenish Schiefergebirge (Kuenen and Sanders, 1956, Plate 2), and recent landslides in Bavaria (v. Freyberg) show that even

FIG. 26. ROCHE MOUTONNÉE, FORMED DURING THE PLEISTOCENE GLACIATION FROM A
PRECAMBRIAN (HURONIAN) TILLITE

Noranda, Canada. The outcrop, therefore, indicates two glaciations separated in time
by perhaps 1,000 million years. (Photograph: M. Schwarzbach.)

FIG. 27. PSEUDO TILLITE FORMED BY SUBMARINE SLUMPING; ORDOVICIAN, QUEBEC
Pencil gives scale. (Photograph: M. Schwarzbach.)

striated pavements may be formed; in the latter case, in a soft clayey substrate (fig. 28). Indeed, even seals can occasionally cause striation, as Jordan observed on Pribilov Island (see Barth, 1956, p. 102). It is at least ice and so a cold climate that is responsible, where striations are produced by grounding icebergs or by ice floes being thrust onto the coast.

Boulders in landslips may also be striated, but Heim points out that the grooves are short, curved, and rough surfaced. They are thus readily distinguishable from the long, straight, smooth grooves of glacial origin. Striated morainic boulders may get caught up in landslides. Then, the striation is not directly related to the pseudomoraine (Heim, 1932, p. 105ff). Striation can be produced even in normal conglomerates by diagenetic processes, because of the greater compaction of the matrix. Heim records examples from the Swiss Molasse (1919, p. 62). W. J. Schmidt has described striated boulders of tectonic origin.

FIG. 28. STRIATED SURFACE IN CLAY CAUSED BY A LANDSLIDE IN 1957, EBERMANNSTADT, BAVARIA.

From B. v. Freyberg, 1957. (Photograph by kind permission of author.)

A general review of the characteristics of moraines and pseudomoraines is given in Table 14. Determination of the origin is often uncertain, but it is sometimes possible, when many features are combined, to suggest that it is glacial. Striated boulders and pavements and a wide areal distribution may be considered as the most typical attributes of true moraines. Little reliance can be placed on association with banded clays, since such sediments are also very common in nonglacial environments (see fig. 66).

Among the more recent literature dealing with this much discussed theme special mention may be made of the papers by Wegmann (1951), Crandell (1957), Crowell (1957), and Schwarzbach (1958).

Many statements concerning alleged pre-Quaternary glaciations are founded on pseudotillites.

Further reading: ACKERMANN, 1951; CRANDELL & WALDRON, 1956.

Glacial Land Forms

Glacial land forms play a decisive part in the reconstruction of the Quaternary Glaciations. They include corries, terminal moraines, roches moutonnées (fig. 26), U-shaped valleys, lakes, kettle holes, eskers, and kames. Morainic features formed during the last glacial phase can be distinguished from those of earlier phases by their individual land forms. In North Germany and Iowa, the Last Glaciation has resulted in incomplete drainage, basins of inland drainage, and lakes (Gripp, Ruhe). Only isolated examples of similar phenomena are to be found associated with older glaciations. U-shaped valleys were produced during the Permo-Carboniferous glaciation of S.W. Africa (Martin and Schalk), Victoria and South Australia (Summers, see Fairbridge, 1953).

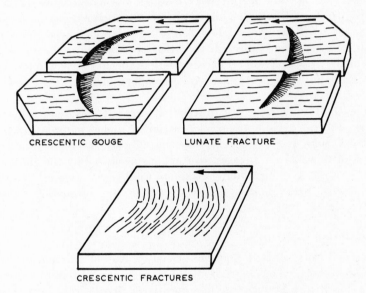

FIG. 29. GLACIAL STRIAE AND SOLE MARKINGS
Arrow indicates the direction of ice movement (after R. F. Flint, 1955).

Direction of Ice Movement

Whence came the glaciers? In present mountain areas, the answer to this important question is usually apparent, but with former glaciations it cannot be answered automatically. The direction of movement is revealed by the *orientation of the boulders*—which do not really lie haphazardly (Richter, 1932; Lundquist; Glen, Donner and West)—and even more by the direction of the *glacial striae*, though these by no means always parallel the ice flow even in valley glaciers. This, Collomb observed as long ago as 1846 for the Rosenlaui glacier in Switzerland. Therefore, it should not always be concluded, as it often has, that different directions of striation on a rock surface indicate several former glaciations. Moreover, one is always faced with a choice between two possible source directions, e.g., with east-west striae, the ice could have equally well come from the east or the west.

Distinction cannot always be made on the basis of crescentic scour markings
on the rock pavement lying at right angles to the direction of flow. Their
concave sides sometimes point in the direction of flow, sometimes in the
reverse direction; and while the flatter slope of the scour feature does in fact
often point in the direction of movement (fig. 29) it by no means always does
so. (Harris, Flint, good photo by Holtedahl, *Norges Geologi*, 1953, II,
fig. 456.)

The analysis of included boulders as a means of determining the source
of old moraines only occasionally produces the desired result, especially if
the rock types are not distinctive. In north Germany, however, it does
serve to distinguish various older Quaternary glaciations because the
direction of ice flow varied. The Ailsa Craig boulder train shows that
Scottish ice swept south through the Irish Sea and onto the neighboring
coastal areas; Scandinavian erratics indicate that that ice sheet once covered
eastern England. Flint (1947) lists American examples of the use of boulder
trains.

In the Quaternary, the orientation of terminal moraines, eskers, and
drumlins, and the asymmetrical long-section of roches moutonnées (with a
flat "stoss" side, and a steep lee side, fig. 25) also serve to indicate the
direction of flow. In a few cases, contortions produced by the glacier yield
the same result, but for older glaciations these structures can hardly be
distinguished from similar features caused by submarine slumping
(Fairbridge).

Transportation by Icebergs

Although Lyell's concept that the glacial erratics of Europe were transported by drifting ice has been abandoned, the word "drift" has continued
to be used in British literature to describe glacial deposits. Nevertheless, it is
certain that icebergs can in fact carry coarse material over vast distances to
deposit it among fine-grained marine sediments (Hough, 1950; fig. 30). At
present, icebergs may occasionally drift to within 40° of the equator. The
investigation of abyssal deposits has revealed numerous such glacio-marine
sediments; many "pebbly shales" of older periods have also been attributed
to this mechanism. Drifting tree trunks and seaweed can also carry rocks for
a long way, as the poet and botanist, Adalbert von Chamisso, observed long
ago off the coast of Radak (in the Marshall Islands) during the world cruise
of the Russian ship "Rurik" (1815–18). In the Jurassic sediments of Solen-
hofen, trees have been preserved with boulders entangled in their roots
(Mayr). Sea lions can also transport individual pebbles as gastroliths
(Emery).

Darwin noted as early as 1855, that the substrate may be striated by
grounding icebergs. Gaertner has suggested, though not on any valid
grounds, that Eo-Cambrian examples of iceberg striation occur at Varanger
Fjord. Contortion of strata could also have been caused by grounding ice.

Ice floes in rivers, like icebergs, may also transport large blocks. This has been observed even in rivers of temperate latitudes (Genieser), but takes place on a large scale only in large Arctic rivers. Boulders of several meters diameter in the Rhine gravels have therefore been taken as proof of a fairly cold, i.e., glacial, climate. Pressure of ice on river banks can give rise to striated boulders (as Bernauer observed on the Neckar near Heidelberg). In the same way, ice pressure on lake shores can also assume considerable proportions. (There is a very informative picture in the textbook *Geology* by Emmons, Thiel, *et al.*, 1955, p. 215.)

FIG. 30. ERRATIC DROPPED BY FLOATING ICE INTO INTERGLACIAL BANDED MARINE CLAYS Fossvogur near Reykjavik, Iceland. (Photograph: M. Schwarzbach.)

Snow Line

The position of the climatically important regional snow line, i.e., the lower limit of eternal snows and hence of glacier formation, can be reconstructed only for the Quaternary Ice Age. Isochion is the name given to the line joining points where the regional snow line lies at the same altitude.

The lowered position of the Pleistocene snow line is revealed by corries on mountains and hills well below the present snow line. They date mostly from the Last Glaciation, and are to be seen, for example, in the Alps or the Cordilleras. Many of the ranges no longer support glaciers, e.g., Vosges, Black Forest, Riesengebirge (fig. 31). Obviously, during the last glacial phase, the snow line lay well below, in places more than 1000m below, its present level. Roches moutonnées and glacial striae are also important though it must be remembered that the snout of valley glaciers often lies far below the limit of eternal snows. In the Alps, 17 glaciers now terminate

FIG. 31. CORRIES FORMED DURING THE LAST GLACIATION
Riesengebirge (Karkenoze), Silesia (now Poland). (From Schwarzbach,
"Geologie in Bildern," 1954.)

more than 1000 m. below the snow line; in the Himalayas several extend over 2000 m. below; the Malaspina glacier in Alaska supports whole woods on its debris-covered snout.

It should always be borne in mind, that in areas like the Himalayas, or Andean ranges, the level of the former snow line may have been displaced by fairly recent tectonic movements (Machatchek, Heim, 1951). This can also affect our opinion of interglacial phases (Lüdi).

The present position of the snow line depends not only on temperature, but also on precipitation. This shows up especially clearly when we trace its level from pole to pole (fig. 110). Certainly, with increasing temperature, it does generally rise toward the equator, but its maximum altitude is attained not there, but in the arid horse latitudes, where at Puna de Atacama, it soars to 6850 m. Moreover, in the Northern Hemisphere, it reaches sea level in Greenland (lat. 81° N) while in the much wetter Southern Hemisphere, it drops to zero height at Heard Island only 53° S of the equator, and therefore in the same latitude as Hamburg, Liverpool, and Lake Winnipeg. In Kerguelen, which lies at the same distance from the equator as the Channel Islands and has a maritime climate, the glaciers descend to only 600 m. above sea level.

For these reasons, the snow line rises inland (fig. 32) both now and during the Pleistocene glaciation. The Pleistocene snow line rose from 1400 m. on the Dalmatian Coast to 3700 m. south of the Caspian Sea (Louis 1944), while in the Pamir plateau, it ascended from 3000 to nearly 5000 m. in a distance of under 200 miles (Zabirov, Büdel, Gerassimov & Markov, Wissmann). Furthermore, the depression of the snow line during the Ice Age was less in arid than in humid areas (fig. 110). Because of their aridity, many parts of the polar zones are not glaciated, nor were they during the Pleistocene; the very limited glaciation of Northern Siberia may be attributed to this cause.

The snow line lies above the tree line. The vertical distance between them varies within wide limits, from 200 to well over 3000 m. (K. Hermes).

PERIGLACIAL PHENOMENA

Outside the true glacial, i.e., glaciated, region, lies the periglacial zone which also affords a wealth of important paleoclimatic phenomena. These have been intensively studied, particularly in fairly recent years, and again they are of greatest importance in Quaternary studies (see the recent papers by Büdel, Cailleux & Taylor, Dücker, Frenzel, Kaiser, Maarleveld, Poser, Schenck, H. T. Smith, Troll, *et al.*).

Intense physical weathering leads to the formation of thick masses of boulder and rubble known as *block-fields*. Where block-fields occur in hill areas of temperate latitudes, they can be regarded as relics of glacial phases.

Another feature of the periglacial zone is *permanently frozen ground* (permafrost, pergelisol, tjäle in Sweden). The subsoil is permanently frozen, sometimes to depths of over 100 m., but flowage (solifluction) occurs readily where a thin surface layer thaws in summer. At the present time, such conditions affect large areas of North America and Siberia (fig. 33). According to Shostakovitch, these areas are characterized by extreme cold, and by slight precipitation in the form of snow. The southern limit coincides approximately with the mean annual isotherm –2° C. Others, including Mortensen (1952) equate it with the –5° C isotherm.

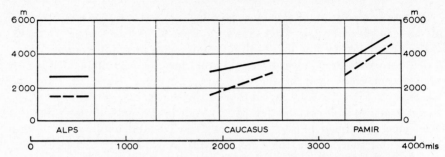

FIG. 32. RECENT AND PLEISTOCENE SNOW LINE IN EURASIA (E.-W. SECTION)
Solid line = present snow line; dashes = Pleistocene snow line. The snow line rises
toward the interior of the continent (after Gerassimov and Markov, 1954).

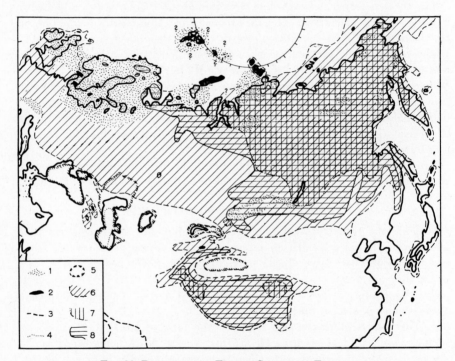

FIG. 33. PERMANENTLY FROZEN GROUND IN EURASIA

1 = ice sheets during Würm Glaciation; 2 = recent glaciers; 3 = Würm coast line;
4 = coast line during postglacial Climatic Optimum; 5 = margins of Black Sea and lakes
during Würm Glaciation; 6 = Würm; 7 = Postglacial Optimum; and 8 = present extent
of permanently frozen ground. Constructed from Russian data by Frenzel, 1960.

Cryoturbation, stone circles, and *ice wedges,* are all typical of the permafrost zone. On the basis of these phenomena, it can be shown that extensive
areas of central and western Europe bore pergelisols during the Pleistocene
glaciations. These may have been as much as 100–150 m. thick, for in a

Saale push-moraine in N.W. Germany great slabs of loose sand penetrate to this depth. This can only have been possible if the sands were frozen at the time.

Rock glaciers are flows of rock and clayey material, often with an arcuate bulging appearance (fig. 34). They occur in high mountain areas. Where they appear at lower levels, they are essentially glacial relics, dating back to

FIG. 34. ROCK GLACIER IN THE ALPS
Duron Valley, South Tyrol Dolomites. (Photograph: M. Schwarzbach.)

periods of intense solifluction. According to Wahrhaftig and Cox, they did not form in the Alaska Range during the postglacial Climatic Optimum, but reappeared later.

Cryoturbation is the term used to describe the contortedly bedded soils (cryoturbates, Würgeboden, etc., see fig. 35) that originate almost entirely by flowage of the summer-thawing layer of permafrost areas. Unlike those of the Pleistocene, recent examples have as yet received little study. Pre-Quaternary examples have not been definitely established, though Wetzel considers the mud-cake conglomerates of the Lower Paleozoic or Precambrian Visingö Formation of Sweden to have formed in this way.

Repeated freezing and thawing of the upper layers of earth, causes geometric arrangement of the larger stones into *stone circles*. On gently sloping terrain, these are drawn out into *stone stripes*. Stone circles and stripes also appear in the zone of eternal snows on the high mountains of the tropics (Troll), in such now unglaciated hill areas (Högbom) as the Riesengebirge, or the Wind River Mountains of Wyoming, and also at lower

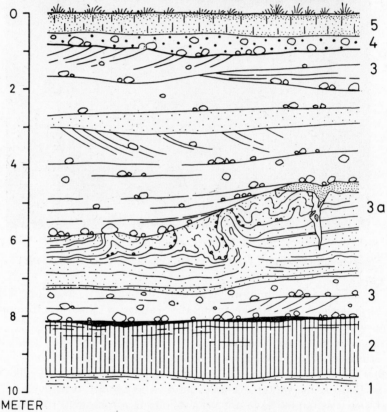

FIG. 35. CRYOTURBATION IN PLEISTOCENE RIVER GRAVELS

Jülich, west of Cologne. 1 = sand; 2 = Pliocene clay; 3 = Older Upper Terrace of the Maas (gravel, sand, and loamy sand) showing cryoturbation (3a); 4 = Younger Upper Terrace of the Rhine; 5 = Würm loess. Above detailed photograph of the cryoturbation. 1 m. rule gives scale.

The Maas sands were in a permafrost area for a long time in the early Pleistocene. Cryoturbation resulted. An ice wedge filled with loamy sand can be seen on the right. The sands were later eroded, then further gravels were deposited. The periglacial phenomena are of the same age as the sedimentation (synchronous cryoturbation) (after L. Ahorner).

levels in Iceland (fig. 36). There they are definitely not associated with permanently frozen ground, so only their optimum development occurs in the periglacial area. Fossil stone nets are rare, though they were formed during the Würm Glaciation (as recorded by Wortmann in Westphalia).

Networks of frost fissures split asunder the pergelisols of the tundras and then fill with ice (fig. 37) to give rise to ice wedges. These wedges may gradually expand to as much as 8–10 m. deep, and 3 m. across (Leffingwell, 1915, 1919, in Alaska; Pataleyev, in Siberia, fig. 39).

FIG. 36. STONE CIRCLES IN POSTGLACIAL TUFFS IN ICELAND, SOUTH OF REYKJAVIK
The formation of stone circles is most common in permafrost areas, but also occurs, as here in Iceland, beyond the limits of permanently frozen ground. Scale given by book. (Photograph: M. Schwarzbach, 1958.)

The ice may later be replaced by sediment, often loess, to give rise to "ice-wedge pseudomorphs" which are usually called ice wedges, loess wedges, or frost fissures, though the latter term is confined by some to the original fissures (figs. 40, 35).

Numerous Pleistocene examples have been described from central Europe (first by Soergel), and later from North America. They are usually seen in cross-section, but occasionally ice-wedge networks are also seen; near Göttingen (Selzer; fig. 38), Prague (Zaruba), in Yorkshire from aerial photographs (Dimbleby), and in Worcestershire (Shotton). It is possible to confuse them with such other structures as infilled joints or tension cracks (Schwarzbach, 1952, Kaiser, 1958).

FIG. 37. ICE WEDGE NETWORK IN THE TAIMYR PENINSULA (SIBERIA)
(Photographed on Arctic Flight of Graf Zeppelin, 1931.) (From C. Troll, 1944.)

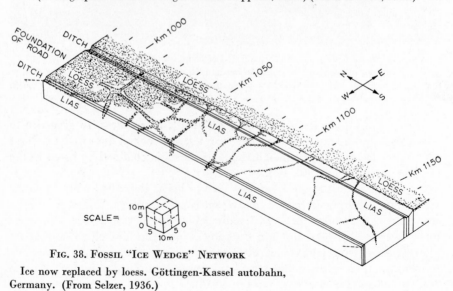

FIG. 38. FOSSIL "ICE WEDGE" NETWORK

Ice now replaced by loess. Göttingen-Kassel autobahn,
Germany. (From Selzer, 1936.)

Many of the valleys in the periglacial zone of central Europe have asymmetric cross-sections with steeper eastern or northern slopes. The asymmetry originated during the Würm Glaciation because the northern and eastern slopes facing toward the sun thawed rather more deeply, with the result that strong lateral erosion set in there (Poser, K. Kaiser).

In the soils of modern tundras, lenticles of ice often gradually push up mounds as much as 10 m. high. These are known as *pingos* or *hydrolaccoliths*. Later, melting of the ice and collapse of the mound gives rise to small circular pools. Maarleveld and Toorn explained similar structures in north Holland as pingos produced during the Würm Glaciation. Cailleux has recorded others near Paris.

Further reading: R. F. BLACK, 1954; GALLWITZ, 1949; HOLMES & COLTON, 1960; HOPKINS & KARLSTROM, 1955; G. JOHNSSON, 1959; KESSLER, 1925; MÜLLER, 1959; WASHBURN, 1956; WOLFE, 1956.

TERRACES

It is probable that many rivers were dominantly erosive during the interglacial phases but tended to become choked with gravel during the glacial

FIG. 39. TWO RECENT ICE WEDGES IN PERMANENTLY FROZEN GROUND AT INDIGIRKA (EASTERN SIBERIA)

The wedges are several meters thick. The ground is frozen here to a depth of some 100 m.; it is covered by woodland (*Larix dahurica*).
(Photograph: Prof. Schanzer, Moscow, 1959.)

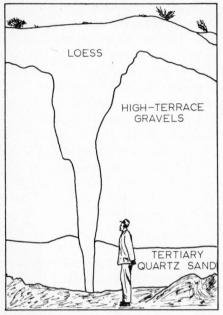

FIG. 40. LARGE "ICE WEDGE" IN QUATERNARY RHINE GRAVELS; LIGNITE WORKINGS NEAR COLOGNE

Length of wedges ca. 6 m. The ice was replaced by loess during the Würm Glaciation (see sketch on right). (From data by Pruskovski, from Kaiser, 1958.)

phases, when more detritus was being supplied than they could transport. This has sometimes been confirmed by the remains of plants and animals adapted to cold conditions, and by syngenetic ice wedges, etc. (fig. 41). The number of terraces leads one to conclude that there were several glacial phases (Soergel, Zeuner, *et al.*). This interpretation is some-

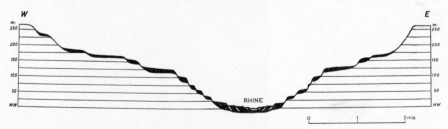

FIG. 41. RIVER TERRACES ON THE RHINE BETWEEN ANDERNACH AND BONN, SOMEWHAT DIAGRAMMATIC

Rhine gravels shown in black. The highest terrace lies 230 m. above the present level of the river. The three highest terraces are of Pliocene age, the remainder are Quaternary. At least part of the Quaternary terrace gravels was deposited during glacial phases, i.e. the succession of terraces partly reflects the Quaternary climatic fluctuations. (Original drawing by Kaiser.)

times open to question because tectonic movements can also produce such structures and because, in rivers near the sea, the opposite conditions prevail. During glacial phases, sea level was greatly lowered and therefore the gradient of the river, and hence its power to erode, increased. Optimal conditions for sedimentation occurred during the interglacials when at times sea level was higher than it is now. For these terraces Zeuner coined the descriptive term "thalassostatic".

The above mentioned variations of sea level are known as "eustatic" changes. During the glacial phases, when much water was withdrawn from the oceans to form extensive ice sheets, sea level probably fell by about 90 m; with all the ice melted, sea level would be 50 m. higher than it is now. Corresponding to each stand in sea level is a marine terrace with wave-cut notches and caves, pebbles, a typical littoral fauna, prehistoric remains, and dunes. These yield important evidence concerning the Quaternary climate and have been especially well studied in the Mediterranean area (Blanc, Pfannenstiel, Zeuner). The altitude of successive terraces decreases continuously in the course of the Quaternary, so obviously another movement is superimposed on the glacially controlled fluctuations of sea level. In interpreting the height of marine terraces for stratigraphic purposes it must always be borne in mind that local tectonic movements can falsify the picture.

In the formerly glaciated areas of Scandinavia, Canada, Iceland, etc., melting of the ice has led to isostatic uplifts which have altered the original levels of the terraces.

TABLE 15

PEBBLE ANALYSES OF TWO GRAVELS, FROM SILESIA (QUARTZ=10, AFTER ZEUNER, 1933)

	QUARTZ	GNEISS	PORPHYRY	KULM GRAYWACKE
Pliocene gravel	10	11·4	11·0	0
U. Pleistocene gravel . . .	10	20·2 ..	12·3	10·2

WEATHERING PHENOMENA AND MINERALOGY

Since chemical weathering is retarded in cold climates, the Quaternary river gravels are much more variegated than those of the Tertiary, in which little other than the most resistant types of pebbles remain (Table 15, and fig. 42). Like desert sediments, they contain such easily weathered minerals as feldspar, hornblende, and pyroxenes. Pebbles of clay and sand are preserved in the gravels, and it is considered that these must have been frozen hard at the time of transport. It has recently been observed that this does happen in Spitzbergen. While this is probably the correct explanation in most cases, it should, strictly speaking, be pointed out that clay pellets can

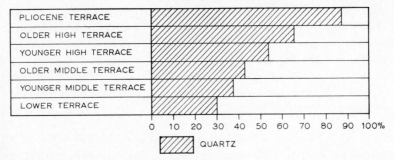

The proportion of quartz pebbles is very high in the Tertiary terraces, subject to intense chemical weathering, but lower in the Quaternary Period. Sometimes as in the lower terrace, it is very low. (From data by Kaiser and Maarleveld, collated by L. Ahorner.)

occur in nonglacial sediments where the distance of transport is very short as, for example, in the Triassic sandstones of the Moenkopi Formation of Utah (McKee, 1954, Plate IVa) or in the Miocene sediments of Trinidad (Kugler and Saunders, 1959) (see also Bell, 1940).

As a result of the temperate climate of the interglacial phases, the upper layers of the calcareous glacial sediments, especially the loess, gravels, and

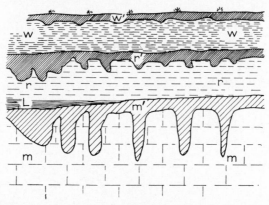

FIG. 43. FOSSIL SOILS AS INDICATORS OF QUATERNARY CLIMATES

Section near Munich. m = Deckenschotter (Mindel); r = High Terrace gravels (Riss); w = Low Terrace gravels (Würm); L = loess. The loamy soils which form in the respective interglacials are indicated by m′ and r′, and divide the section into 3 glacial and 2 interglacial phases. w′ indicates postglacial soil. The relative lengths of the postglacial, Riss-Würm Interglacial, and Mindel-Riss Interglacial phases = 1:3:12. Thickness of section 10 m. (From Penck & Brückner, 1909.)

calciferous boulder clays, were decalcified and altered with the formation of loams (fig. 43). The different lengths of the interglacials show up in the variable thickness of the leached zone (10 cm. to several meters). By

Fig. 44. *Glossopteris*, an indicator of cool Permo-Carbo-niferous climates in Gondwanaland

Leaves some 10 cms. long. (From Gothan, Vorgesch. d. Pflanzenwelt, 1912.)

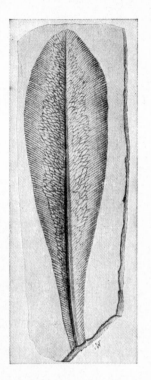

comparison with the amount of postglacial weathering, it has been possible to make a rough estimate of the duration of each interglacial (Penck and Brückner in the Alps, G. F. Kay in North America). In doing so it is assumed that the interglacial climates remained constant and re-sembled that of the postglacial period. This is by no means certain, and Hunt and Sokoleff, for example, consider that the thick early Pleistocene soils in the Rocky Mountains were produced by a climate unlike ours. Climatically controlled local differences in the Pleistocene soils of south Ger-many (Brunnacker) and Lower Austria (Fink) can be readily demonstrated. Thus chernozems formed in the drier parts of the loess belt, and "sol lessivé" in the wetter ones.

Taber (1950) put forward an unusual type of climatic interpretation when he suggested that the presence of well-preserved liquid inclusions in quartz crystals in Carolina showed that the soils containing them could not have developed in the periglacial zone since there, large liquid inclusions are damaged by frost.

"Ice crystals" provide doubtful evidence of climate. It seems certain that these delicate needles, crystallized in wet mud by freezing, may be preserved, but it is not certain that all the things so identified really are ice crystals. They have been described from the Precambrian of Russia (Lungers-hausen), the Devonian of North America (Clarke, Schuchert), the Gondwana Beds of Southwest Africa (Martin), the Verrucano of Tuscany (Redini, Häntzschel), the Rotliegendes of the Nahe Basin (Reinecke), the Muschel-kalk of Baden (Pfannenstiel), the Upper Cretaceous of South Dakota and Texas (Udden), and the Pleistocene of Lake Bonneville (Mark). Crystals other than ice, e.g., gypsum, may have been responsible. Besides, ice crystals do not prove a cold climate but only the action of frost, which can occur quite close to the equator, e.g., in the Sahara at the present time.

It has occasionally been assumed that the green iron silicate glauconite forms preferentially in relatively cool sea water, but Galliher's (1935) map of the distribution of glauconite in Recent sediments shows no such relation-ship. It can probably be said, though, that glauconite is not diagnostic of very warm seas (see Cloud, 1955). This would explain why it is not known

from the sediments of the hot equatorial zone of the Upper Cretaceous and
Tertiary Periods (Shatski, 1954).

PLANTS

Plants are of prime importance in the Tertiary and, above all, in the
Quaternary. Among pre-Tertiary plant occurrences, only the Gondwana
floras, with the "ferns" *Glossopteris* (fig. 44) and *Gangamopteris*, merit
attention since they were associated with glacial deposits and so may be
held to have flourished in a cold climate. Typical of the plants of the
Quaternary glacial phases of Central Europe, are *Dryas octopetala*, the arctic
willow (*Salix polaris*), and the dwarf birch (*Betula nana*) (fig. 45). Nowadays,

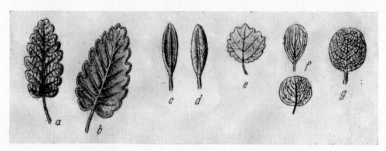

FIG. 45. PLANTS OF THE ARCTIC TUNDRA DURING THE QUATERNARY GLACIATION

a-b, *Dryas octopetala*; c-d, *Loiseleuria* (*Azalea*) *procumbens*; e, *Betula nana*; f, *Salix polaris*;
g, *Salix herbacea*, about actual size. (From A. Heim, 1919.)

these plants appear mostly in the far north or in high mountains, but then
they were widespread throughout the treeless tundras of Central Europe.
Since the southern limit of the present tundra more or less coincides with the
10° C isotherm for the warmest month, it has been calculated that the
Pleistocene temperatures of the areas where these shrubs occur must have
been 6–10° C lower than today's.

Contrariwise, the remains of the beaver (*Castor fiber*) in the tundras of
eastern Siberia indicate that this region must once have supported temperate
woodlands—an ingenious example of an "indirect" climatic indicator
(Arembovski).

The conifers are generally regarded as indicators of cool climates. Some,
e.g., juniper, spruce, larch, pine, spread right into the polar zone and fig. 39
shows a locality where *Larix dahurica* is thriving in the permafrost area.
They are almost completely absent from tropical lowlands; in these latitudes
they favor the mountains where, as Humboldt saw in Mexico, they are
often associated with palms. Conifers obviously migrated far south through
North America during the Ice Ages, for *Picea glauca* and *Picea mariana*,
which now grow around Lake Huron and farther north, were flourishing in
Texas during the Last Glaciation (Potzger & Tharp) while *Picea* and *Abies*
were living in Florida (Davis).

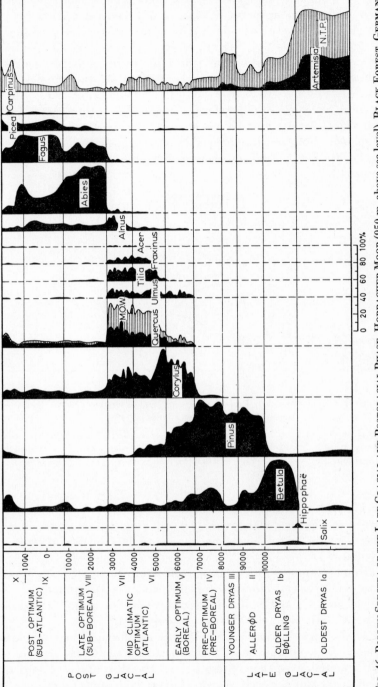

Fig. 46. Pollen Spectra of the Late Glacial and Postglacial Phase, Horbacher Moor (950 m. above sea level), Black Forest, Germany. The section about 6 m. deep through peat and gyttja covers a period of 15,000 years. Cold climates are best shown by a great increase in the amount of birch and non-tree pollen (N.T.P.), warm climates, by the predominance of oak, elm, lime, etc. (mixed oak woodland, M.O.W.), e.g. in the postglacial Climatic Optimum (after G. Lang).

Generally speaking, the interglacial strata contain floras similar to those which thrive in the same areas today with, in addition, particularly in the earlier interglacials, some species which require more favorable conditions. In this category may be included the vine, *Vitis sylvestris*, and the Pontian Alpine rose, *Rhododendron ponticum*, which no longer grow in the Inn valley but are present in the Höttinger Breccia of the Mindel-Riss Interglacial.

Pollen spectra have proved to be of great importance as they enable us to detect even slight climatic fluctuations in the Quaternary and even in the Tertiary (fig. 46). Fundamental papers on this subject include those of Erdtmann, Faegri, Firbas, Godwin, Iversen, Overbeck, Pflug, Pokrovskaya, and Thomson.

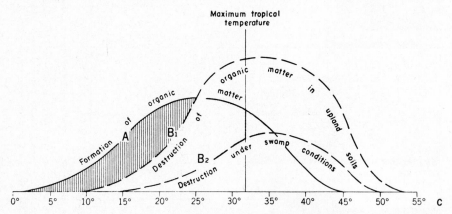

FIG. 47. RELATIONSHIP BETWEEN PLANT GROWTH, DECOMPOSITION AND RATE OF ACCUMULATION OF PLANT DEBRIS

A= rate of plant growth (maximum at temperature of about 25° C); B_1= decomposition of plant material in soils, B_2, in swamps. The shaded areas indicate where growth is faster than decomposition, i.e. where organic matter can accumulate (after Mohr, and van Baren, 1954).

The possible *sources of error* in pollen analyses include:

(*a*) the resistance of the pollen grains to weathering. They can, therefore, easily survive erosion and redeposition in a quite different bed (Iversen's "secondary pollen");

(*b*) the distance through which many pollens are carried by wind and water. Aario found Recent *Tilia* pollen in Lapland almost 400 miles north of the limits of the lime, and Erdtmann has discovered many tree and grass pollens in the Atlantic 550 miles from the nearest land.

Nowadays, the great majority of *peat bogs* are forming in temperate climates which offer conditions most favorable to the abundant accumulation of plant material, even though they are not the areas of most luxuriant vegetation (fig. 47). This is clearly shown by every map of peat distribution (fig. 48) and A. W. Giles has calculated that more than 90% of all present-day peat bogs lie more than 40° N of the equator. It is plain, however, that peat can also appear in quite different climatic conditions wherever the tectonic environment is favourable; rapid subsidence of the substrate and consequent rapid sedimentation also give rise to peat formation. These tectonic conditions were fulfilled in many parts of the world during the Carboniferous and Tertiary periods, and we have reason to believe that at those times, unlike now, a great many peat swamps formed in the tropics. Isolated peat bogs do occur in the tropics even at the present time (Straka, 1960).

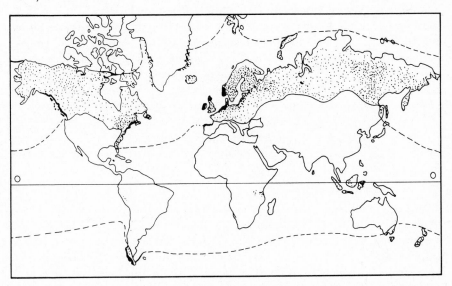

Fig. 48. Present Distribution of Peat Bogs (after Früh & Schröter, simplified from von Bülow's "Moorkunde" 1925)

Schlechtendahl, in 1896, described frost markings on the leaves of *Carpinus* and *Fagus* from the Miocene of Niederlausitz, but it is very doubtful whether they really are frost markings. In any case such markings, like ice crystals, do not by any means form only in cold climates.

Further reading: BADER, 1960; L. S. BERG, 1958.

ANIMALS

Land Animals

In this field too, most is known about the Quaternary. During the Ice Age, the tundras were inhabited by white grouse (*Lagopus*), lemmings (*Myodes*), arctic fox (*Canis lagopus*), arctic hare (*Lepus variabilis*), reindeer (*Rangifer tarandus*), and musk ox (*Ovibos moschatus*). Even the now extinct large mammals, mammoth (*Mammotheus primigenius*), woolly rhinoceros (*Rhinoceros tichorhinus*), etc., roamed there. Among this fauna, the mam-

moth, in particular, has been shown to have lived in a great many areas,
e.g., Europe, Siberia, Hokkaido, and North America. It is noteworthy that
the woolly rhinoceros is absent from North America. The famous discoveries
of complete corpses of mammoth in the ground ice of Siberia (comprehensive
account by Popov, 1956), and of woolly rhinoceros in oil-saturated silt in
Galicia, as well as the graphic drawings and paintings of prehistoric man
have all revealed the adaptations required for life in cold climates. Zeuner
has also carefully analyzed a Pleistocene insect fauna from Galicia.

The mountain marmot too, was much more widely distributed during
glacial phases than it is now, and its presence in north central New Mexico
proves that there the snow line was lowered by 1500 m.

Interglacial phases are characterized by the presence of a modern fauna,
together with such extinct species as *Rhinoceros merckii* and *Elephas
antiquus*. It should also be mentioned that there lived in central Europe,
the marsh turtle (*Emys orbicularis*), which now occurs only sporadically, and
many gastropods which have now migrated to southern Europe, e.g.,
Belgrandia marginata in interglacial strata at Lehringen in Lower Saxony
(Boettger); *Helicigona banatica* which is now found only in the southern
Carpathians was present in Czechoslovakia (Ložek).

Further reading: FARRAND, 1961

Marine Organisms

Marine organisms also afford important information concerning the
Quaternary climates. For example, the polar lamellibranch, *Yoldia* (*Portlandia*) *arctica* has been found in late glacial sediments of the eastern Baltic.
On the other hand, the present Lusitanian lamellibranch *Tapes aureus*
characterizes sediments of the last interglacial in the Eem Sea of central
Europe. In Greenland, Franz Josef Land, and Spitzbergen, raised beaches
dating from the postglacial Climatic Optimum, carry the edible mussel,
Mytilus edulis, which no longer survives in these latitudes. Cold and warm
water forams can likewise be distinguished from each other, and are of some
significance in working out the stratigraphic succession in deep-sea cores.
Warm water forams which appear in the Atlantic include *Globigerinoides
sacculifera* and *Globorotalia menardii*; *Globigerina bulloides*, and *Globigerina
inflata* live in cooler water. In *Globigerina pachyderma*, the test is most
commonly sinistrally coiled in cold, but dextrally coiled in warm water in
the North Atlantic. The boundary between the two forms coincides more
or less with the 7·2° C April isotherm (Ericson, 1959, Bandy, 1960).

The Greenland whale (*Balaena mysticetus*), detected by Jux and Rosenbauer in the Lower Low Terrace of the Rhine, is indicative of an arctic
climate in that area during the Younger Dryas period (*c.* 10,500 B.C.).

Further reading: ANTEVS, 1928.

6

Evidence
of
Arid Climates

"Figurez-vous, disait-il, qu'un certain soir, en plein
Sahara . . ."
Alphonse Daudet, Tartarin de Tarascon, 1872.

RED BED AND SALT DEPOSITS

It has already been pointed out, that red beds are indicative not of
extreme aridity, but only of a certain degree of dryness. The really important evidence of hot, arid climates is afforded by deposits of *evaporites;* rock
salt, potash salts, and gypsum (Lotze). Precipitation of salts takes place,
most commonly, on or below the surface of the soils of arid regions—more
especially in steppes than in deserts since a certain amount of water is
required for transport of the salts—or in the salt lakes and lagoons of these
areas, e.g. Caspian Sea, Aral Sea, Dead Sea, etc. Therefore the world's
evaporite zones are arranged in two great belts, one north and one south of
the equator (fig. 121), corresponding on the whole to the two hot arid belts
of fig. 11. In places, e.g. in Central Asia, the evaporite zone extends far to
the north, but high temperature undoubtedly favors salt precipitation.

There is a possibility of error, for salt formation does occur on coasts and
even in the cold dry wastes of the Arctic, though certainly in much smaller
quantities and only as a temporary phenomenon (e.g. salt crusts in Greenland, Spitzbergen, etc.). Avsjuk, Markov, and Shumski describe similar
deposits from the ice-free "oases" of Antarctica. Moreover, salt separates
from sea water during freezing (Thomson and Nelson; see also Bain's
remarks), and moderate amounts of gypsum can also precipitate outside of
the evaporite zones, even in the muddy tropical mangrove swamps of New
Caledonia (J. Avias). Such cases may only very rarely, however, achieve any
paleoclimatic significance, and the same may be said of the few salt deposits
resulting from volcanic steam. Geologists have available as climatic indicators, not only really extensive beds of salt, such as the salt "seams" of the
German Zechstein sediments but also *halite pseudomorphs,* i.e. former individual salt crystals which have been replaced by sand, etc. (fig. 49). They may

form partly in salt impregnated soils (Linck, Schwarzbach) and partly on the surface (Knetsch). Sandy gypsum crystals are also common in present-day deserts (Macfadyen), but to us these are of little importance because

gypsum pseudomorphs admit of several interpretations (see section on ice crystals). Lotze has collected numerous instances of fossil occurrences of salts and has constructed maps which reveal that the evaporite belt has gradually shifted from the north polar region in the Lower Paleozoic to its present position (fig. 121). Unfortunately, corresponding data for the Southern Hemisphere are not yet available. Lotze concluded that there must therefore have been a migration of the arid zone, which probably corresponded to a gradual wandering of the equatorial zone and so of the poles.

FIG. 49. HALITE PSEUDOMORPHS Zechstein sandstone, Silesia. Specimen from Geol. Inst., Breslau (Wroclaw). Actual size. (Photograph: M. Schwarzbach.)

Rain Pits

Rain is an unexpected indicator of dry climates. Individual raindrops striking sand or mud can leave characteristic rounded impressions which are known in the fossil state from the Rotliegendes, Buntsandstein, etc. (fig. 50). They were recognized by Lyell as early as 1851 (p. 239). Of course,

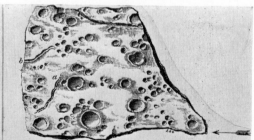

FIG. 50. RECENT AND FOSSIL RAINPITS (X1)

Left: Recent pits from a mud, Ziebice, Silesia. (Photograph: M. Schwarzbach). Right: fossil pits from Carboniferous green shale Cape Breton, Nova Scotia; from Lyell, 1851. This specimen also shows supposed animal trails (a, b). According to Lyell, the rain fell from the right.

not all impressions that have been regarded as rain pits really are so. Rising air bubbles or fish feeding on the bottom may sometimes produce similar structures (Hornstein, Strigel, Jüngst, Reineck, R. Richter). Rain pits, being indicators of isolated showers are to be expected more in arid climates than in humid. Therefore, paradoxical as it at first appears, fossilized evidence of rain is often nothing less than an indication of an arid climate. The size of fossil rain prints compares with those found today, i.e. mean diameter 5 mm. Hence Lyell long ago deduced that the density of the atmosphere must always have been the same as it is now.

DESERTS AND WINDS

Deserts are the characteristic land forms produced by very arid climates. In them, physical weathering caused by temperature changes predominates. Exfoliation, contraction cracks, and the like form continuously, and chemical weathering is retarded. Thick deposits of pebbles and gravel are therefore developed. These are carried by sheet-floods during periods of heavy rain to build up blankets of unsorted, mostly unbedded, conglomeratic sediments which Lawson called fanglomerates because they are deposited in fan-shaped alluvial cones. Fossil examples occur, for example, in the Rotliegendes of Europe.

Rather finer-grained sediments carrying small unweathered pebbles of feldspar (arkoses) likewise appear in arid regions, though Krynine's observations in the present savanna lands of Mexico show that they are certainly not confined to extremely arid areas.

Silicification is another characteristic of dry climates (as was already mentioned in dealing with laterites, Chapter 4). The petrified forests of the Rotliegendes of Germany, or the Trias (Chinle Formation) of North America (Petrified Forest National Monument, Arizona), or the beds of carnelian in the Buntsandstein all afford fossil examples.

Crusts of calcite cover extensive tracts of the steppe lands (pedocals: caliche). In the highlands of Mexico, they appear where the annual rainfall is below 25 inches and the temperature for the greater part of the year above 25° C. They are associated with xerophytic vegetation (Arellano). In the southeastern part of New Mexico, they characterize the relatively arid phases of the Plio-Pleistocene period (Bretz and Horberg). Among older sediments, they appear in the Rotliegendes of Germany, in the Pliocene of Queensland (Whitehouse), and in the Quaternary "pluvials" of Spain (Rutte) and elsewhere.

In areas which lack a vegetational cover, the effect of the *wind* is very apparent, as it heaps up the sand into dunes. (These can, of course, originate in coastal areas with a heavier rainfall). Many of the cross-bedded sandstones of the Permo-Trias of Europe or North America belong in this category. Ripples are very abundantly developed, but in the older sediments, it must first be established that they are not water ripples. According to Twenhofel, differentiation is possible on the basis of the ripple index, i.e. the ratio of wave length to amplitude. In wind ripples, this exceeds 15, i.e. they are very flat; in water ripples, on the other hand, it is less than 15 (fig. 51). Thus the ripples in the Coconino Sandstone of Arizona were formed by the wind (McKee) while those of the Triassic Moenkopi Formation developed in water (McKee, 1954).

As a result of transport by wind, the sand grains are often fine-grained and well-rounded, and have a matt surface (Cailleux, fig. 52). The driving sand frequently gives rise to wind abrasion with the formation of ventifacts

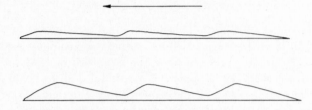

FIG. 51. WIND RIPPLES (ABOVE), AND WATER RIPPLES (BELOW)
(after Twenhofel, 1926)

(dreikanter). But none of these phenomena is restricted to hot deserts; they also appear in the cold wastes of Northern Greenland (Fristrup) and else-where, and in the unvegetated windswept steppes of the Pleistocene and post-Pleistocene periods (fig. 53). In fact, ventifacts are very uncommon in the Rotliegendes or the Buntsandstein—individual finds are described as something special—whereas they are exceedingly common in the Quaternary (see fig. 59). A shortcoming of ventifacts as climatic indicators is that they

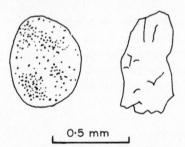

0·5 mm

FIG. 52. SAND GRAINS BLASTED BY WIND (LEFT), AND NOT (RIGHT)

The sand-blasted grain is rounded and has a matt surface (Weichsel i.e. Vistula sand, Warsaw); the other is clear and angular (fluvio-glacial sand from an esker near Stockholm) (after Cailleux, 1942).

occasionally appear to originate in non-arid regions; Mülleried observed them in the tropic zone in Mexico. Flowing water, too, can produce facetted pebbles similar to ventifacts (Taljaard, Kuenen, Frankel).

Fine dusty *loess* is a sediment that is unusually widely distributed over cool or even cold steppe lands. In general, as its distribution and fauna clearly show, it is of glacial origin. The Pleistocene cold phases with their barren, almost unvegetated, outwash fans, gravel spreads, and steppes did in fact afford optimum conditions for the transport and deposition of loess, though dust storms certainly also occurred at times during the interglacials (e.g. loess in Alsace) and, indeed, loess is still being formed in China (Frenzel, 1960). Pre-Quaternary loess deposits have been described from the Devonian of Siberia, and by Woodworth from the Permo-Carboniferous of South America.

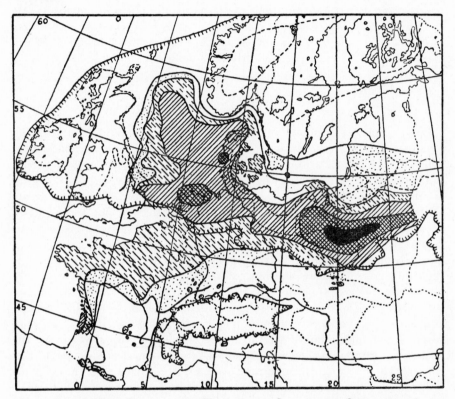

FIG. 53. MEAN FREQUENCY OF WIND-WORKED SANDS IN THE QUATERNARY

Black > 80%, ▨ 60–80%, ▥ 40–60%, ▧ 20–40%, ⬚ 10–20%, unshaded (in areas examined) < 10%. The maximum extent of ice is also shown. Intensity of reworking by wind particularly great in periglacial area; it also increased eastward (after Cailleux, 1942).

Inselbergs form striking topographic features in hot arid and semiarid regions. They rise abruptly and steeply from flat plains often for no known petrological reason (e.g. unusual hardness of the rock and the like). Only rarely do they appear in the polar zone (e.g. in Lapland and Newfoundland) (H. Schrepfer). Brinkmann has described fossil inselbergs from the Miocene of Spain and has pointed out further examples in the Buntsandstein of Spain and Triers and the Rotliegendes of Northern Bohemia. This land form always attests a desert origin.

Many geological processes which now occur only in arid regions did undoubtedly operate in humid areas too in times past, when there was little or no vegetational cover on dry land. Then probably it was possible for ventifacts to form in areas adjacent to coal swamps and be washed into the swamps and included in the coal seams, as H. C. Mantle records in Leicestershire. The Paleozoic fanglomerates, arkoses, etc., could probably also form in most land areas, and from their presence therefore, it is by no means safe to conclude that the climate was very arid. E. Kaiser, Beurlen, and others have pointed this out; in this connection, J. Walther, E. Stromer, and others have spoken of "Urwüsten", i.e. primitive deserts.

Further reading: BAGNOLD, 1954; GRAHMANN, 1932; HIGGINS, 1956; MORTENSEN, 1927; v. WISSMANN, 1938.

PLANTS

Plants adapt themselves in many ways to life in arid climates, and botanists, in fact, recognize a group of characters (xeromorphic characters) which develop under arid conditions. Small size and sparse development of the leaves, and sunken stomata are distinctive features. A "physiological aridity" is also to be found, however, in upland moors, where such plants as the Ericaceae display "xerophytic" characters that are not dependent on an arid climate. Moreover, such an apparent "xeromorphism" is not uncommonly developed, in the tropical rain forests, and in the Japanese umbrella pine (*Sciadopitys*) which is often present in the Tertiary lignites of the Rhine. If we knew nothing of modern trees, we would probably incorrectly conclude from the sunken stomata of *Sciadopytis* that the climate was very arid. The Devonian Psilophyte *Rhynia*, one of the first land plants, also shows "physiological aridity", in the relatively small transpiration surfaces and high relative area of conduction of its vascular strand; the cause is probably that the plant possessed only an imperfect vascular system (Filzer). Therefore, all these features can only be utilized with care.

The *density of veining* of the leaf increases with increasing aridity, because in arid areas, increased evaporation must be compensated for by a more closely spaced vascular system. The leaves on the sunny and shady sides of a single tree differ for this reason; hence it is understandable that Zeuner's stimulating attempt to assess the paleoclimatic significance of this feature for the Miocene flora of Oeningen has, as yet, yielded no reliable results. However, it will probably be rewarding to pursue this method further.

ANIMALS

The frequent *preservation of tracks* of large animals may be mentioned first since these are often the sole surviving fossils in rocks deposited under arid conditions, e.g. *Cheirotherium* in the Buntsandstein. Their preservation as fossils is in accordance with the retention of wheel marks, etc., in modern deserts for tens or even hundreds of years (Mortensen).

The two lungfish, *Lepidosiren* and *Protopterus*, which now live only in Queensland, Africa, and South America are adapted to life in arid conditions. Unlike a third genus, *Epiceratodus*, they can survive even complete drying out of their pools. Whether this is true of their much more widely distributed Mesozoic ancestors is not known but from the accompanying climatic evidence, it appears that *Ceratodus*, common in the Trias of Germany and elsewhere (fig. 54), really was an inhabitant of the arid zone.

FIG. 54. TOOTH OF LUNG-FISH *Ceratodus*, KEUPER SANDSTONE, UPPER SILESIA
Specimen in Geol. Inst. Breslau (x3). (Photograph: M. Schwarzbach.)

Of the modern inhabitants of the cooler steppe areas, the jerboa (*Alactaga*) the earless marmot (*Spermophilus*), the steppe marmot or bobac (*Arctomys bobac*), the dwarf rat-hare (*Lagomys pusillus*), the saiga antelope (*Antilope saiga*) and several others are known from Pleistocene deposits, and indicate a dry, continental climate when they lived. The saiga antelope, which at present dwells in eastern Russia and southwest Siberia, occurred even in the west of France. The Irish elk (*Megaceros hibernicus*), which became extinct in the postglacial period, also testifies to parkland and steppe; its 4-meter spread of antlers certainly must have excluded any possibility of life in close woodlands.

As Thenius showed, the proportion of Lower Pliocene steppe dwellers in Europe increases toward the southeast, i.e. in the direction of increasing aridity.

Further reading: NEHRING, 1890; STROMER, 1939.

7

Evidence
of
Humid Climates

Harris said: "How about when it rained?"
J. K. JEROME, Three Men in a Boat, 1889.

INORGANIC EVIDENCE

Humid and not too cold climates differ from deserts in that chemical weathering is very active. The widely distributed white clayey sediment, *kaolin*, which originates from the weathering of feldspar-rich granites, porphyries, etc., is a typical deposit which is of economic importance as a china clay. It is often carried into basins to form the lignitic clays and the like, included in the Tertiary succession. We have already seen (Chapter 4) that kaolin appears in the deeper parts of laterite profiles, but it also seems possible for it to develop in slightly cooler but still sufficiently humid climates.

Traces of the once greater rainfall of the Pleistocene "pluvial" phases are

FIG. 55. OLD LAKE TERRACES OF LAKE BONNEVILLE, UTAH
Evidence of a pluvial phase (after Gilbert, 1890). See fig. 56.

conspicuous in all deserts, where they show up in widely ramifying river systems, fossil remains, prehistoric artifacts, and in classical fashion in the splendidly preserved lake terraces of Lake Bonneville and Lake Lahonton in the now almost dry Great Basin (figs. 55–56; fundamental papers by Gilbert, and Upham). These terraces were correctly identified by the Franciscan monk Sylvestre Veléz de Escalante as early as 1776 (Ives).

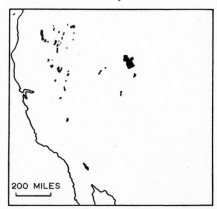 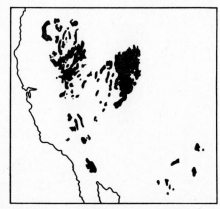

FIG. 56. PRESENT LAKES (LEFT), AND PLEISTOCENE (PLUVIAL) LAKES (RIGHT) IN THE GREAT BASIN, UTAH

In the N.E., compare the present Great Salt Lake, with the vast Pleistocene Lake Bonneville (after Meinzer and R. F. Flint, 1947).

PLANTS

Peat bogs, and thus coal seams too, are always associated with wet, and often also with cool, climates (Chapter 5). This applies to an unusual degree to the constantly waterlogged raised bogs where *Sphagnum* moss is typical.

A fluctuation between wetter and rather less wet periods is apparent in postglacial peats in the now greater, now lesser humification. In relatively arid phases, the peat decomposed to a greater extent and gave rise to light beds (recurrence surfaces); among these, the much discussed *Grenzhorizont* of the north German peat bogs has been equated with the postglacial Climatic Optimum. Research by Granlund, Overbeck, and others has shown that there were several dry phases in the postglacial period.

The Tertiary floras also provide important pointers to the amount of rainfall, for they may be compared with Recent genera. From such comparison, it is evident that the aridity of the Great Basin continuously increased during the Tertiary period (fig. 101). Chaney has calculated the following values for the annual rainfall of that area:

Bridge Creek, Upper Oligocene	40 inches
Mascall, probably Miocene	27 inches
Sonoma Tuff, Lower or Middle Miocene ..	20 inches or over
Santa Clara, Upper Pliocene..	20 inches or over
Altura, Upper Pliocene	16 inches or over

The present rainfall of the John Bay Basin also amounts to 16 inches. Axelrod has, in fact, reconstructed a Miocene-Pliocene rainfall map for southwest U.S.A.

Tree ferns are moisture-loving plants which flourish luxuriantly in the heavy rainfall areas even in cool latitudes, e.g. in parts of New Zealand which have winter snows.

In very wet climates, the leaves of many plants develop conspicuous *drip-points* (fig. 57). These serve to drain off rain water quickly. Drip-points are especially common in tropical and subtropical rain forests, but also occur in the wetter parts of the temperate zone; they are unusual in rain-deficient areas. G. Schindehütte pointed out the climatic significance of drip-points in the Miocene flora of Eichelskopf in central Germany as early as 1907, and F. Kirchheimer systematically studied several German Tertiary floras from the Aquitanian to the Pliocene for leaves showing this feature. From the differing proportion of such leaves in the whole flora, it may probably be deduced that rainfall conditions varied in the course of the Tertiary period. In Germany, the Lower Miocene floras of Lauterbach and Eichelskopf, for example, are rich in drip-pointed leaves; so is the flora of Wiesa near Kamenz.

FIG. 57. DRIP-POINT OF A LOWER TERTIARY LEAF

Apocynphyllum dechem, Oligocene, Rhineland (xl) (after Weyland, Paleontogr. 1943.)

More precise statistical results are afforded by the work of Chaney and Sanborn (Table 16); from these figures, it is apparent that the Goshen flora was a moisture-loving type. The opposite may not, however, be deduced from the smaller percentage of drip-points in the Bridge Creek flora as this developed in a temperate climate, and must, therefore, be compared with, say, the present redwood forests of high rainfall areas (annual precipitation 20–60 inches).

TABLE 16

PROPORTION OF LEAVES WITH DRIP-POINTS
(DICOTYLEDONS; AFTER CHANEY AND SANBORN)

Modern floras	Panama lowlands (tropic)	76%
	Californian Redwoods (temperate)	9%
Fossil floras	Goshen flora (Eocene)	47%
	Bridge Creek flora (U. Oligocene)	10%

8

Atmospheric Pressure Distribution and Thunderstorms

I would give part of my life to know the mean barometric reading in Paradise.

G. C. LICHTENBERG (1742–1799)

THE RECONSTRUCTION OF PRESSURE SYSTEMS

The approximate position of high- and low-pressure areas is revealed by climatic maps, and when the distribution of climatic belts during any one epoch in the past is known sufficiently accurately, the pressure distribution can also be given in broad outline. But our climatic maps for past ages are far too inaccurate, and suffice at most to allow only isolated statements of this kind. Thus, for example, the desert belts, in so far as they are known, can be equated with high-pressure areas. In any case, such theoretical considerations produce only fairly vague details of pressure distribution.

Wind is of much greater paleoclimatic significance, for since its origin and direction are controlled by the pressure gradient it likewise permits the reconstruction of pressure distribution. The direction of the wind in past periods can be demonstrated directly, and leads to precise conclusions regarding pressure distribution. Here, we are interested, not so much in the fact that the wind did blow, for we have already discussed its geological effects where they were particularly conspicuous, namely in deserts (Chapter 6). Its strength and, above all, direction are now of much greater significance.

More than with other climatic phenomena, it must be borne in mind that random events may be recorded which need not always correspond with average conditions throughout the year (see section on wind direction, particularly under 1, 5, 11 and 12).

Wind Strength

Only rarely can the wind strength be determined with fair accuracy from geological data though it may, in many cases, be estimated from the grain

TABLE 17

RELATIONSHIP BETWEEN WIND VELOCITY AND GRAIN
SIZE OF SAND (AFTER SOKOLOV)

WIND VELOCITY IN M.P.H.	MAXIMUM GRAIN SIZE IN mm.
10·3–15·4	0·25
15·4–19·3	0·5
22·5–26·2	1·0
26·2–29·9	1·5

size of the sediments (Table 17). H. Poser found, thereby, that the late glacial dunes of north Germany were formed largely by winds with a velocity of 5·6 m/sec. (12 m.p.h.), which corresponds to strength 5 on the Beaufort Scale 2 m. above the ground.

Typhoons, with wind velocities of as much as 190 m.p.h., can leave coarse, poorly sorted pebble beds behind on atolls. McKee observed such sediments on Jaluit-Atoll, in the southern part of the Marshall Islands, after hurricane "Ophelia" on 7th January 1958 and considered that he could detect similar older deposits.

Wind Direction

Wind direction may be determined in a number of different ways.

1. Form of dunes and wind ripples.—Transverse dunes have a cross-section which has a gentle windward slope and steeper lee-slope. The horns of barchans curve around to point in the direction in which the wind is blowing unlike those of paraboloid dunes, whose extremities are fixed by vegetation so that the central part migrates more quickly (fig. 58). Seifs lie parallel to the wind direction.

SOURCES OF ERROR.—The position of the flatter and steeper slopes may be altered by later winds. Solger regarded the postglacial sickle-shaped inland dunes of north Germany, whose west faces were flattened, as barchans, formed by east winds, but developing flat western slopes because of later winds. Louis and Woldstedt, however, look upon them as paraboloid dunes formed at a time when the west wind was already blowing. Ripples can indicate small-scale local conditions. Prevailing winds need not have coincided with dominant winds, i.e. those which had the greatest effect in producing sedimentary structures. Thus, according to Ives, the dune-like mega-ripples of the Great Salt Lake area were produced by the stronger N.W. winds, although the wind blows most often from the S.E.

EXAMPLES.—The asymmetrical "sand ridges", up to 10 m. high, under the Kupferschiefer (Lower Zechstein—"Weissliegendes") were recorded as dunes by Meinecke; since their flat sides face S.W. the wind blew from that direction. From the orientation of the barchans, in the Permian red beds of Central England—opening to the S.W.—Shotton deduced a N.E. wind.

Keilhack described 1500 m. long seif dunes running dead straight from N.W.–S.E. in the Miocene sediments of Hohenbocka, and produced by a N.W. wind (the dune orientation alone, of course, indicates either a N.W. or a S.E. wind). Northerly winds gave rise to wind ripples in the Permian Coconino Sandstone (Reiche, McKee; see Chapter 6).

2. Cross-bedding in the dunes.—Cross-bedded units accumulate on the lee side of the dune, but the dip directions vary greatly because the plane of deposition is curved. (Jungst, Shotton.)

SOURCES OF ERROR.—Flowing water can also give rise to cross-bedding: too few measurements can lead to a false conclusion.

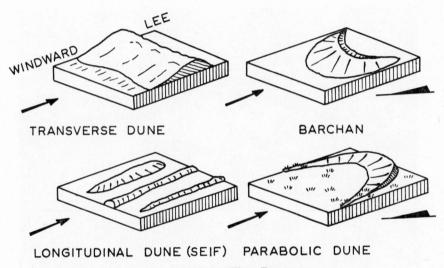

FIG. 58. DUNES AND WIND DIRECTION

EXAMPLES.—Permian dunes in England (Shotton)—Paleogene dunes in the western foreland of the Urals formed by a N.E. wind (Lungershausen)—late glacial dunes near Valdivia (Chile) caused by N. to W.N.W. winds. (Illies).

3. Wind-abraded pavements.—Polished surfaces produced by wind abrasion face into the wind.

EXAMPLES.—Ventifacts near the base of loess of Würm age in Silesia face S.E. (fig. 59), so the wind was southeasterly. Postglacial facetted blocks east of Cologne were caused by west winds (Jux)—Pleistocene ventifacts in the Big Horn Mountains by N.W. winds (Sharp).

4. Position of source areas.—The grain size of the eroded material decreases away from source till, in extreme cases, loess finally appears as the finest sediment.

SOURCES OF ERROR.—The relation of dunes, etc., to their source area is not always sharply defined. Grain size varies not only horizontally but also vertically, often to a much greater degree; even when we are dealing with what we consider to be a single horizon, we may in fact be comparing sediments which are not strictly contemporaneous.

EXAMPLES.—East of the Rhine plain near Cologne, there is a sequence, sand, sandy loess, loess (Breddin, Jux), suggesting that the wind blew from the west. The eolian sands of the Last Glaciation are coarser in Holstein than they are further west, hence the wind was easterly (Dücker).

5. Rain pits.—These are elongated in the direction of the wind, and because of the oblique impact of the drop, have unequally developed ramparts which are absent on the side from which the wind blew (Reineck).

FIG. 59. WIND-BLASTED PAVEMENT BELOW UPPER PLEISTOCENE LOESS, Niemcza, Silesia
Arrows indicate the larger wind-polished faces. These face south-east (after Tietze, 1914).

SOURCES OF ERROR.—The wind direction at the time of an individual shower may vary greatly from the prevailing direction, thus giving a chance value.

EXAMPLES.—Rain drops described by Lyell (fig. 50, right) from the Carboniferous of Nova Scotia, and in the Rotliegendes of Martinstein (Nahe Basin, Reinecke) where the wind blew from the southwest.

6. Accumulation of mussels, etc.—In bays or inlets of seas and lakes, mussels and other shells tend to accumulate on the shore against which the wind-generated waves break. Mistakes can occur, because we usually can only see a small section of the shore line.

EXAMPLES.—In west Holstein, the beach sands of a narrow arm of the Eem Sea, which dates from the Last Interglacial, carry winnowed valves of mussels virtually only on the east shore (Dittmer): therefore the wind was westerly. Pollen accumulations tend to occur on the eastern margins of pools of Eocene age in the Geiseltal moor (Voigt), another indication of a west wind.

7. Water ripples.—Ripples formed in shallow water may also reflect the prevailing wind direction, though often the trend of the coast line has a greater influence on ripple orientation than has wind direction. This constitutes a possible source of error.

EXAMPLES.—The N.W.–S.E. trending ripples in the Lower Carboniferous Bedford Formation of Ohio. According to Hyde (1911) these were occasioned by the N.W.–S.E. trend of the coast, but Bucher, Pepper, de Witt, and Demarest all regarded them as products of a monsoon wind blowing alternately to and from a land mass in the northeast.

8. Ocean currents.—These do, in fact, correspond to the earth's major wind systems, but fossil currents can only be reconstructed from indirect evidence (see, for example, the Tertiary climatic map, fig. 105) and so they yield only very uncertain results.

9. Disposition of coral reefs.—The convex side of horseshoe atolls faces into the wind; the finer coral debris accrues mostly on the lee side (Ladd, Tracey, Wells and Emery). The attitude of the Niagaran (Silurian) reefs in North America resulted from a south wind (Lowenstam).

10. Arrangement of corries.—There is a preferential arrangement of corries on the lee slopes of mountain crests, for snow is driven there from across the crest and accumulates to give rise to corrie formation (Enquist, 1916–1917). Most of the Pleistocene corries lie on the N.E. slopes of the Black Forest and on the N.E. and E. slopes of the Riesengebirge, hence the wind was westerly.

11. Volcanic tuffs.—Numerous recent examples have shown that during volcanic eruption, ashes are carried for long distances by the wind, the deposits becoming finer-grained and thinner with increasing distance of transport. Icelandic examples are afforded by the eruptions of Hekla in 1300 and 1947 (fig. 60) (see Thorarinsson's maps), Asja in 1875, and Oerafaejökull in 1372.

SOURCES OF ERROR.—During long transport, the wind direction may change several times, e.g. the Hekla outbreak in 1947 deposited tuff in Finland (Salmi, Thorarinsson; fig. 61)—see also the Glacier Peak example dealt with later. The wind can blow in quite different directions at different altitudes. The direction of stratospheric winds during the 1883 eruption of Krakatoa is indicated by the S.W. and N.W. drift of the ash, which was thrown more than 30 miles upwards. The British National Antarctic Expedition of 1901–1904 observed that the smoke of the 13,000 ft. high Mount Erebus was borne towards the west and southwest by an easterly wind while a west wind prevailed at the foot of the mountain. Inclined vents likewise give rise to a unilateral distribution of tuffs formed of coarse, quickly deposited material. For this reason, the lapilli from the 1906 eruption of Vesuvius lie to the east of the volcano, though the wind at the time was blowing from the N.N.E. (Alfano & Friedländer, 1929, p. 61).

The earliest observations stem from the noted Swedish chemist Berzelius, who, in 1822, together with "Baron Goethe", examined the tiny Pleistocene Kammerbühl volcano near Eger. He found that ashes and scoriae had been carried to one side by the west wind. The stratigraphically oldest example

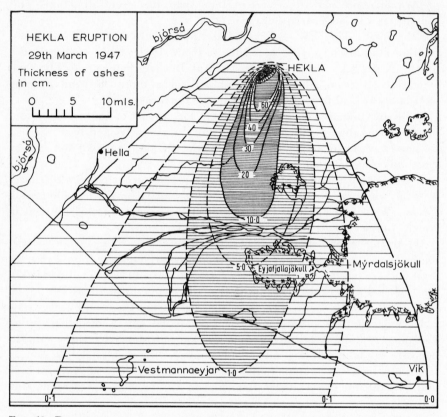

FIG. 60. DISTRIBUTION AND THICKNESS OF VOLCANIC ASH ERUPTED FROM HEKLA, ON 29th MARCH, 1947

Wind northerly (after S. Thorarinsson, 1954. Compare with fig. 61).

is the Lower Carboniferous volcano of Arthur's Seat, Edinburgh, whose tuffs lie to the south because of north winds (Peach, Oertel). The Lower Eocene tuffs of north Germany thicken northward, therefore the wind blew from the N. and N.E. (Illies). Characteristic bipyramidal quartz crystals from Mount Dore (Auvergne) occur in the Villafranchian *Mastodon* sands of Le Puy (Bout); this indicates a N.W. wind. Because of easterly winds, the tuffs of the early Quaternary Kahusi volcanic massif in the Congo are only found to the west (Boutakoff). Near Olot, in northeast Spain, tuffs lie to the east of a Quaternary volcano, and near the Laacher-See (Eifel) the pumice tuffs of Allerød age were carried partly eastward, over a distance of as much as 300 miles, and partly southward, because of W. and N.W. winds. In the case of the Glacier Peak eruption, 6700 years ago, most of the ashes were blown toward the N.E. by the prevailing S.W. wind. Rigg and Gould have explained that aberrant occurrences of ashes were caused by a depression moving eastward.

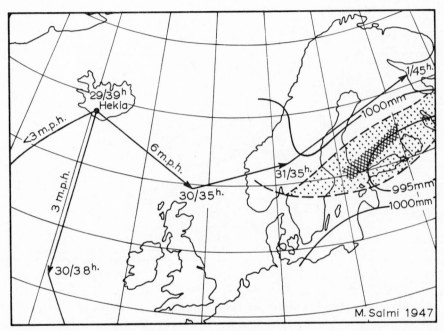

FIG. 61. TRACK OF THE HEKLA ASH FROM 29TH MARCH TO 1ST APRIL, 1947, UNDER THE
INFLUENCE OF VARIABLE WINDS

In Iceland, the fall-out was affected by northeast winds, up to an altitude of 5,000 m., between 5,000 and 9,000 m. north winds blew, above 9,000 m. ash was carried first S.E., then N.E.; over Finland, it was brought down by rain (after Salmi, 1948).

12. Overturned trees.—Trees may be overturned in the direction in which the wind is blowing. Other factors may be involved, however, e.g. the slope of the ground (Dorf, 1933), flowing volcanic ash (Dickerson, Pliocene petrified forest north of San Francisco), avalanches, and meteorites (as in Siberia, 1908). Tornados may not travel in the same direction as the prevailing wind. The many overturned tree trunks in the Oligocene lignites near Bitterfeld (central Germany) are mostly suggestive of west or northwest winds (Hintze).

13. Tree roots.—On the windward side of the tree, the roots run more nearly horizontally than on the leeward side. The roots of Carboniferous trees near Sheffield (Sorby, 1875) are indicative of west winds; winds blew from the same quarter while the Miocene trees grew near Cologne (Krames).

14. **Cross-section of tree trunks.**—The maximum diameter of the stem often lies in the direction of the prevailing wind (E. Assmann, G. Müller, fig. 62). But there is also a tendency for it to be either in a north-south orientation, or else downslope, so errors can arise. (See Chapter 25.)

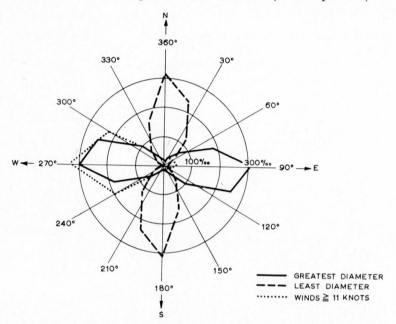

Fig. 62. Eccentricity of Spruce Trunks, and Wind Direction in Bavaria

Measurements taken 4 ft. above ground. Rose shows the frequency distribution of orientation of greatest and least diameters of the trunks, and wind direction (of winds greater than 11 knots). Prevailing west wind, therefore greatest diameter E.W. (after G. Müller, 1959).

The various climatic indicators enumerated here vary greatly in reliability and applicability; some have little more than curiosity value, since the phenomena required for the reconstruction of wind direction can probably be observed only rarely.

THUNDERSTORMS

The frequency with which thunderstorms occur varies greatly from place to place; on average, the number of thundery days each year is 322 in Java, 17 in Europe, 0·7 in Greenland. K. Andrée has given us a comprehensive account of the little that is known about thunderstorms in past epochs.

Sand-fulgurites (Blitzröhren) are of the greatest significance; they originate when lightning strikes sand and causes the sand grains to fuse together in chains which are often several meters long (fig. 63). The first description probably stems from Hermann, the learned parson of Massel, near Breslau, in 1711, although he, in fact, regarded the structure as a petrified root. Priestley's observations (1790), and Darwin's detailed account of fulgurites in the La Plata district (1832) should also be mentioned; so too should those of the Atlantic seaboard, described by J. J. Petty. The Sahara fulgurites described by Lacroix are probably partly subfossil, and correspond to a period when thunderstorms were more frequent than they are today (Schoeller).

There are, seemingly, only two known examples of real fossil fulgurites; one from the Cretaceous sands of New Jersey (Barrows, 1910), the other from the Miocene sands of Oberlausitz (W. Fischer, 1927). In neither of these cases, however, can the possibility of a very recent origin be ruled out completely.

Rock-fulgurites, caused by the melting of solid rocks, and their resolidification as glass, are known to occur on mountain peaks, e.g. Mont Blanc (Saussure, 1787). They have not yet been observed in the fossil state, for it is very unlikely that such exposed sites could ever remain uneroded.

Chapman and Alexander (1929) also regard australites, the tectites found in Australia and elsewhere, as fulgurites. Unlike other investigators, they do not explain these enigmatic vitreous rocks as meteorites, but rather as atmospheric dust fused by lightning. G. S. Hawkins (1960) considers all tectites to be fulgurites.

The fragments and beds of charcoal in the Tertiary lignites of Germany are probably a direct result of lightning: they may have originated through forest fires caused by lightning. T. M. Harris has described similar charcoal from the Jurassic rocks of Yorkshire, and from the Mesozoic strata of Greenland. Whether the fusain of the Carboniferous

FIG. 63. RECENT SAND FULGURITE, Mecklenburg.

Length 70 cm. Specimen in Geol. Inst., Rostock. (Photograph by kind permission of v. Bülow.)

bituminous coals may be explained in like manner, remains to be seen. Shattered wood fragments in the Lower Tertiary amber of East Prussia, and a Carboniferous Cordaite stem, coalified in the middle, have also been attributed to lightning.

Lastly, we must mention the Chilean saltpeter, for according to Pissis, Rogers, and van Wagenen, the nitrate resulted from nitrogen fixation caused by lightning discharges.

Further reading: ARBENZ, 1923; GRUND, 1928.

Hail

The appearance of hail is nearly always associated with thunderstorms. Over 100 years ago, Redfield interpreted the oval to angular markings in the Lower Trias Shale of New Jersey as the imprints of hailstones on mud. Though this is possible, it remains unproven.

9

Seasonal and Long-term Climatic Variations

Well, you know what I think it is—I think it's sunspots.

T. WILDER, Mrs. Antrobus, in "The Skin of Our Teeth", 1942.

SEASONAL BANDING

Banding in Recent and Glacial sediments

There is no reason to assume that the earth's axis has not been inclined throughout the last thousand million years, so we may take it for granted

FIG. 64. LATE GLACIAL VARVED CLAYS, LEPPÄKOSKI, FINLAND
Thickness of section 3–4 m. (Photograph: H. Kinzl, from R. v. Klebelsberg, 1949.)

that there have been seasons ever since the Archaean era. Both their nature and the degree of change from season to season may, however, have varied as is shown by a comparison of the present equatorial zone with temperate

Fig. 65. Banded Slates below the Huronian Tillites
Probably a varvite, Cobalt, Ontario. (Photograph: M. Schwarzbach.)

latitudes. In any event, demonstration of seasonal banding is of interest both for its own sake and also for chronological purposes.

Where there is a considerable seasonal variation in climate, the conditions of sedimentation must also change greatly, and distinct seasonal banding may form (general account by R. Brinkmann, 1932).

The best-known example of this is afforded by the Pleistocene banded clays, which were first investigated in masterly fashion by de Geer, working in Sweden. They were deposited in glacially impounded lakes, into which, in summer, a great deal of relatively coarse material was swept by abundant melt waters. In consequence, the "summer bed" formed there was thick, light-colored, and sandy. In winter, the finest mud settled as a thin, dark, very clayey, "winter bed" (fig. 64). Two such related beds, at the most several centimeters thick, are known by the Swedish term varve. The number of varves naturally permits us to determine the number of years required for their formation. Fig. 65 shows an example of very old, probably glacially banded shales.

The varves are most sharply defined in cold water where the increased viscosity and consequent decreased rate of settling of suspended sediment

FIG. 66. SILURIAN GRAPTOLITIC SHALES SHOWING BANDING. MALMÖYA, OSLO FJORD

The very regular banding strongly resembles glacial varved clays (cf. figs. 64 and 65), but this banding is certainly not of glacial origin. Whether it is annual is not known. (Photograph: M. Schwarzbach.)

lead to an especially marked separation of the different grain sizes (sorting; Sauramo's diatectic varves). It is not, however, permissible to conclude from indistinct varves (symmictic varves) that the water was warm (as H. Korn did for varves in the Upper Devonian and Lower Carboniferous sediments of Thuringia) since other factors, especially the electrolyte content of the water, may be involved. Salts can produce rapid flocculation of all the particles and hence give rise to a poorly banded sediment. Fresh- and salt-water beds can be distinguished in this way in the Pleistocene varved clays of Finland. Seasonal change in the supply of sediment often appears to be less abrupt in the sea than in inland lakes. Marine lamination is best developed in anaerobic sediments where there is no benthonic fauna to disturb the bedding, e.g. graptolitic shales (fig. 66), and the Oxford Clay in England. In many cases, fine banding originates solely through periodic admixture of organic material and not through any change in grain size (Bradley).

Among recent examples of well-laminated, probably annually banded, lake sediments are those of Lake Louise and Lake Cavell in the Canadian Rockies (Johnston, Kindle) where the varves are ½ cm. thick, Lake Zurich (fig. 67) where some of the beds are dateable historically (Nipkov, Minder), and lakes in France (Dangeard). Marine laminations are to be seen in the Black Sea (Archangelski), and in the littoral zone of the Adriatic (Seibold).

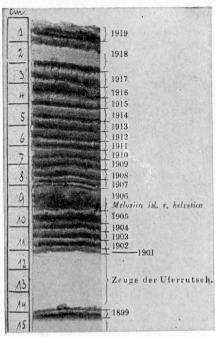

FIG. 67. RECENT MUD SHOWING ANNUAL BANDING, LAKE OF ZURICH

Deposited between 1899 and 1919. The sediment laid down in 1918, and more especially in 1900, is unusually thick, because of slumping from the banks. 1906 marks the first appearance of the calcareous alga *Melosira islandica* var. *helvetica* (after Nipkov, 1920, from Minder, 1938).

[Zeuge der Uferrutsch=Evidence of bank slumping.]

Banding in Non-glacial and pre-Quaternary Sediments

Apart from the banded clays of the Pleistocene period, there are many examples of regular lamination from Precambrian times onward, but hardly ever has any attempt been made to prove that this banding is annual. We should not, therefore, speak of beds of uncertain origin as varves or varvites, as B. Misař (1960) and others have proposed.

There are several cases where the annual nature of the bands appears to be fairly well established. In the Faulenseemoos, on the southern shore of Lake Thun, Welten has shown that the fine laminae of the postglacial deposits contain differing pollen assemblages. The lighter beds developed in summer, the darker beds in autumn, winter, and early spring. The thickness of the annual bands varies between 0·5 mm. and 2·4 mm.

In the siliceous earths of Lüneburg Heath in northwest Germany (Dewall), the light beds of the banded diatomaceous sediments are composed almost entirely of tests of *Melosira italica*, whose optimum development occurs in autumn. In contrast to this, the dark bands contain numerous other diatoms, such as *Synedra ulna*, which are most abundant in May. The light bands were therefore deposited in autumn, the dark bands during the rest of the year (see also Giesenhagen).

H. Remy has suggested that pollen analysis indicates that the fine bedding of the Villafranchian beds at Villaroya, Spain, is probably also annual.

At Rott, near Cologne, the exceedingly fine (0·03 mm.) bands in the Oligocene leaf-coals are alternately pollen-rich and pollen-poor, though the pollen-poor bands contain a relatively high content of *Pinus* pollen (Krieger; see Schwarzbach, 1952). This is probably a seasonal variation, caused either because *Pinus* bloomed later than the other pollen-bearing plants, or because its pollen took longer to settle (fig. 68).

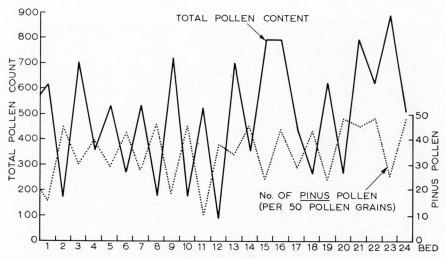

Fig. 68. Rhythmic Variation in Pollen Content of a Banded Leaf Coal, Oligocene, Siebengebirge (Germany) (from research by W. Krieger)

The coal examined was 0·8 mm. thick, and contained 24 layers; some pollen rich, others pollen poor (solid line). The content of *Pinus* pollen (dotted) varies inversely with the total pollen content. Rhythms probably seasonal.

In the sandstones of the Oligocene Molasse, near Lausanne, in Switzerland, there are fine lignitic intercalculations, 1·64 mm. apart, which may be attributed to the fall of leaves of poplar, alder, acacia, etc., in autumn (Bersier).

The Eocene oil shales of the Green River Formation of the western United States are very finely banded (some of the laminae are only 0·014 mm. thick). The dark layers have a high organic content which is probably due to plankton production in summer.

In the thick salt deposits of the Permian and other systems (Borchert, Fiege, Fiweg, Lotze, G. Richter-Bernburg) a distinct banding, "Jahresringe", involving clay, anhydrite and halite, is often apparent. Those in halite beds have an average thickness of 5–10 cm., in anhydrite 0·5–1 mm. If they are interpreted as annual, it is found that the period required for the whole deposit to form is so short that long breaks in

sedimentation have to be assumed (Borchert, Newell, Richter-Bernburg).
Deposition of individual beds of salt may, however, take much more than
a year.

Here, and in the Upper Devonian and Lower Carboniferous sediments of
Thuringia, whose history was investigated by Korn, it has been said that
sunspot rhythms can be detected (fig. 73) in order to prove that the banding
is really annual. Clear evidence of such rhythms would indeed constitute
a proof, but in every case the observations are uncertain. Hence they can
tell us little about whether the banding is annual.

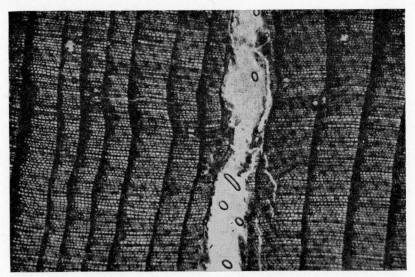

FIG. 69. ANNUAL RINGS IN A CONIFER STEM, FROM THE CRETACEOUS OF KING CHARLES
LAND (78° N.) (after W. Gothan, 1908)

Seasonal Growth of Organisms

The best-known example of seasonal growth is afforded by annual rings
in trees (fig. 69). These readily enable determination of the age of both
modern and fossil trees. Sequoias in the Miocene strata of Niederlausitz
lived for as much as 3,000 years (Teumer).

Annual rings are usually also present in the tropics. Yet, because of the
scarcity of its rings, the wood which formed the Carboniferous coals has
been attributed to a completely uniform climate without seasons (especially
by H. Potonié). But the Carboniferous climate can hardly have been more
uniform than the present equatorial climate. It is more probable that, at
that time, plants were still insufficiently advanced to be able to react to
seasonal variations by the development of growth rings of varying thickness
(Antevs, Schwarzbach). Finds from the colder Gondwanaland, where
annual rings appear rather more frequently, suggest that only where the
seasons were very marked did this ability manifest itself.

Conifer branches too, sometimes exhibit growth cycles by an alternation of long and short shoots. This cycle has been observed in the conifer *Elatocladus* from the Lower Tertiary of Saxony (E. Fischer), and in the Carboniferous seed fern *Neuropteris* (R. Potonié).

By analogy with present conditions, seasonal variation can often also be regarded as the cause of structures in fossils. The hard parts of organisms frequently exhibit growth rings, e.g. in the brachiopods, pelecypods, corals, fish scales and otoliths. In many cases, these, too, are probably annual—the age of fish is estimated by means of their scales—but other much shorter growth cycles also occur (see p. 91). In belemnites, it has been shown directly with the help of the $O/^{18}O^{16}$ method that the animal produced several growth rings per year (Chapter 11).

The existence of an unfavorable season can also be inferred from certain adaptations of organisms. To this category belong the cysts of the water flea (*Daphnia*), very common in the Oligocene sediments of Rott, near Cologne.

Seasonal Nature of Geological Processes

On the few occasions when the course of the seasons is known, there exists the possibility of classifying geological processes seasonally, and vice versa of delineating the seasons of the past by means of certain phenomena. In this connection, people have spoken rather daringly of fossil phenology (Heim, see also Deecke, 1930).

Thus, animal tracks are found only in the "summer beds" of the Pleistocene varved clays of Silesia (Schwarzbach). E. Voigt observed that the otoliths of the Eocene fish of Geiseltal all terminated with the same ring, and thereby concluded that the fish perished in a sudden seasonal catastrophe (summer drought). O. Heer could state accurately the season in which certain shale laminae from Oeningen were formed; the spring laminae contained blossoms of the poplar and camphor tree; the summer ones, flying ants and fruits of the poplar, elm, and willow, and those formed in autumn, the fruits of the camphor tree, persimmon, and traveller's joy (*Clematis vitalba*). In the same way, Murr (1926) was able to ascertain that the land-slide which gave rise to the famous interglacial "Höttinger Breccia", near Innsbruck, took place in May because as well as young leaves of the Pontian Alpine rose and of *Salix glabra* there are also fruits of the sycamore. According to T. Einarsson, the postglacial beds of volcanic ash in Iceland originated, at least partly in late summer or autumn, because the vegetation was not harmed, and there was no erosion by melt waters.

It is amusing to note that similar considerations were among the earliest paleoclimatic speculations, for in the eighteenth century, attempts were made to determine from fossils, when the Flood began. Woodward (1702) and Scheuchzer (1723) thought it occurred in May; Parsons (1758), in autumn (see E. Dorf, 1955).

Changes in Weather Throughout the Year

There are other climatically controlled beds apart from seasonal banding; due firstly to the influence of weather, and corresponding to only a short period of time such as a day, and secondly to long-term climatic fluctuations of the order of several years or even centuries. It is extremely difficult to distinguish between all these cases, though it is very desirable to do so in order to prevent false conclusions from being drawn regarding the climate or the time required for the beds to be deposited.

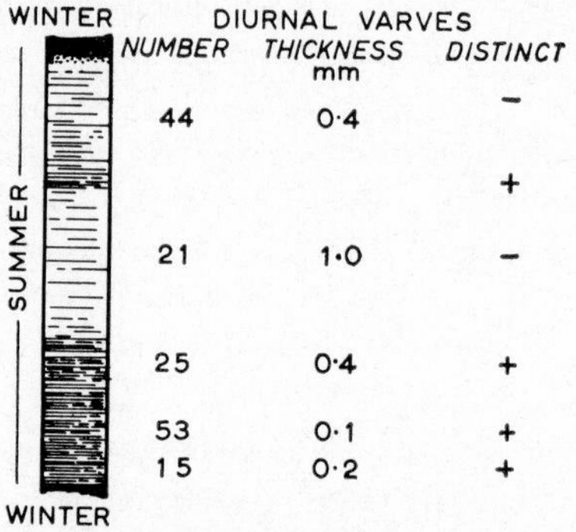

	DIURNAL VARVES		
WINTER	NUMBER	THICKNESS mm	DISTINCT
	44	0·4	–
			+
	21	1·0	–
	25	0·4	+
	53	0·1	+
	15	0·2	+
WINTER			

Fig. 70. "Diurnal Varves" in an Annual Layer of a Pleistocene Banded Clay. Riss or Mindel Glaciation

Silesia (*cf.* fig. 64). The supply of sediment changed at least 158 times in a year in the glacially impounded lake (see fig. 71), from Schwarzbach, 1940.

Where climatic factors change over a period of days or weeks, it is better to speak not of climatic changes but of changes of weather, since these changes vary irregularly from year to year and are completely dependent on more or less chance factors.

The Pleistocene banded clays often exhibit, within the sharply defined annual varves, very fine laminae which are especially common in the summer beds (fig. 70). These may be designated "diurnal varves", although they need not always correspond to one day. In general, there is no reason to fear that annual and diurnal varves may be confused one with the other, although Hansen says that de Geer himself once did so, and consequently, in Denmark, counted 2,500 years instead of 129.

The origin of diurnal varves is easily explained when one considers that the volume of water in present glacial outflow streams varies not only between summer and winter, but also quite regularly between day and night (fig. 71). This means that the mud content, and hence the character of the sediment, changes from day to night. The finer beds form at night. It is, of course, quite possible for only one bed to form in several days, as in periods of bad weather, but it cannot be assumed that several beds can form in one day. Now, in a carefully studied example, dating from the Saale or Elster Glaciation in Silesia (Schwarzbach), up to 158 diurnal varves could be counted, whence it follows that considerable melting of snow and ice occurred on at least 158 days of the year; the climate at the time was no longer strictly polar. Yet at that time the Scandinavian Ice still had not attained its maximum extent; so the greatest development of ice lagged behind the climatic minimum.

Diurnal beds also appear, according to the description given by Banks,

Loveday, and Scott, in the Permian "varves" of Tasmania. It is, of course, unusually difficult to recognize short-term beds in pre-Quaternary sediments, where, indeed, even annual banding cannot be definitely established. Fourfold division of a bed has occasionally been interpreted as the result of two rainy seasons per year, with the conclusion that the area was near the equator. This has been done in the Lower Carboniferous of Thuringia by H. Korn, and in otoliths from the Eocene sediments of the Geiseltal, near Halle, by E. Voigt, but their conclusions are not reliable.

Tidal lamination is a special case of short-term bedding. Ebb and flow give rise to a fine banding in the tidal flat sediments investigated by Johnstone (Fraser River delta, British Columbia), and on the North Sea

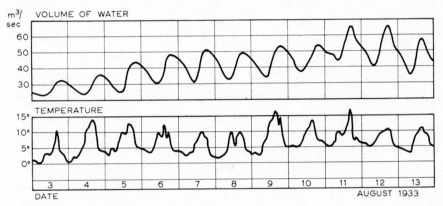

FIG. 71. VOLUME OF WATER IN GLACIAL RUN-OFF STREAM, DORABALTEA, SOUTHERN ALPS
(after Alfieri, 1938)

Distinct rhythmic diurnal variations closely parallel the temperature variation and result in oscillations in the amount of mud carried in suspension. Diurnal varves (fig. 70) can then form.

coast by Van Straaten, R. Richter, Trusheim, Häntzschel, and others. But this is of little paleoclimatic interest.

That growth lines, which may correspond to a day or a few days, also appear in the hard parts of animals, has best been shown by Orton's observations on *Cardium edule*, and Davenport's on other Recent pelecypods. Davenport ascertained that *Pecten* in Cold Spring Harbor developed up to 145 daily growth lines followed by one thick winter line corresponding to the winter pause in growth. In the warmer area of Florida, *Pecten gibbus* shows no winter line, but *Pecten eboreus* from the Miocene of Virginia shows a very clear one. Davenport goes too far in deducing that the Miocene winters were more severe than today's, and also in his other conclusions; the results of so few Recent observations may not be applied so definitely to determining past conditions, though these observations open up an interesting prospect.

LONG-TERM CLIMATIC VARIATIONS

Secular variations in climate, long-term cyclic changes extending over tens, hundreds, or even many thousands of years, must also be expressed in the character of the sediments, but they are even more difficult to recognize than annual banding.

Tree Rings

The Quaternary Period provides the only exception; the repeated changes between glacial and interglacial phases are reflected in many geological findings. One need only recall the floral and faunal changes, the river and marine terraces, or the exceedingly important deep-sea sediments. These climatic variations took place over the order of tens of thousands of years.

Very much smaller climatic changes are indicated by the varying widths of successive annual rings in trees. The cause of this variation in width lies only partly in climatic changes, among which it is difficult to distinguish between the effects of temperature and rainfall; condition of the site of growth, insects, grubs, etc., can all have some effect. The effect of climate is, however, always dominant, so that one may attempt to draw conclusions regarding the climate from the curves showing the width of the annual rings. Different trees are compared with each other, and the different curves related to each other in time, to build up a "dendrochronology". This type of study has been particularly widely developed in North America (Douglass, Schulman; Huber in Europe), but of course spans only the last few thousand years.

Sunspot Cycles

Attempts have been made to detect in the annual rings of trees, one of the best known present-day cycles, the sunspot cycle.

Sunspots vary fairly regularly in frequency over a period of, on average, just over 11 years (with a range of from 7 to 17 years; fig. 72). Riccioli suggested as early as 1651 that sunspots affected the weather, and the question has been repeatedly investigated since then, e.g. by Köppen. Regular observations of sunspots are available from 1820 onwards. In fact, there is a relationship, but not a very close one. To be sure, the temperature curve of the tropics follows a course which largely parallels that of the curve of relative number of sunspots[1], but deviation from the mean still never reaches 1° C. Generally speaking, no clear relationship may be recognized in other latitudes.

Yet, according to Willett, major fluctuations in sunspot activity affect climate in middle latitudes of the Northern Hemisphere (Table 18). Each major fluctuation comprises three or four 11-year cycles. Accordingly, in

1. Relative number $R = 10g - f$, where g is the number of sunspots, and f is the number of individual spots.

these latitudes, the period of about forty years when there is a high relative number of sunspots is characterized by slightly higher temperatures. Rainfall behaves differently from area to area.

It would, therefore, be most astonishing if we could recognize the effect of sunspot cycles in fossil sediments. Yet such cycles are claimed to have been detected in many places—in the Precambrian of the Urals and

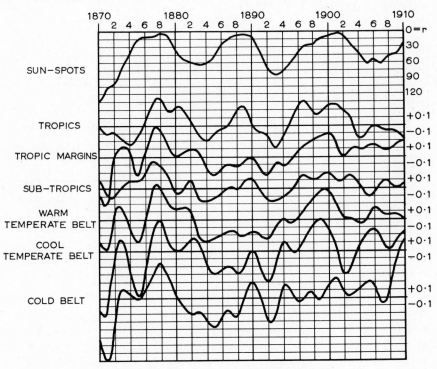

FIG. 72. SUNSPOTS AND TEMPERATURE

Above, relative number of sunspots (r); below, deviation of temperature from mean value (°C). Only in the tropics does the temperature curve parallel the sunspot curve (from Köppen, 1914).

Angaraland, in the Upper Devonian and Carboniferous of Thuringia, in the Permian of Australia, South Africa, Texas, Siberia, and Germany, in the Upper Jurassic and Eocene of North America, in the Pleistocene varved clays and dunes, and in the Recent silt of Lake Sakski in the Crimea. H. Korn, and Richter-Bernburg have probably investigated this problem most thoroughly, but their results are not conclusive. The unbiased observer can detect no regular 11-year cycle in Korn's curves (fig. 73), nor in those given by Anderson and Kirkland for the Jurassic Todilto Formation, by Bradley for the Eocene Green River Shales, or by Lungershausen. The most objectionable feature of Richter-Bernburg's curves is the fact that they were

TABLE 18

MAJOR VARIATIONS IN SUNSPOT ACTIVITY AND CLIMATE (MIDDLE LATITUDES OF THE NORTHERN HEMISPHERE; AFTER H. C. WILLETT)

SUNSPOT MAXIMUM		MEAN RELATIVE NUMBER	TEMPERATURE	RAINFALL
YEAR	RELATIVE NO.			
1750	83			
1761	86			
1769	106	102	Above average	
1778	154			
1787	132			
1804	48			
1816	46	55	Mostly below average	
1830	71			
1837	138			
1848	124	124	Partly above average	Mostly below average (but high in N)
1860	96			
1870	139			
1883-4	64			
1893	85	71	Below average	Partly above average
1905	64			
1917	104			
1928	78	112	Above average	Below average (but higher in N)
1937	115			
1947	152			

obtained not from exact measurements (this would certainly not have been easy in view of the fineness of the banding), but by counting the number of bands between "anomalous" ones, by which were understood—quite subjectively—unusually thick, or sharp, or doubled, or in some other way distinctive beds. "Surprisingly, an anomaly was present on an average about every 11 normal beds." Because of its subjective bias, the impressive diagram with its maximum every 11·1 or 11·2 years has very little appeal for a more severe critic.

Attempts to recognize a longer cycle by the same methods must also be regarded with scepticism. These include a 23- or 50–60-year cycle (Bradley,

FIG. 73. "SUNSPOT" CYCLES IN UPPER DEVONIAN BANDED SHALES, THURINGIA

Curve indicates the ratio of clay to lime in the bands. The horizontal axis, graduated in 10-yearly intervals, covers a period of 160 years (after H. Korn, 1938, pl. XIII, curve I, 315–475 years). According to Korn, the 11-year rhythm is "clearly recognisable", but in fact, it is not particularly pronounced.

Lungershausen *et al.*) and a 170-, 200-, or 4,500-year periodicity in the Zechstein of Germany (Richter-Bernburg). Bradley even believed that he could recognize a 21,000-year cycle, the astronomical precession of the equinoxes, in the Green River sediments.

SEASONAL BANDING AND ABSOLUTE DATING

True annual banding permits the period required for the deposition of a bed to be determined directly. A single section, of course, usually only provides information about a short period of time, but by cleverly combining various sections, it is possible to obtain an overall picture, and thereby make a valuable contribution to our knowledge of the absolute chronology of the earth's history.

G. de Geer applied this method in classic fashion at the beginning of the century; by counting the varves in postglacial impounded lakes of Sweden, he was able to calculate the duration of the postglacial period. Here, too, the profiles from many localities had to be combined, by comparing graphically, successive individual varves of different thickness. The values given in Table 19 were computed in this way.

TABLE 19

ABSOLUTE CHRONOLOGY OF LATE-GLACIAL PERIOD (IN YEARS B.C.)

	DE GEER, LIDÉN	SAURAMO
Central Swedish moraines.	7912	7858
Salpausselkä II (end-moraine in Finland) . . .	8204	8150
South Swedish moraines	13219	

In North America, E. Antevs, one of de Geer's pupils, pursued similar lines of research. There, since the sections are not complete, the figures are not completely certain. Dendrochronology works in much the same way although for much shorter periods of time. The section in the Faulenseemoos of Switzerland, investigated by Welten, may also be mentioned here, since its annual beds can be dated back from the present time; it yielded the following dates: disappearance of ice from the Faulensee depression 7,700 B.C., appearance of hazel and oak mixed woodland 5,050 B.C., appearance of beech 3,200 B.C.

Such favorable conditions as prevail in postglacial times, due to the retreat of the ice sheets, are never found in earlier periods. At best, one can only attempt to calculate the length of individual periods of time with the help of annually banded sediments. Some examples of such estimates include: Chattian-Aquitanian of Switzerland $2\frac{1}{2}$–3 million years (Bersier), Mid-Oligocene-Mid-Miocene of the Caucasus $7\frac{1}{4}$ million years (Archangelski),

Eocene Green River Formation 5–8 million years (Bradley), therefore duration of Eocene 22·9 million years (Bradley). Two Silurian graptolite zones in the Lake District, England, 700,000 years; hence duration of the Ordovician and Silurian $9\frac{1}{2}$ million years (Marr) (see also fig. 66).

In part, these values agree fairly well with those obtained with the help of radioactive minerals; in part—especially for the Ordovician-Silurian—they are much lower. That implies either that there are great breaks in sedimentation or that no true annual bands are present.

Further reading: KORRINGA, 1957 (moon cycles); A. J. WELLS, 1960.

10

Mathematical Investigation of Past Climates

While I was writing this chapter (April 1830), I attended
a meeting of the Geological Society of London, at which
the President, in his address used the expression "a
geological logician". Smiles appeared on the faces of all
who were present, and some, like Cicero's augurs, could
not suppress a laugh; so amusing appears the combination of geology and logic.

C. LYELL, Principles of Geology.

FORMULAE FOR TEMPERATURE DETERMINATION

Climatic indicators do not represent the only way of reconstructing
paleoclimates. It is possible, in theory at least, to approach the problem in
a quite different, deductive fashion, and to attempt to treat it mathematically. There appears to be such a close interrelationship between climate and
geography (particularly the distribution of land and sea) that the paleogeographic situation must permit some definite conclusions to be drawn
about paleoclimates (morphogenic climate).

As early as 1861, Forbes developed an empirical formula expressing the
mean present-day temperature of any line of latitude ($T\varphi$) as a function of
the latitude (φ) and the percentage of land along the line (n).

$$T\varphi = -10 \cdot 8° + 32 \cdot 9 \ \cos \tfrac{5}{4}\varphi + 21 \cdot 2n \ \cos 2\varphi$$

Kerner-Marilaun applied such a formula to Neumayr's map of the Jurassic
Period and calculated the following temperatures for different latitudes:
70° N = 5·8° C; 30° N = 20·7° C; Equator = 26·2° C; 30° S = 18·3° C.

Kerner-Marilaun later devised complicated formulae in which, for
example, distance from the Gulf Stream and its temperature, etc., were
taken into account. He applied these formulae to past periods, and thereby
attempted to allow at least for that part of temperature variation which was
due especially to the changing distribution of land and sea. Semper also
attempted this sort of thing for the Eocene. He considered the effects of
warm ocean currents to be of prime importance. Brooks has calculated
temperatures of the Holarctic region during each Period; these are based on

continentality (derived from very uncertain paleogeographic maps), mean height above sea level (which again is only an "intuitive" estimate), oceanic circulation (i.e. breaches in the circumpolar land ring), and volcanic activity. He has compared these estimated temperatures with "observed" temperatures derived from climatic indicators.

Uncertainty of Such Formulae

These papers are mentioned only because the methods are interesting; they are of no practical value in determining paleoclimatic data because climate is influenced by too many different factors. As a general rule, nothing definite is known about these factors. They cannot therefore be used in formulae. At most, one may arrive at reasonable values only for the very recent past, when paleogeographic conditions were already extraordinarily similar to those of the present day. In fact, Brooks's estimates—e.g. for the period of the *Littorina* transgression in the Baltic, i.e. 4,000–7,000 B.P.— usually agree fairly well with the values which have long been established from climatic evidence.

11

Physical Methods of Determining Paleotemperatures

The medieval doctors of divinity who did not pretend
to settle how many angels could dance on the point of a
needle, cut a very poor figure as far as romantic credulity
is concerned beside the modern physicists who have
settled to the billionth of a millimeter every movement
and position in the dance of the electrons.

G. B. SHAW, preface to "St. Joan", 1923.

THE OXYGEN ISOTOPE METHOD

The most modern technique available to paleoclimatologists is an outcome of the atomic age; it is based on isotope research and enables us to obtain "direct" temperature data. We could speak of "geological thermometers", were the term not already applied quite differently in mineralogy, to minerals which can be used to determine their temperature of formation.

This method derives from H. C. Urey who, with others, worked on oxygen isotopes and thereby ascertained that the ratio of O^{18}/O^{16} in calcium carbonate, for example, was dependent on its temperature of formation— "I suddenly found myself with a geological thermometer in my hands." He, Lowenstam, Epstein, and McKinney published their first remarkable results in 1951; these were based on Jurassic and Cretaceous belemnites. Each of the 24 growth rings of a Jurassic belemnite from Skye was investigated by this method, and the results were produced in the diagram, fig. 74. The temperature curve showed four "winters" and three "summers"; hence the animal produced several rings per year, and had lived for four years. On the whole, the temperature was slightly higher during the early part of its life than later, the seasonal range of temperature was about 6° C, the annual mean 17.6° C. Upper Cretaceous belemnites from England yielded temperatures of 14°–19° C (24° C in one case), those of the Maestrichtian of Denmark gave 12°–14° C, and 12°–18° C was recorded for the Upper Cretaceous of southeastern U.S.A. Najdin, Tejs, and Tchupachin calculated comparable values from the Upper Cretaceous belemnites of the Soviet Union (see also Tejs *et al.*, 1957, and Table 28).

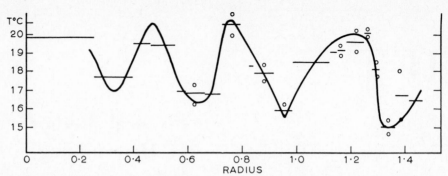

FIG. 74. TEMPERATURE CURVE OF THE JURASSIC SEA IN SKYE (SCOTLAND) DURING THE
FOUR-YEAR LIFESPAN OF A BELEMNITE

Samples were removed at various distances from the center of the belemnite (abscissa),
and investigated using the O^{18}/O^{16} method. The temperature varied between 15° C and
21° C (after Urey, Lowenstam, Epstein, and McKinney, 1951).

Difficulties in the Use of the Method

Corresponding investigations of brachiopods and oysters gave different
results. The cause is to be found in the more porous nature of the shell,
which permitted slightly different $CaCO_3$ to deposit later in the pores. This
admixture falsified the temperature data. Such a difficulty is to be expected
in many, if not most, fossils. Belemnites have unusually dense skeletons so
this source of error is absent. In other shells, it becomes more important
with increasing age of the sediment.

Another source of error is that organisms need not form calcite throughout
the year; thus the material analyzed only gives the temperature of some
months. This factor can put the results out by at least a few degrees. For
example, the Recent *Globigerina inflata* of the North Atlantic, yielded a
temperature of 18° C by the O^{18}/O^{16} method, when the sea temperature
there in fact varied between 18° C in February, and 25.5° C in August
(Emiliani, 1958, p. 256). On the other hand, *Globigerinoides rubra* and
Globigerinoides sacculifera probably reflect the summer temperature of the
surface waters.

Further, it must be observed that the O^{18}/O^{16} ratio in sediments is
dependent on the initial ratio of the two isotopes in sea water which, in turn,
is dependent on such factors as location of the ocean (tropical waters contain
more O^{18} than those of the Arctic, because the water vapour pressure of
H_2O^{16} is higher than that of H_2O^{18}). Moreover, the ratio is different in ice
and water, so that a correction is advisable for glacial and nonglacial periods.
It may also be supposed that the ratio has varied in the course of the earth's
history, although probably not by any substantial amount. At any rate
there are a series of factors, known and probably unknown, which complicate
the issue and make the technique applicable only in certain cases.

Further reading: VALENTINE and MEADE, 1961.

Application to Abyssal Sediments

This technique has been widely applied to the investigation of abyssal sediments because the tests of calcareous forams in abyssal deposits are also suitable for O^{18}/O^{16} analysis. Systematic investigation of cores, particularly by Emiliani, has shown that it is possible to obtain temperature curves for the Quaternary Period and also, probably, for the Tertiary. The curves can

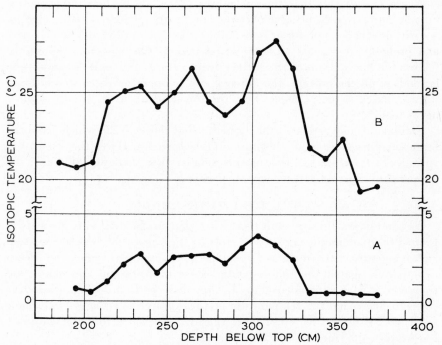

FIG. 75. CURVES OF PLEISTOCENE TEMPERATURES OF SURFACE WATERS AND FLOOR OF THE OCEAN BY O^{18}/O^{16} INVESTIGATION OF A DEEP-SEA CORE FROM THE EQUATORIAL ATLANTIC (Core 234, depth 3,577 m.)

Interglacial phase? A = sea bottom, B = surface waters (after Emiliani, 1958)

probably be equated in some way with the subdivisions of the Ice Age as they have long been known on the continents, although in what way is rather controversial. We know the life habitat of the forams which sank into the deeps after death and which are used for analysis. Many, such as *Globigerinoides rubra* and *Globigerinoides sacculifera*, lived near the surface of the ocean, and therefore provide an indication of the temperature at that level, though, as we have already seen, it may only be a seasonal temperature. Other forams can be employed for analysis of the temperatures of the deeper parts of the ocean.

Figure 113 shows an example from the northern part of the mid-Atlantic (core 280, depth 4256 m.). In the upper 10 m. of abyssal sediments, the recorded temperature of the surface waters fluctuates between 11° C and 18° C; "glacial" and "warm" phases are readily distinguishable from the curves. These beds represent a time span of at least several 100,000 years. The rise and fall of the curves correspond in every respect with the results of the straightforward stratigraphic-paleontological investigations of forams from deep-sea cores by W. Schott and others.

Figure 75 indicates that the curves of surface and bottom temperatures may be contrasted by using planktonic and benthonic forams. This example is derived from the equatorial zone of the Atlantic (core 234, depth 3577 m.), and probably represents an interglacial period. The bottom temperature follows the fluctuations of the surface temperature, although the amplitude is smaller; on the bottom, the difference in temperature between cold and warm phases is only about 4° C (in the Pacific, it is usually almost negligible).

Emiliani also investigated the deeper part of this core 234 which, from the foram evidence, probably belongs in the Tertiary. Here, the calculated variations of surface temperature are smaller than in the Quaternary; the temperature fluctuated between 21° C and 25° C.

THERMOLUMINESCENCE

Certain minerals clearly emit light when they are heated. This property is termed thermoluminescence. It depends on the amount of natural radiation and temperature to which the rock has been exposed. Zeller and Pearn (1960) investigated the thermoluminescence of Antarctic limestones and compared it with experimental data. They deduced that during at least the last 170,000 years, the temperature of the Antarctic can at no time have exceeded 25° C for a period of more than 125 hours, i.e. that the Antarctic has been "cold" for at least 170,000 years.

The method is still in its infancy, and, since it contains many sources of error, we still cannot be certain that these results are reliable.

12

Paleoclimatology and Economic Deposits

*Einem ist sie die hohe, die himmlische Göttin, dem andern
eine tüchtige Kuh, die ihn mit Butter versorgt.*
J. W. v. GOETHE (1749–1832).

Weathering and sedimentation, both of which are dependent on climate, are the dominant factors controlling the formation of numerous economic deposits. A close relationship exists between paleoclimatology and the study of ore deposits. Salts and coal are only two examples of sediments which clearly show this relationship. Hence paleoclimatology has a direct practical significance. Naturally, all magmatic ores are excluded here, or else we are primarily interested in their climatically controlled weathering phenomena. By no means all sedimentary ores come within the scope of this chapter either.

Since the climatic evidence provided by different types of deposit has been dealt with fully in the chapters dealing with climatic indicators, and since their stratigraphic distribution is indicated in that part of the book dealing with historical paleoclimatology, it will suffice here to give a brief summary (see also the textbooks on different types of ore deposits, e.g. those by Bateman, and Schneiderhöhn, and the paleogeographic maps by Chain and Ronov). As well as ores and "non-ores", several sediments of particular importance, e.g. building stones, have been included here.

Examples of Climatically Controlled Economic Deposits

1. Deposits in Warm Climates.—Nickel silicates in serpentine (New Caledonia, Urals, Silesia); magnesite gel in serpentine (Styria, etc.); bauxite (see Krotov); salts; limestone.

2. Deposits in Cold Climates.—Economic accumulates of blocks of ore in moraines (e.g. below the primary Cu_2S chalcocite deposits of Kennecott, Alaska). Erratic blocks of ore give an indication of *in situ* ore bodies (e.g. the discovery of copper deposits of Outokumpu, in eastern Finland by O. Trüstedt, 1910—see Laitikari, 1941); fluvio-glacial gravels (including probably the gold-bearing Witwatersrand conglomerates); loess.

3. Deposits in Arid Climates.—Ore deposits produced by concentration in arid regions; copper of red bed type (U.S.A., Urals foreland, Riesengebirge, etc.); silver (Silver Reef, Utah); uranium-vanadium (carnotite in Colorado, Utah, Urals foreland); lead-zinc (deposits at Mechernich, on the northern edge of the Eifel are possibly of this type). Rich oxidation zone of ore deposits and often very thick cementation zone, especially in warm arid climates. Wind-blown eluvial and fanglomerate placers (diamond placers in Southwest Africa, many cassiterite placers). Gypsum, anhydrite, rock salt, potash salts, saltpeter.

4. Deposits in Humid Climates.—Alluvial placers; lake and bog iron ores. In climates with wet and dry phases, bauxite, limonite and iron-manganese weathering deposits. In humid tropical climates, both the oxidation zone and the cementation zone of ore deposits are poorly developed; both are better developed in humid temperate regions. Coal; kaolin.

With regard to coal, it should at least be mentioned that for certain petrographic reasons—which are of economic importance—it is thought that the cooler climate of the Younger Tertiary was responsible for the lignites of central Germany (H. Jacob).

Part 2

HISTORICAL PALEOCLIMATOLOGY

Development of Climate throughout the Earth's History

13

Introduction and Precambrian

> While the Earth remaineth, seedtime and harvest, and cold and heat, and summer and winter, and day and night shall not cease.
>
> GENESIS 8, 22.

HISTORICAL PALEOCLIMATOLOGY

The nature of the earth's climate at any given time in the past may be inferred from a great many different pieces of evidence. The main objective of geologists engaged in this field is to collate this evidence, and thereby build up the most probable, and most internally consistent, climatic picture for each stage in the earth's history.

Of the many difficulties which have to be overcome, one of the greatest is that, because each geological period occupies some tens of millions of years (Table 20), the climatic evidence afforded by the strata of each system in different localities is not strictly contemporaneous. Since we know from studies of the Pleistocene Period that major climatic changes can occur over periods of only thousands of years, it follows that, in the present incomplete state of our knowledge, any reconstruction which we may attempt for earlier periods will necessarily be very imperfect, even when we have considered every possible piece of climatic evidence at our disposal. Only from the beginning of the Tertiary Period are we on fairly safe grounds, and the Quaternary climates can already be reconstructed in fair detail; but as we go further back in the earth's history, the picture becomes increasingly uncertain.

In Precambrian strata, the absence of fossils not only deprives us of invaluable organic evidence of climate, but also makes correlation of other evidence very difficult, thereby producing great chronological uncertainties.

General references: BRINKMANN (1959); V. BUBNOFF (1956); DUNBAR (1959); MÄGDEFRAU (1956); MACGINITIE (1958); MOORE (1958); RUEDEMANN (1939); STRAKHOV (1960); TERMIER (1952).

Climates of the Past

TABLE 20
OUTLINE OF GEOLOGICAL SYSTEMS

Era	System (Period)	Stage (especially in Europe)		Estimated Absolute Age (Millions of Years)	
				Older Scale	Kulp, 1960
CENOZOIC	Quaternary	Holocene Pleistocene		1	1
	Tertiary	Neogene	Pliocene		
			Miocene		
		Paleogene	Oligocene		
			Eocene		
			Paleocene	60	63
MESOZOIC	Cretaceous			130	135
	Jurassic	Malm Dogger Lias		155	180
	Triassic	Keuper Muschelkalk Bunter		185	(225)
	Permian	Zechstein Rotliegendes		210	(275)
PALEOZOIC	Carboniferous	Pennsylvanian Mississippian		265	350
	Devonian			320	405
	Silurian			360	430
	Ordovician			440	500
	Cambrian			520	(>560)
PRECAMBRIAN	Algonkian (Proterozoic)			>3000	
	Archean				

PRECAMBRIAN CLIMATE

Evidence of Glaciation

That moraine-like deposits are present even in the Precambrian and, in fact, even in the Archean, is of fundamental importance. In this section, we shall not consider the numerous tillites that occur in the youngest Precambrian (Eo-Cambrian) strata, as these are discussed more fully later (Chapter 14), but shall deal only with the older "true" Precambrian examples.

FIG. 76. PRECAMBRIAN TILLITE SHOWING STRIATED BOULDERS
Cobalt Series, Kekeko Lake (Quebec) (after M. E. Wilson, 1939).

In Europe, only a few rather doubtful glacial deposits have been discovered in Finland, but much more widespread finds have been made elsewhere, particularly in North America and South Africa. One should add also Australia, where, in the Adelaide system, a clear stratigraphic succession of older tillites have been followed back from the Eo-Cambrian glacial stage (see further in Chapter 14).

In North America, the most important and most accurately dated occurrence is the Cobalt (Gowganda) tillite, which can be traced for at least 500 miles, from Lake Huron, via Cobalt and Noranda to Lake Chibougama (fig. 26). Here, striated boulders (fig. 76) and glaciated pavements have been observed. Moreover, in places, e.g. at Cobalt, the tillite is interbedded with banded "varved-slates". Coleman considers this "Huronian Ice Age" to have been one of the earth's greatest glaciations. It is thought to have occurred more than 1,000 million years ago. Recently, however, the morainic character of even the Gowganda tillite has been questioned (personal communication from Winterer to Crowell, 1957).

The Cobalt tillite can probably be correlated with rocks of the Medicine Bow Range in southern Wyoming (Snowy Range Series). This series, first described by Blackwelder, is considered by C. L. and M. A. Fenton to be of early Huronian age. The 8,000 m. thick succession contains three tillite horizons, 40 m., 8 m., and 30 m. thick.

The appearance, in the upper part of the succession, of dolomites which contain large algal reefs, suggests that the cold phase was followed by a period of warmer conditions.

Other Precambrian tillites or glacio-marine sediments in North America include the Fern Creek tillite series of Michigan, described by H. L. James, and biotite schists from the southern part of the Deep Creek Range in Utah which contain erratic blocks (Misch, Hazzard, Turner). These, too, are probably of Huronian age. Other undoubted Pre-Huronian examples, for the most part well over 2,000 million years old, are the tillite-like rocks in the Keewatin of the Upper Lake (Doré Conglomerate), in the Timiskaming Series (Lake Timiskaming, Canada), in the Seine Series west of Lake Superior, and in the Sudbury Series (Wanipigow Conglomerate). Both the exact stratigraphic position and the mode of formation of these occurrences is very uncertain. Even Coleman, who was strongly inclined to glacial interpretations, has not ruled out the possibility of other modes of origin in some cases.

The chronological sequence of the more important North American occurrences, together with that of the younger Proterozoic-Eo-Cambrian rocks dealt with in the following chapter, is indicated in Table 21.

In recent years, a great many new "tillites" have been discovered in South America; but while some are definitely Precambrian, their stratigraphic position and mode of origin is still doubtful. They include the tillites of the Lavras Series in the Brazilian states of Minas Gerais and Bahia (the so-called "conglomerates" of Leonardos and Ebert, from the base of the Carandai Formation). These are, in part, metamorphosed, and contain diamonds; according to Maack, they cover an area of over 20,000 square miles (fig. 91). They may be Precambrian, in which case they are probably no older than "Eo-Cambrian", but they could also be Cambrian.

In South Africa, a whole series of old tillites occur at different stratigraphic horizons. Those which belong to the uppermost part of the Precambrian are discussed in the next chapter; it must, however, be emphasized that opinions regarding the age of the tillites are widely divergent.

The Chuos tillite described by Gevers and Beetz from western Damaraland, Southwest Africa, appears to be very old. The whole series, which may attain a thickness of over 650 m., covers an area of 19,000 square miles.

TABLE 21

STRATIGRAPHIC POSITIONS OF PRECAMBRIAN TILLITES
OF NORTH AMERICA

STRATIGRAPHIC DIVISION		TILLITE BEARING SERIES	AGE (MILLION YEARS)
ALGONKIAN (Proterozoic)	Belt	Near Great Salt Lake, and in Wasatch Mountains	>600
	Keweenawan U. Huronian L. Huronian	Gowganda; Medicine Bow Range?; Fern Creek?	>1000
ARCHEAN	Timiskaming Keewatin	Timiskaming, Seine, Sudbury Doré	>2000

Bedding is absent and the contained blocks are angular and indistinctly
striated. The original feldspar of the tillite is now partly converted to
epidote. Banded slates are also present. The Chuos tillite was classified by
Martin as belonging to the much younger Transvaal System.

The next tillites are probably those of the Witwatersrand System in the
Southern Transvaal. Striation and facetting of the boulders have been
recorded. In the east, there is only one tillite, but in the west there are
usually two or three; the glaciers probably advanced from the northwest.
The famous gold-bearing conglomerates of the Witwatersrand have also
recently been interpreted as fluvio-glacial deposits (Wiebols).

TABLE 22

STRATIGRAPHY OF SOUTH AFRICAN PRECAMBRIAN, AND
ITS TILLITES

TILLITE	SYSTEM	AGE (MILLION YEARS)
Schwarzkalk	Nama	
Numees, Griquatown, Daspoort; "Grand Conglomérat", and "Petit Conglomérat" in Katanga	Transvaal	>620 in part
Witwatersrand	Witwatersrand	
Chuos	Damara	ca. 1000

In the Transvaal System lie the 200–300 m. thick Numees tillite of southwest Africa, and, at a slightly higher horizon, the Griquatown tillite of west
Griqualand. The Daspoort tillite of the Transvaal is probably of the same
age (cf. Table 22). The Numees tillite, described in great detail by Beetz, has

an areal extent of over 12,000 square miles. Striated boulders are present
in all three of these sediments.

Lastly, a tillite is known to occur in the Little Kharas mountains of
southwest Africa, in the Schwarzkalk Series of the Nama Formation; but it
is probably of very early Cambrian age. Glacially striated pavements have
been observed here. The glaciers (valley glaciers) probably advanced from
the north.

Correlation with the equally widely distributed tillites further north,
particularly in the Congo, is difficult. The more important occurrences are
indicated in Table 23 of the next chapter, and in the map, fig. 81. Absolute
age determinations indicate that the "Grand Conglomérat" in Katanga
(Lower Kundelungu Formation) is more than 620 million years old, and
therefore probably does not belong to the Eo-Cambrian glaciation. The
tillite series, which in Katanga is as much as 500 m. thick, includes two
tillites; the "Grand Conglomérat" and the overlying "Petit Conglomérat".
Their glacial origin is considered certain by some authors because striated
boulders are known to occur. Certain facies variations have been said to
indicate periglacial conditions. A synopsis of the more important Precambrian tillites of South Africa is given in Table 22. (See Table 23 for the
uppermost Precambrian.)

Other Climatic Indicators

Apart from these "moraines", little other climatic evidence need be
mentioned. Fairly warm conditions in the upper part of the Precambrian
can be inferred from the limestones and dolomites which occur here and
there in Siberia, North Africa, and Australia. In the late Algonkian Belt
Series, in the Belt Mountains and Glacier-Waterton Lakes Parks areas of
Montana and southwest Alberta, there are bioherms up to 50 m. thick. These
have been studied by C. L. and M. A. Fenton (1957), who also consider that
fairly arid conditions existed for a time, because the red color of the
sediments is combined with desiccation cracks and other phenomena. A
similar argument may be applied to such other late Precambrian red beds
as the Keweenawan of Lake Superior and Canada, the Torridonian sandstone of Scotland, the Dala and Jotnian sandstones of Sweden, and the
Vindhyan of India.

It is noteworthy that no Precambrian evaporites are known to occur
anywhere, though a few traces of salt formation have been found; for
example, the "salt crystals" of the Belt Series (Fenton & Fenton, 1957,
p. 109).

14

The Eo-Cambrian Glaciations

Of all the pieces of evidence relating to the climate of the Precambrian, the tillites are of fundamental importance, since they must surely indicate the existence of glacial conditions, even at this far distant time in the past. They do not, however, provide us with a paleoclimatic datum, because their precise stratigraphic position is all too uncertain. The first time this situation changes is immediately preceding the appearance of Cambrian trilobites. This particular horizon has been designated "Eo-Cambrian" (Broegger) or "Infra-Cambrian" (Menchikoff, Pruvost). Tillites are known to have been formed at this time in many different parts of the world. As their stratigraphic position is now more definitely fixed than that of the older tillites, it is possible, for the first time, to represent them on a map. Of course, such a climatic map still has many serious deficiencies. Other definite evidence of climate is absent, and it has not been established that the "tillites" undoubtedly represent moraines or other types of glacial deposit. Furthermore, the age of many of the deposits is uncertain.

DISTRIBUTION OF GLACIAL PHENOMENA

The evidence of Eo-Cambrian glaciation has all been brought together in Table 23 (and also in fig. 81), where general characteristics are compared. Also included in this table are those tillites which are presumed to be slightly older and which, strictly speaking, belong in the preceding chapter, where they have already been mentioned.

To the table may be appended a few remarks about the more important glacial deposits, whose age is not in question because of the presence of overlying Cambrian strata. In Europe, the numerous tillites of the Sparagmite Series of Scandinavia are of particular significance. Classic exposures resting on a glacially striated pavement are to be seen at Varanger Fjord in north Norway (fig. 77); Kulling, therefore, gave to this Ice Age the name "Varanger Glaciation". As the orientation of the striae does not correspond with that of the boulders, Gaertner concluded that the former were produced by a grounding iceberg. Research on Recent glacial striae indicates that this assumption is quite unnecessary. At no great distance from these Norwegian tillites (fig. 78), lie the various Eo-Cambrian glacial deposits of

FIG. 77. EO-CAMBRIAN TILLITE RESTING ON A STRIATED PAVEMENT. BIGGANJARGA,
VARANGER FJORD, NORTHERN NORWAY

Left: Drawing by H. Reusch, 1890, from O. Holtedahl, Föyn & Reitan, 1960.
Right: Photograph, H. R. v. Gaertner, 1943.

FIG. 78. MOELV-TILLITE, EO-CAMBRIAN, LAKE MJÖSEN, SOUTHERN NORWAY
(Photograph: M. Schwarzbach).

the Polar region. In east Greenland, two tillites occur within the 540 m. thick sandstone-shale-limestone succession of the Cape Oswald Formation (Katz 1954, Poulsen 1956). Most of the boulders of the lower tillite are of limestone, while those of the upper consist of gneiss, granite, or quartz porphyry. This suggests two separate glaciations. In the succeeding Tillite Canyon Formation, there are glacial varves, and a Lower Cambrian fauna appears about 400 m. above the tillites. Fränkl (1953) has questioned the glacial origin of the beds. The tillites which occur in Peary Land (North Greenland lat. 82°) are up to 100 m. thick and, since they contain large striated boulders, their morainic character seems assured. Cambrian fossils do not, however, appear until 800 m. higher; hence these tillites may be older than those of east Greenland.

FIG. 79. STRIATED BOULDER FROM EO-CAMBRIAN TILLITE, ADELAIDE
(after David, from Kayser's "Lehrbuch der Geologie", 1923).

Neither in North nor in South America are there any important relics of Eo-Cambrian glaciation, and only in Utah are supposed Eo-Cambrian beds overlain by Cambrian strata. Here Blackwelder has recorded a tillite 100 m. thick, overlain by varved slates, which grade up into supposed Lower Cambrian deposits. The earliest fossils are, however, of Middle Cambrian age, so it is possible that this tillite may be early Cambrian.

In Africa, most of the tillites are probably older by about 100 million years, but there are numerous exposures in Australia. In the south, these can be traced for over 900 miles, and in the Flinders Range the tillite series attains a thickness of 6,000 m. (figs. 79–80). It is probable that the greater part of these deposits is of glacio-marine origin, and that they formed in an area of geosynclinal downwarp. The series can often be divided into the main (Sturt) tillite and a higher tillite. Glaessner and Parkin consider that the glacial center lay to the north, over Lake Frome and Lake Eyre. Above the tillite series comes the predominantly arenaceous and argillaceous Marinoan Series, which is up to 3,000 m. thick. Locally, this contains yet another thin tillite horizon, the Elatina and Umberatana tillites (Mawson). The Marinoan Series is followed upward by the basal Cambrian Pound Quartzite. The

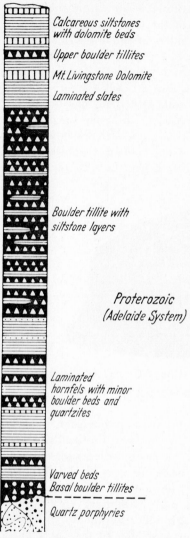

*Calcareous siltstones
with dolomite beds*

Upper boulder tillites

Mt. Livingstone Dolomite

Laminated slates

*Boulder tillite with
siltstone layers*

*Proterozoic
(Adelaide System)*

*Laminated
hornfels with minor
boulder beds and
quartzites*

Varved beds
Basal boulder tillites

Quartz porphyries

Fig. 80. Profile of an Eo-Cambrian Tillite Series in Australia

Mt. Fitton, northern Flinders range. Thickness of section, 7,500 m. Sediments possibly deposited from floating ice (after Glaessner and Parkin, 1958, fig. 2).

thickness of the Marinoan Series is so great that the lower tillites may be older than the Eo-Cambrian.

In Asia, the most important tillites are those which, near Nantung, attain thicknesses of up to 35 m., and are overlain by Cambrian strata with a *Redlichia* fauna. According to Schuller and Ying, they also appear in all nine provinces of South China, in the Tienshan Mountains of North China, and probably also in Shansi. The Yenisei "tillites" have recently been ascribed by Grigoriev and Semichatov to Lower Cambrian submarine slumping.

The Blaini Tillite of the southwest Himalayas, which has sometimes been considered as Eo-Cambrian, is not included in the Table. Later work, particularly by T. H. Holland (*Lex. stratigr. internat.* 1957) indicates that it is an equivalent of the Talchir (Permo-Carboniferous) Glaciation.

Map of the Eo-Cambrian Tillites

The various tillites vary greatly in their degree of certainty. Undoubted morainic deposits or other glacial deposits may be designated M, and beds of doubtful origin, m. Where their Eo-Cambrian age is certain, this is indicated by E; those whose age is questioned are shown by e.

The various occurrences may, therefore, be subdivided into four groups:

(*a*) Group ME: occurrences 2, 6, 7, 8, 21a–c, 22a, 22b (in part) of Table 23.

(*b*) Group Me: 3, 4, 10, 15, 16, 17, 18, 19, 20, 21e.

(*c*) Group mE: 23 (in part).

(*d*) Group me: 1, 5, 9, 11, 12a, 12b, 13, 14, 22b (in part), 22c, 23 (in part). Group (*a*) includes the most certain, group (*d*) the most doubtful occurrences. The degree of certainty, regarding the nature and age of each exposure, is

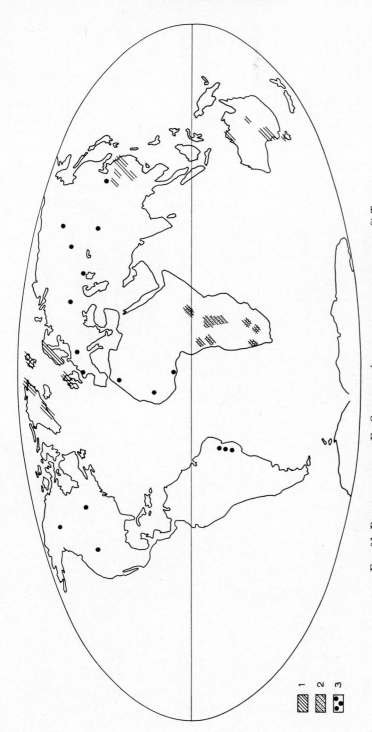

FIG. 81. DISTRIBUTION OF EO-CAMBRIAN (AND A FEW SLIGHTLY OLDER?) TILLITES

1 — Widespread distribution, stratigraphic position relatively certain; 2 — possibly slightly older than Eo-Cambrian; 3 — age rather doubtful.

TABLE 23
EO-CAMBRIAN (AND SLIGHTLY OLDER) TILLITES

LOCALITY	STRIATED PAVEMENT	STRIATED BLOCKS	OVERLYING CAMBRIAN	REMARKS	IMPORTANT, MAINLY RECENT LITERATURE
1. Russian Platform and Urals	–	–	–	Tillite-like conglomerate in U. Riphean	Lungershausen 1960 Shatzki 1958
2. Scandinavian mountains	+	+	+	Traceable over 900 miles, figs. 77, 78	Asklund 1958 Föyn 1938 Holmsen 1957 Holtedahl 1960 Kautsky 1949 Kulling 1931, 1955
3. Scotland, Ireland	–	–	–	Traceable over 250 miles; probably glacio-marine	Anderson 1953, 1954 Bailey 1937 Elwell 1955 Sutton and Watson 1954
4. Normandy	–	(+)	–		Dangeard, Graindor and Wegmann 1950 Graindor 1957
5. Bohemia	–	–	–	Uncertain	Fiala and Svoboda 1956
6. Spitzbergen	–	+	?	Probably glacio-marine	Harland 1960 Kulling 1931, 1934
7. East Greenland (lat. 72–74°N)	–	+	+ *Olenellus* (400 m above)	Cape Oswald Fm.; 500 m tillite series with two tillites	Fränkl 1953 Katz 1954 Poulsen 1956, 1958
8. North Greenland (a) Pearyland	–	+	+ (750–800 m above)	Up to 100 m thick	Troelsen 1956

(b) Yukon Territory, Bonnet Plume River	−	+	+	Boulder Clay 600–700 m thick; extent 7 sq.miles quartzite boulders	P. A. Ziegler 1959
9. South shore of Lake Superior	+	−	−	Only striated pavement known near L'Anse, Michigan; age uncertain	Murray 1955; Gussow thinks caused by coastal ice
10. Utah (Great Salt Lake Wasatch Mts.)	−	(+)	+	Up to 100 m thick	Blackwelder 1932, 1937; Ives 1950
11. Brazil (Minas Gerais, Bahia)	−	−	−	Age uncertain (Lavras Series). Area ~19,000 sq. miles (Maack)	Barbosa 1948; Ebert 1957; Leonardos 1940, 1941; Maack 1957
12. North Africa (a) Anti-Atlas	−	−	+ (15,000 m above) +?	Probably older; Precambrian II (G. Choubert; 15,000 m below "Lie-de-vin" = Cambrian) "Infra-Cambrian"	Houpé 1958
(b) West Sudan	−	−	−		Dars and Sougy 1958
13. Gold Coast	−	−	−	Locally in Buem Series (Precambrian III?)	Junner 1954
14. French Equatorial Africa	−	−	−	Niari "Tillite" (= Tillite Superieure of Congo?)	Furon and Nicklès 1956 (Lex. strat.)
15. Congo	−	+	−	Widespread "tillite" series in Katanga up to 500 m thick; Grand Conglomerat in Lowest Kundelungu, Petit Conglomerat above). Absolute dating suggests age 620 m.y. But younger age not impossible. Correlation with Precambrian "Tillite Superieure" and "Tillite Inferieure" of Lower Congo uncertain	Cahen 1958; Cahen and Lepersonne 1951, 1954 1956 (Lex. strat.); Krenkel 1934

LOCALITY	STRIATED PAVEMENT	STRIATED BLOCKS	OVERLYING CAMBRIAN	REMARKS	IMPORTANT, MAINLY RECENT, LITERATURE
16. Uganda	—		—	Bunyora Series (area 1500 sq. miles)	K. A. Davies 1937 Pallister 1956
17. Angola	—	+	—	"Tillites" of Bembe Fm. Some can be correlated with "tillites" of Katanga or Lower Congo	Krenkel 1934 Mouta 1956 (Lex strat.)
18. Northern Rhodesia	—	+	—	"Tillites" in Kundelungu Fm. (Lufubu Glacial? conglomerate)	Krenkel 1934 Brandt et al. 1956
19. South West Africa (a)	?	+ (Du Toit 1954 fig. 25)	—	Numees Tillite (200–300m) of Transvaal System. At Luderitz, Witpitz, etc. (area 11,500 sq. miles). Correlation with 20 uncertain; compared with Katanga Tillite by Du Toit.	Du Toit and Haughton 1954 Gevers and Beetz 1937 Krenkel 1934
(b)	+	+	—	Schwarzkalk "tillite" of Nama Fm. Local deposit younger than Transvaal System (a) and (b) probably early Paleozoic	Haughton and Martin 1956
20. South Africa (a) West Griqualand	—	+ (Du Toit 1954 Pl. 7)	—	Griquatown "Tillite" (Transvaal System) up to 30 m thick	As in 19
(b) Transvaal	—	+	—	Daspoort Tillite	As in 19
21. Australia (a) South Australia	—	+ (David Pl. 5)	+ (100–several 1000 m above)	Main (Sturt) Tillite and Upper Elatina Tillite (in N.). Outcrop 950 miles long, thickness several 100 m. Figs. 79, 80	David 1950 Glaessner and Parkin 1958 Mawson 1948 Noakes 1956

Locality				References
(b) Kimberley	−	(+)	Walsh Tillite	Guppy 1953 Noakes 1956
(c) Tobermory District (Central Australia)	−	+		Traves 1956 Noakes 1956
(d) Nullagine (West Aus.)			Pre-Permo-Carb. (Noakes)	David 1950 Noakes 1956
(e) Tasmania and King Island			"Zeehan Tillite", age uncertain, recently regarded as Middle Cambrian	Banks 1956
22. China				
(a) Nantung	+	+ *Redlichia* (700 m above)		Lee 1924, 1937 Wang 1955
(b) Other occurrences in S. China	Some +		Up to 400 m thick in S.	Schiller and Ying 1959 Wang 1955
(c) Wutai-shan Shansi			Slightly metamorphosed. 600 m thick, age uncertain	Schiller and Ying 1959
(d) E. Tienshan (N.E. margin of Tarim Basin)		+ (U. Camb. −700 m above)		Norin 1941
23. Asiatic Russia				
(a) Ulu-Tau	−	?		Grigoriev and Semichatov 1958
(b) Kusnezk-Alatau Area	−	+	Probably glacio-marine (Yenisei-Kutenbuluk Series)	Lungershausen 1960 Shatski 1958
(c) Yenisei Mountains	−	+	Recently interpreted as non-glacial and L. Cambrian	Sokolov 1958
(d) Patom Highlands	−	+		Tchurakov 1932, 1937

shown in roughly similar fashion on the map, fig. 81. As was pointed out when dealing with the Congo tillites, the tillites probably comprise the products of several Ice Ages, namely, the true Eo-Cambrian and one or more rather earlier glaciations. But, in any event, the Eo-Cambrian represents a glacial culmination. The upper Algonkian and Eo-Cambrian glaciations correspond to a long period of time; this is also true of the late Paleozoic glaciation, whereas the Quaternary Ice Age, by comparison, is very short. However, this latter may be a false yardstick, because we cannot be certain that the Pleistocene glaciation is finished. In any case, the possibility of using glaciations as time planes is rendered more difficult by the length of the Ice Ages.

Only in some cases does the Eo-Cambrian Ice Age serve satisfactorily as an approximate datum. The widespread occurrence of tillites throughout every continent is as yet difficult to understand, but it suggests that many of the exposures may be of pseudomoraines of nonglacial origin. It further indicates that in Precambrian times, the Southern Continents were nearer to the Pole than they are at present. They remained close to the Pole throughout the Paleozoic Era. The Precambrian North Pole lay close to the west of what is now the Pacific Coast of Canada (see fig. 130). During Paleozoic times, the pole position swung gradually in a great arc across the Pacific and into northeast Asia.

15

The Older Paleozoic

TEMPERATURE AND PRECIPITATION

Introduction and Reef Belts

The Cambrian marks the first appearance of richly fossiliferous rocks, and, therefore, the beginning of organic evidence of climate. At first, this is scarce, but later, particularly after the development of land plants in the Upper Paleozoic, the indications become more numerous. On the whole, little can be said with certainty about the climate of the Older Paleozoic, although we know more about it than about the Precambrian.

The Cambrian, Ordovician, Silurian, and Devonian periods can be dealt with as a whole. They are characterized, primarily, by the presence of a warm, and often arid, climate throughout all of the Northern Hemisphere. Figure 122 clearly shows that the reef belt lays far to the north. "Reef Belt", both here and in other periods, is to be taken to indicate a belt of particularly intensive development of limestones. Several examples may be mentioned. In the **Cambrian,** there are Archaeocyathid limestones several hundreds of meters thick. These are to be found in Silesia, in Sardinia, in the Anti-Atlas of North Africa, in almost mountainous occurrences in the North American Cordilleras (e.g. at Mount Robson), and on into Alaska and Greenland. Limestones and dolomites are also widely developed in Siberia. The 500 m. thick Cambro-Ordovician Durness Limestone of Scotland may be equated with the similar Beekmantown Formation of North America. The North American continent and Greenland form the site of the most abundant development of **Ordovician** limestones (e.g. Chazy, Trenton, etc.). In the **Silurian** System, there occur the highly fossiliferous Wenlock and Aymestry limestones of the Welsh Borderlands with their abundant reef-knolls, the oft-described coral reefs of the Swedish island of Gothland (Hadding, Jux, and Rutten), and the particularly widespread Niagaran reefs of east and northeast North America. These extend from Illinois and Indiana—only 4° N of the present poleward limit of reefs—to Cornwallis Island in lat. 75° N (fig. 82). Lowenstam considers that "this depicts the most extensive areal spread of reefs in North America during geologic time". Some of the reefs form economic oil traps. Similar reef limestones are to be found in Nevada (Winterer and Murphy, 1960) and in Siberia, at Verkhoyansk and on the islands of Novo-Sibirsk.

Thick **Devonian** reefs are developed in Europe (Devon, Ardennes, Rhineland, etc.) and in North America (Helderberg, Gaspé, Onondaga). Givetian
bioherms have also been described from as far north as Novaya Zemlya
(71° N). From the distribution of Devonian tetracorals showing particularly
large annual increments, Ma has reconstructed the position of the equator

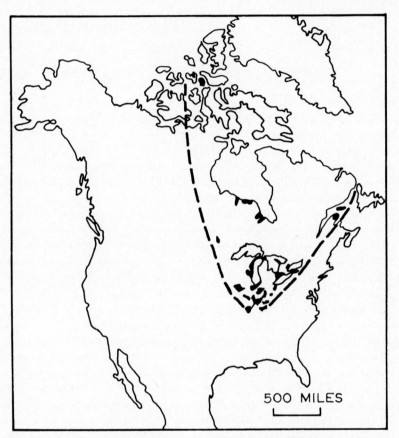

500 MILES

FIG. 82. DISTRIBUTION OF REEFS IN THE NIAGARAN (SILURIAN) IN NORTH
AMERICA (after Lowenstam, 1950).

at that time; he considers that it ran from the north Urals through South
China, West Australia and the northwest of South America. While the
method is interesting, it is not certain that the results are completely
reliable (*cf.* Chapter 4).

Australia, too, is the site of abundant calcareous sedimentation. The
Lower Cambrian Archaeocyathid limestones, which in places are almost
1,000 m. thick, outcrop in South Australia through a distance of almost 400
miles. They have occasionally been compared with the Great Barrier Reef
which lies off the east coast of Australia at the present time. Such a warm

environment seems more likely than Öpik's suggested "cool" climate for the Cambrian of Australia. The "ice crystals" which have been described are exceedingly doubtful. Silurian coral reefs extend intermittently from Queensland to Tasmania, a distance of more than 1,500 miles. Teichert in particular has recorded Middle and Upper Devonian reefs in Western Australia. Even though they are isolated, the discovery of Archaeocyathid limestones is noteworthy in the Weddell Sea region of Antarctica, and at Mt. Buckley at the head of the Beardmore Glacier.

Further reading: BAIN (1960).

Evidence of Arid Climates

Evaporites are of prime importance. For them, Lotze has drawn up a detailed stratigraphic classification, which will also be referred to for other periods (fig. 121).

Cambrian salt deposits are very rare in Europe, North America and Australia. Gypsum occurs in the Middle Cambrian of Devon Island off the Arctic coast of North America (Kurtz and others), and in the Macdougal Stage of the Mackenzie Range; gypsum and halite pseudomorphs occur in the Middle Cambrian of Australia. Evaporites of very great thickness are developed in Siberia (Lena, Yenisei), and in India, in the Salt Range, whose name is derived from its beds of rock salt. The age of these deposits has been disputed, but it now seems certain from Schwindewolf's work, that the evaporite series may be closely correlated with *Redlichia*-bearing Lower Cambrian strata. The *Redlichia* beds also contain such other indications of a dry climate, as desiccation cracks and salt pseudomorphs.

Thicker red beds, containing halite pseudomorphs, occur in the Cambrian of South Australia; particularly in the Middle Cambrian of the Lake Frome area (Daily).

There is little evidence of **Ordovician** aridity except for red beds in the Upper Ordovician of the Appalachians—Juniata Formation. A drier **Silurian** climate is suggested by halite pseudomorphs and salt springs (presumably from beds of halite) in the eastern Baltic area of the Russian Platform, and by abundant occurrences of halite and gypsum in Siberia and North America, where evaporites 600 m. thick, are present in the Upper Silurian of the Michigan Basin. Rock-salt production in the Great Lakes States exceeds 6 million tons. Silurian gypsum deposits have been worked in New York State, Michigan, and Ohio. The **Devonian** System contains both gypsum and halite, especially in the south of the Russian Platform. There are also salt deposits in North America, where they are best developed in the southern part of Canada.

Even more abundant in the Devonian are red beds, thick red clastic deposits washed down from the Caledonian fold mountains of Europe and from the Acadian mountains of eastern North America, to accumulate on the dry lee sides of these mountains. Red coloration, cross-bedding and sun-cracked surfaces, together with gypsum and halite, and a specialized fauna of armored fish, are the characteristics of this "Old Red" facies. A very similar type of sedimentation is encountered in the Permian and Bunter of Europe (i.e. the "New Red" facies).

The Old Red facies is widely developed throughout the northern parts of Europe and Asia. In North America, the Catskill red beds of the eastern United States belong to this facies; so do the Upper Devonian sandstones of East Greenland, which contain the first Tetrapods.

The development of arid climates is obviously closely linked with major periods of mountain-building. The Silurian and Devonian evaporites and "Old Red" sediments are related to the Caledonian and Acadian Orogenies. The arid climate was produced as a result of the driving back of seas and expansion of continents, and by the rain-shadow effect of the mountains.

Evidence of Wet Climates

The bauxite occurring in the Middle Devonian and in the lower part of the Upper Devonian of the Urals (Gladkovski, Krotov, and Sotova) indicates a certain amount of rainfall. The presence of bauxite in this locality fits in with the development of less saline deposits on the adjoining Russian Platform, and also with the reef belt of the Northern Hemisphere. Bauxite is also present in the Lower Devonian of Leon, Spain (Font Alba & Closas, 1960). A humid climate may also be proposed for Bear Island where Upper Devonian coal swamps formed.

Evidence of Glaciation

Those glacial traces that have been recorded from the Northern Hemisphere have either been refuted or are very doubtful. This applies to Ordovician pebble slates in Thuringia and in Britain, and to the widely distributed Ordovician "boulder conglomerates" of Quebec, etc., which Bailey et al (1928) have shown to be the products of submarine slumping. Kirk mentions as Silurian moraines, some 100 m. thick "boulder conglomerates" from Heceta Island, Alaska, latitude 55°–60° N. Other moraines are recorded from British Columbia (Shepard) and Maine (Smith). The Russians also consider that there were Ordovician (Lungershausen) and Silurian (Miloradovitch, Novaya Zemlaya) glaciations. The Devonian tillite of the Mediterranean island of Minorca, described by Schindewolf, has been shown by Gomez de Llarena and Schwarzbach to be probably the result of submarine slumping. Clarke's so-called "ice crystals", in the Lower Devonian of New York State, were later denied as such by Clarke himself. Striae in the Portage of Pennsylvania (Willard) can readily be assigned to nonglacial causes.

Another possible moraine is the Squantum-"tillite" of Boston, Mass., described in greatest detail by Sayles. Its distribution is certainly very restricted and its boulders are at best only indistinctly striated. The "tillite" is accompanied by well developed "varved shales". Unfortunately its strati-graphic position is not well established, but it does not, as has hitherto been supposed, seem to be late Paleozoic. Bell considers it to be Devonian. The glacial origin of the Squantum-"tillite" (fig. 83) has recently been queried by Crowell, and by Dott (1961), who considers that this bouldery mudstone formed during the Mid-Paleozoic diastrophism, by gravity movement of volcanic-rich sediments with periodic resedimentation by turbidity cur-

FIG. 83. SQUANTUM-"TILLITE" NEAR BOSTON (Photograph: M. Schwarzbach).

rents. He points out that there is no striated pavement and that striated clasts, and facetting, can be produced in nonglacial sediments. Fairbridge (1947, p. 108) earlier showed that the intraformational folding, originally ascribed to grounding icebergs, was simply the product of submarine slumping.

A different state of affairs exists in the Southern Hemisphere. Certainly, in Australia, there are only doubtful tillites, including the already-mentioned Zeehan tillite of Tasmania, which was considered as Eo-Cambrian, but could also be of Middle Cambrian age. On the other hand, there do appear to be Lower Paleozoic glacial sediments in South Africa and South America.

In South Africa, there is the 30 m. thick Table Mountain tillite which outcrops near Cape Town, and again 60 miles further north, near Clan-william, where it can be traced for nearly 20 miles. Individual boulders are very well striated. Since the overlying strata form the Lower Devonian Bokkeweld Series, the glacial sediments are probably Silurian or Lower Devonian (Du Toit, 1954).

In South America (fig. 91), striated blocks in the Lower Ordovician conglomerates of the Andean foothills of northern Argentina are considered, by Keidel, to be of morainic derivation. However, this interpretation is open to question. Then, in the Sierra Sao Joaqim in Parana, there are two tillite horizons in the Iapo Formation (Caster, Maack, Rich). These are traceable for over 20 miles, and contain striated boulders, mostly of granite, porphyry, and quartzite. The Iapo Formation underlies the "Lower Devonian" Furnas Sandstone and succeeds Taconic quartz porphyries. Its stratigraphic equivalence with the Table Mountain glaciation is therefore very striking. The Zapla tillites in northwest Argentina are probably also of Silurian age (Schlagintweit); the same tillite is also present at Yapacani in neighboring Bolivia (Rod, 1960), 40–50 m. below basal Devonian sediments.

Devonian "glacial" sediments have also been found in Brazil. There are the tillites in the Furnas and Barreiro Sandstones of Parana, and striated pavements in Piaui, above the Serra-Grande Sandstone (which is regarded by Malzahn as the equivalent of the Furnas Sandstone). The Carolina tillite in the Upper Devonian Longa Formation of Piaui (Kegel) is said to be at the same horizon as the tillite in the Andean foothills of San Juan in west Argentina, described by Frenguelli.

The nature of many South American "tillites" still requires critical appraisal. Nevertheless, we get the impression that, in this continent, climatic conditions remained favorable for the formation of glaciers throughout a long period of time, from the Eo-Cambrian or early Paleozoic to the beginning of the Permian. The same seems to apply to South Africa.

SUMMARY

A few general conclusions can already be drawn in spite of the fragmentary nature of the details. In the Older Paleozoic, all of the Northern Hemisphere, including even high latitudes, enjoyed a warm climate; so did Australia. In these areas, the prevailing climate was sometimes arid as well. This aridity was related to the Older Paleozoic mountain building, and hence was most marked in the Upper Silurian and Devonian. Some traces of glaciation are to be found, especially in South Africa and South America. It is possible to draw a climatic map of the Devonian Period (fig. 84); on it may be entered the position of the poles and equator as deduced from paleomagnetic measurements. The resulting picture is in many ways surprisingly uniform. It shows a "tropic" zone running through North America and Europe, and a south polar region over the South Atlantic. Strakhov recently arrived at a similar reconstruction; Spjeldnes (1961) did likewise for the Ordovician. In Strakhov's (1959) map, however, the position of the equator, as revealed by climatic indicators, is somewhat different

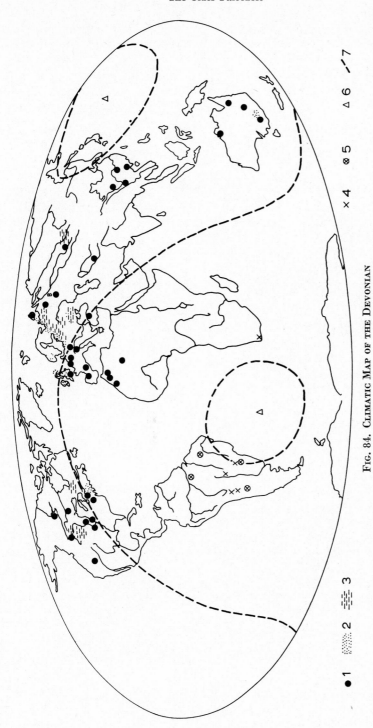

FIG. 84. CLIMATIC MAP OF THE DEVONIAN

1—Coral limestones, 2—Old Red Facies, 3—Evaporites (after F. Lotze), 4—Iapo Formation and Table Mountain Tillite, 5—Upper Devonian Tillite, 6—Paleomagnetic South Pole (after Runcorn) and North Pole from which the equator and polar circles have been constructed (7), B—Bauxite (after M. Schwarzbach, 1958).

from the palaeomagnetically calculated position shown in fig. 84. Thus, in Europe, he considers the equator to have lain north of Scandinavia, some 1,300 miles north of the position shown in fig. 84. Central and western Europe, then, lie in the southern arid belt, while the northern desert zone trends south-eastwards from Spitzbergen.

16

Younger Paleozoic, and the Permo-Carboniferous Glaciation

> I have been laughed at by country people riding their
> mules to market, while I chipped striated stones from
> tillite, well within the tropics, not far from plantations
> of coffee and bananas in Brazil.
>   A. P. COLEMAN, Bull. Geol. Soc. Amer., 1939.

In the Northern Hemisphere, the climatic features displayed by Carboniferous and Permian strata vary greatly; the Carboniferous beds often suggest a wet climate: the Permian sediments indicate aridity. Nevertheless, the two periods are here treated together as the Younger Paleozoic for in the Southern Hemisphere, the Permo-Carboniferous Ice Age is the dominant feature of both periods. Absence of traces of this glaciation from the Northern Hemisphere is also, in a negative sort of way, a common characteristic of both periods. For other reasons, too, paleoclimatologists regard the Carboniferous and Permian Systems as unusually interesting; both contain deposits of great economic importance, which have been thoroughly investigated, and owed their origin to particular climatic conditions. The bulk of American and European coals are included in Upper Carboniferous strata; rich Permian seams are present in other continents. The Permian system also contains the world's most important salt deposits. In the Northern Hemisphere, then, there are separate developments of beds indicating both high rainfall and extreme aridity.

TEMPERATURE AND PRECIPITATION

Reef Belt

As in the Lower Paleozoic, the warm areas, characterized by prolific formation of organic limestones, lie well within the Northern Hemisphere. According to D. Hill, the belt of Lower Carboniferous reef corals lies between 20° N and 60° N (fig. 122).

Among Lower Carboniferous (Mississippian) limestones, the Carboniferous Limestone Series of Europe merits particular mention. This name is applied to calcareous deposits underlying the main coal-bearing formations. In places, the series is 700 m. thick; its rich fauna of corals, large productids, etc., has been the subject of classic research work, particularly in England, Ireland, and Belgium.

In Eastern Europe (Russian Platform), Asia, and North America, both the Lower and Upper Carboniferous (Pennsylvanian) contain very thick calcareous deposits. Large calcareous forams are often the dominant element of the fauna in these younger beds of North America, the eastern Alps, the Russian Platform, Central Asia, Japan, China, and even the Arctic (Spitzbergen and Bear Island). Examples of North American reefs built largely of the alga *Cryptozoon*, include Upper Pennsylvanian occurrences in New Mexico which, according to Plumley and Graves, may be as much as 1 mile long and 60 m. thick, and the Upper Carboniferous–Lower Permian reef masses of the Horseshoe Atoll in northwest Texas. This atoll was detected only by drilling. It forms a 90-mile diameter semicircle and is of economic importance as an oil reservoir (Stafford, Burnside, fig. 20).

There is a great deal of other evidence of Carboniferous climates, including the gay colors of the marine organisms, the presence of *Lingula*, gigantism and heterometabolism of insects. All suggest a warm climate, and so does the flora of the coal seams.

Most of the Younger Paleozoic limestones are situated, stratigraphically, in the Lower Carboniferous; figs. 122, 123 show quite clearly how the area of the calcareous sedimentation decreased during the Permian period. The afore-mentioned foraminiferal limestones of the Upper Carboniferous often continue to develop in the same areas in the Permian. Reefs also occur in the South Urals, where they range in time from the Upper Carboniferous to the Artinskian. Here they are more than 50 m. thick and form important oil traps (Theodorovitch, Levet). They appear in the Kasan stage of the Upper Permian in northern Russia (Tumanskaya) and in eastern Greenland (Maync). Other American reefs include those of West Texas (fig. 20) and the Lower Permian Wolfcamp Formation. The latter form important oil reservoirs (Kornfeld). The Upper Permian Capitan Reef of the Guadeloupe Mountains, New Mexico, which is exposed over a distance of 45 miles has been intensively studied by Newell and his co-workers. In England and in Germany, the Bryozoa stand out as important Zechstein reef-builders.

In view of the very considerable development of limestone in the far north, e.g. the thick Permian limestones of Alaska (Moffit), one cannot agree with Stehli that a cold climate may be inferred on a statistical basis from the "impoverished" fauna. He does not appear to have taken proper account of either the difficulties of finding fossils there or the possibility of later destruction.

In the Southern Hemisphere, reefs are prominent only in Australia, where such distinct calcareous facies as the Burindi Limestone are developed basally in the Lower Carboniferous succession, and in Timor where, according to Gerth, the unusually prolific Permian fauna, with corals, etc., constitutes a warm water assemblage.

Further reading: BOND, 1950; D. PARKINSON, 1957; ZEKKEL, 1941.

Coal Forests as Evidence of a Warm Humid Climate

The Carboniferous Period, particularly in its middle stages, appears to have been a time of unusually high rainfall. This is indicated primarily by the extensive swamps from whose peat deposits the coal seams have arisen. The development of the luxuriant land vegetation which gave rise to the peat began, as we have already seen, in the Upper Devonian, and attained a maximum in the Westphalian stage of the Upper Carboniferous. Thus the greatest part of the bituminous coals of Europe and North America, the Urals, the northern part of Asia Minor, and North Africa are of Upper Carboniferous age. The large number of coal seams—more than 100 in many places—shows that conditions favoring the formation of coal swamps persisted over a long period of time. Seams undoubtedly developed intermittently throughout a period of some tens of millions of years.

With the arrival of the Permian, the swamps disappeared almost completely from Europe and North America, except for such areas as the Massif Central of France, where there are many Autunian coals, and the Pennsylvania-West Virginia area where the Dunkard coals formed. Instead, they now spread into the great Siberian basins of Kuznetzk, Minussinsk, and Tunguska; and into China, India and the Southern Hemisphere. The bituminous coals of Australia, South Africa, and South America all belong to much the same stratigraphic horizon, in the middle of the Lower Permian; those of the Siberian coalfields continue on into the Mesozoic.

Whether or not the flora of these coal measures indicates a warm climate at that time, has often been discussed. The particular characteristics of many of the Carboniferous plants do, in fact, suggest warmth (Chapter 4). On the other hand, the vast amount of vegetable material which has accumulated in the coal seams does nothing to support this argument, for it has been shown before (Chapter 5) that at the present time, the vast majority of peat bogs are to be found in areas with a cool climate. In Europe, however, the Carboniferous coals all originated under rather exceptional conditions in the tectonically mobile foredeeps and intramontane basins of the Variscan mountain chains. In the United States, the developing Appalachian mountains exerted a similar control. Such conditions are almost unknown at the present time. Because of this tectonic control, formation of the Carboniferous coals was largely independent of climatic factors, or at least of temperature.

While the Carboniferous flora of Europe and North America may be described as "tropical" or at least "subtropical" in character, the same cannot be said of the Permian flora of the Southern Hemisphere which has as a typical member the seed fern *Glossopteris* (fig. 44). On the basis of other

Climates of the Past

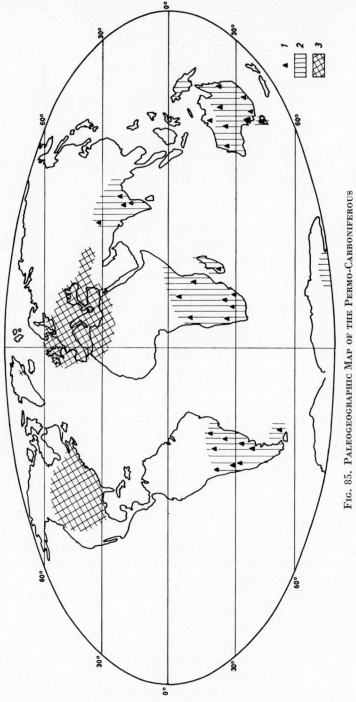

FIG. 85. PALEOGEOGRAPHIC MAP OF THE PERMO-CARBONIFEROUS

1—Tillite, 2—*Glossopteris* flora, 3—Euramerican flora (floras after Gothan-Weyland, 1954, slightly modified).

climatic evidence, this flora must be regarded as being the product of a cooler climate.

Generally speaking, the Upper Carboniferous and Permian periods are characterized by clear geographical differentiation of the different floras (fig. 85); in the Lower Carboniferous, on the other hand, more or less the same type of vegetation is developed everywhere. During Carboniferous times, belts of abundant coal formation migrated southward from a relatively northerly position over Spitzbergen, Scotland, and the Moscow Basin

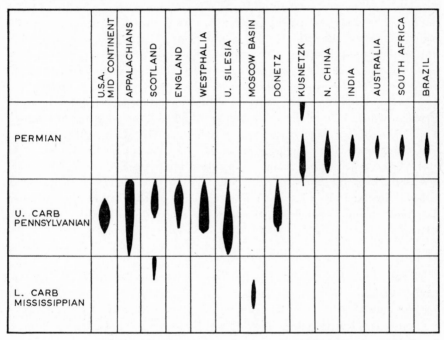

FIG. 86. COAL FORMATION IN THE UPPER PALEOZOIC

The area of extensive development of coal shifted from North America and Europe in the Upper Carboniferous to Asia and the Southern Hemisphere in the Permian. The unimportant Permian Dunkard Coals of Pennsylvania and West Virginia are not indicated.

(fig. 86), to the Saar Coalfield and the Massif Central. This latter position was reached by the end of the Upper Carboniferous. The coal belt then shifted to other continents. Migration was controlled partly by climatic factors, and reflects the slow displacement of a belt of heavy rainfall throughout the Carboniferous and Permian periods. Tectonic factors played a lesser part in this southward movement of the coal forests.

Evidence of Carboniferous Aridity

From the widespread distribution of wet climates during the Carboniferous period, it follows that evidence of aridity will tend to be sparse. Evaporites are absent from Europe, but in North America, gypsum and rock salt occur in the Mississippian of Michigan, Ohio, Virginia, Nova Scotia, and Newfoundland. The same salts occur very infrequently in the Upper Carboniferous, e.g. in the Paradox Formation of the Lower Pennsylvanian of Colorado and Utah. The Upper Carboniferous gypsum deposits of Spitzbergen and East Greenland are particularly noteworthy. In other continents there are only isolated, and often doubtful, occurrences of evaporites. Only toward the end of the Carboniferous Period do the indications of aridity in Europe and America start to multiply. The red bed facies, which was to be dominant in Permian times, appeared during the Westphalian stage in Scotland, during the Stephanian in the Saar district and in Silesia, and during the Pennsylvanian of Colorado (Fountain Formation). The red beds tend to appear in the north rather earlier than they do further south. Therefore, the belt of semiarid climates which gave rise to this facies must also have advanced slowly southward in Upper Carboniferous and Lower Permian times, behind the rainy belt in which the coal swamps developed. The Carboniferous fireclays of Scotland, Silesia, the Moscow Basin, China, and the Appalachians suggest seasonally arid conditions to Harrassowitz and others, who regard them as degraded laterites. Krivsov has recently described kaolinite-bauxites from the Lower Carboniferous of northern Russia; silicification of the Namurian peats of the Ruhr, described by Teichmüller and Schonefeld, may also have been connected with lateritic weathering.

Evidence of Arid Permian Climates

Those developments which have been described resulted in places in extremely arid Permian climates. There is hardly any climatic contrast greater than that between Westphalian conditions in central Europe, when luxuriant tropical rain forests flourished, and Upper Permian conditions, when the area was a barren desert. The increasing aridity found its best expression in red beds with footprints, rain pits, silicification, ripple marks, ventifacts, inselbergs, etc. Extreme aridity resulted in the vast salt deposits of this age; the greatest of the world's potash deposits occur in Permian strata (fig. 121).

In Europe, the typical red bed formation is the continental, Lower Permian "Rotliegendes" of Germany, or the Lower New Red of the English Midlands. This type of sediment is developed throughout most of Europe, and in 1849 Murchison coined the name of the system from outcrops in the foothills of the Urals. In places, it can be established that the climate repeatedly alternated between wet and dry phases—occasional periods of coal formation have already been mentioned—before very dry conditions became firmly established in the Saxonian. Precipitation of salts had already begun in Lower Permain times in Schleswig-Holstein, over large parts of the eastern sector of the Russian Platform, and at Solikamsk, where potash deposits formed; it reached a maximum in the Upper Permian, with the formation of thick halite and potash beds in Germany and northeast England (see fig. 49).

Evaporites are also present at a number of localities in Asia. Sheynman depicts an extensive arid zone stretching from the Urals to the upper reaches of the Yangtse Kiang, and the Hwang Ho. North America, too, has many enormous Permian deposits of gypsum, halite and potash salts. It has been estimated that the area covering Kansas, New Mexico, and west Texas, has reserves of 95·5 billion tons of rock salt. Just as in Europe, the evaporites are accompanied by red bed formations in both eastern and western United States. An example of such red sediments is the Coconino Sandstone of the Grand Canyon of Arizona.

Further reading: SHERLOCK, 1947.

WIND DIRECTION

There are few records of the direction of Carboniferous winds. Sorby's work on tree roots suggested that around Sheffield in the north of England, the prevailing wind was westerly; a north wind is supposed to have affected the Midland Valley of Scotland during the eruption of the Lower Carboniferous tuffs of Arthur's Seat (see Chapter 8). According to Bucher and others, a "monsoon" wind blew in Ohio; the land mass lay to the northeast, the sea to the south. There are not many more records from the arid deposits of the Permian, where the wind direction is usually deduced from ripples and from the shape and internal structure of dunes (Table 24). Schove, Nairn, and Opdyke have attempted to fit these observations into the overall climatic picture of the Permian; they have attributed the directions given in the Table to trade winds. At this time, the equator is supposed to have run through Europe and North America, but naturally, these few observations of Permian wind directions afford only a very sketchy indication of this.

TABLE 24

PERMIAN WIND DIRECTIONS

LOCALITY	HORIZON	WIND DIRECTION	AUTHOR
Nahe Basin (Hunsrück, W. Germany)	Rotliegendes	SW	Reineck, 1955
Central Germany	Zechstein	SSW–ESE	Ludwig, 1927 and Richter-Bernburg
England	Permian	E	Shotton, 1956
Colorado Plateau	Permian-Trias	N, NE	Reiche, 1938; Poole, 1957
Wyoming, Utah	Pennsylvanian-Permian	NE	Opdyke, and Runcorn, 1960

CLIMATIC VARIATION

Seasonal Variation

In dealing with "laterites" we have already touched upon the problem of seasonal climatic variation during the Carboniferous Period. This subject has been much discussed, particularly with regard to the structure of tree stems (Gothan). In Europe and North America, these show hardly any annual rings; rings are somewhat more common in Gondwanaland. There are only very isolated records of growth rings in the Northern Hemisphere, and these have been explained as belonging to trees swept down from cooler mountainous areas. In the tropical lowlands there was supposedly no seasonal variation to produce rings. It is very probable, though, that the absence of growth rings is related more to the primitive state of development of the plants than to extremely uniform climatic conditions, for the rocks adjacent to the coal seams are often laminated, and the bones of reptiles and amphibians often exhibit an apparent annual growth structure, as Peabody has recorded in the Lower Permian of Oklahoma. Both the lamination and the bone structures are almost certainly due largely to seasonal climatic variation. Korn has even attempted to demonstrate a four-membered annual rhythm in the Thuringian sediments. This rhythm is supposedly due to the two rainy and two dry seasons found in equatorial regions, but his observations are not convincing.

Long-term Rhythms

The question of climatic rhythms is raised when we consider the often very regular cycles of sedimentation, or cyclothems, which occur in very many Carboniferous coalfields. A rhythm of the following type is often encountered.

Marine Shale
Coal
Rootlet Bed
Sandstone   } Rhythm several meters thick.
Sandy Shale
Marine Shale
Coal

Cyclothems may be explained either tectonically, i.e. as resulting from a variable rate of subsidence of the area, or climatically, by such indirect processes as variations in sea level, and changes in the base level of erosion. It is as yet very difficult to establish any climatic factor which would cause such a regular variation in sea level. Only eustatic changes of the type encountered in the Quaternary seem adequate. Yet, in the present state of our knowledge, it appears that the Permo-Carboniferous glaciation did not comprise a hundred or more glacial phases. However, if it lasted, as King has suggested, from the early Carboniferous to the Middle Permian, it might have produced enough sea-level variations to account for the relatively few megacyclothems. Moore (1958) has shown that most of the small-scale rhythms could have been produced by the normal processes of deltaic sedimentation. If the cause is held to be tectonic, one may add that tectonism could have produced simultaneous slight climatic changes, and thus indirectly affected the formation of cyclothems. Weller, in particular, has advocated this theory.

Unconvincing attempts to explain rhythms in the Carboniferous gray-wackes of Thuringia, and banding in the Permian evaporites, on the basis of 11-year or longer cycles of sunspot activity have already been mentioned in Chapter 9.

Further reading: WHEELER & MURRAY, 1957.

TRACES OF GLACIATION

The Northern Hemisphere

As the prevailing climate of North America and the greater part of Europe and Asia was warm during the Carboniferous Period, no undoubted evidence of glaciation has been discovered there. The Squantum tillite near Boston (fig. 83), the most likely moraine, is now considered by some authors to be older[1]. Other "tillites" are now thought, probably correctly, to be due to some such other cause as submarine slumping. These "tillites" include the Caney Shale of the Ouachita Mountains in Oklahoma, which contains striated boulders as large as houses (Waterschoot *v.d.* Gracht, Kramer), and boulders in the slightly younger Johns Valley Shale of the same district (Moore) and in the Haymond Formation of west Texas (King, Hall). In 1957, Misch and Oles again suggested that the boulders of the Johns Valley shale were of glacial origin, and derived from drifting ice. It is of historical interest only to note that in 1892, at the time when the theory of the great Gondwana glaciation was being developed, the Culm conglomerates of Lower Silesia were considered to be of glacial origin. The Lower Carboniferous "pebble-slates" of Thuringia need not be glacial, as Kalkovsky suggests; they could be the products of normal sedimentation (Eigenfeld, Korn).

Geologists have also been tempted to interpret the Permian fanglomerates as glacial deposits; indeed, they were the subject of the first, incorrect, report of pre-Quaternary moraines (Ramsay, 1855). More recently, so-called Permian tillites have been recorded from the mouth of the River Lena in Siberia, and from the Valle de las Delicias in northern Mexico (Humphrey). Suggestions that these two deposits are glacial have been questioned by Meshwilk and Newell respectively.

Gondwanaland

Suess, in his great synthesis, "The Face of the Earth", clearly showed that India and the continents of the Southern Hemisphere all have many features

---

1. M. P. Billings still believes it to be Permo-Carboniferous (personal communication to author, 1961).

in common. It is therefore reasonable to assume that in Upper Paleozoic times they formed one great land mass, which he named Gondwanaland. Today, the problem of this ancient continental block no longer seems quite so simple, although one of its main characteristics is apparent; unlike the Northern Hemisphere, it abounds everywhere with evidence of widespread glaciations, though the exact stratigraphic position of those glaciations is still uncertain. The main glacial phase obviously lies somewhere near the Permo-Carboniferous boundary, for Teichert has recently observed that, in Australia, it took place at the start of the Permian, while in India and South America in particular, it is still regarded as Upper Carboniferous in age. In any event, early glacial phases took place in the Carboniferous, while late phases occurred in the Permian. Hence it is still best to speak of the Permo-Carboniferous or Younger Paleozoic glaciation of Gondwanaland.

India.—This Ice Age was discovered by W. T. Blanford (1856), while he was working in India, the only part of Gondwanaland situated north of the equator. The tillite (Talchir Tillite) is in places more than 30 m. thick, and contains striated blocks. A striated pavement was also discovered by Fedden in the Penganga River area (lat. 19° N). The striae ran from southwest to northeast. In the Umaria coalfield the tillite is overlain by a marine horizon with *Productus*, so the ice probably advanced through the lowlands to reach the sea; in the Salt Range, marine sandstones containing *Eurydesma* and Conulariids are closely associated with the tillites.

Figure 87 shows that the main glacial deposits lie in eastern and central India, between latitudes 17° N and 24° N, in a belt over 600 miles long. There are other outcrops in the Salt Range, in the Himalayas, where there occurs the Blaini Tillite of Kashmir, thought by some to be Eo-Cambrian, and in east Nepal and the Kosi Gorge. The latter was first described by Auden and Dutta in 1946.

In the main outcrop, the boulders may have been derived from the south; this would mean that the ice came from the direction of the present equator. Jacob, however, inclines more to the view that the ice center lay in the region of the Vindhyas and Aravallis, and that from there, the ice streamed away to the south and east (see fig. 87). He assumes that the tillites of the Salt Range were derived from a separate center in the Sargodha region.

The succession above the tillite shows the effects of a gradual amelioration of the climate. Moraines of the glacial phase are followed by beds containing a *Glossopteris* flora, which may also be regarded as an indicator of a cool climate. These, in turn, are overlain, in the Salt Range, by sandstones containing the pelecypod *Eurydesma* and Conulariids, which also suggest cool conditions. Above come sandstones with a richer flora, interbedded with seams of coal (Damuda Series), and with *Productus* limestones whose fauna is warmth-loving. Not far from India, tillites have recently been described from southwest Oman, Arabia, by Hudson (in King, 1958). There, the tillites are underlain and succeeded by sandy limestones containing

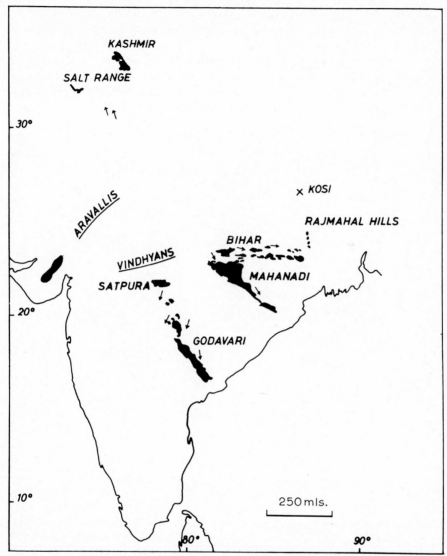

FIG. 87. DISTRIBUTION OF THE LOWER GONDWANA BEDS (WITH THE TALCHIR TILLITE) IN
INDIA

Direction of ice movement (after K. Jacob) shown by arrows.

Metalegoceras. The boulders were derived in part from the Precambrian
shield.

South Africa.—Here, too, glacial deposits were recognized long ago by
Sutherland (1868). The most important moraine is the Dwyka "conglomerate", for which Penck (1906) coined the term "tillite", now applied to all
consolidated morainic deposits.

The Dwyka Tillite Series is usually some 300–400 m. thick though it may
occasionally swell to as much as 700 m.; the thickness diminishes northward.
The boulders and some of the pavements are beautifully striated. The source
of some of the boulders may be accurately pinpointed; they were derived
from the north, often from a distance of more than 700 miles. Using these
boulders, it has proved possible to reconstruct a fairly accurate map of this
glaciation (fig. 88). In the south, the deposits have been interpreted as

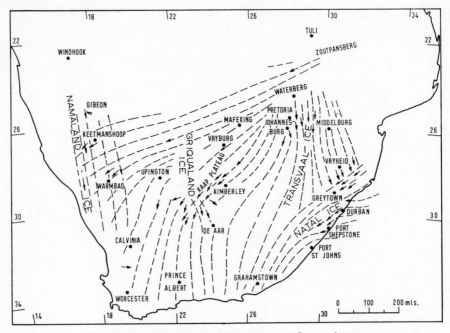

FIG. 88. UPPER PALEOZOIC GLACIATION OF SOUTH AFRICA

Arrows showing direction of movement of ice sheets. Four glacial centres (after Du Toit,
from Krenkel, 1928).

glacio-marine sediments. In the nearby Kaoko-Feld, in the northwestern
part of Southwest Africa, banded shales, *roches moutonnées* with southerly lee
slopes and U-shaped valleys, have all been observed by Martin. He even
believes that he has seen corries at Grootberg, but his evidence for these is
not very convincing.

The tillites and their glacio-marine equivalents cover the southern tip of
Africa and stretch more or less continuously as far north as lat. 25° S,
throughout an area of well over 400,000 square miles. As with the Pleistocene
continental ice sheets, several ice centers can be detected. The Namaland
Ice in the west is followed eastward by the smaller Griqualand Ice, by the
extensive Transvaal Ice, and finally, by the Natal Ice, which must have
originated in the area now occupied by the Indian Ocean. Whether or not

we should assume that there were several ice ages remains unsettled, but there may be as many as five tillite horizons.

Here, too, the tillites are followed by shales containing *Glossopteris* and, at Keetmanshoop, a marine fauna in which *Eurydesma* is prominent. These, in turn, are succeeded by the Karroo Beds with their well-known reptilian remains.

The South African continental ice must also have had some outlet to the north. The tillites of North Angola (lat. 10° S Lutoe Series, Mouta) and the Congo (Niemba bed of the Lukuga Series) may well represent its deposits. So too may the conglomeratic basal beds of the Nyassa Coalfield and the typical Dwyka tillite of South Madagascar. The latter rests on crystalline rocks and is overlain by coal seams, red beds, and marine limestones with *Productus* (Besairie).

Australia.—Traces of glaciation in Australia are of even greater significance, for in this continent their time span is greater than in any other. The first clear indication of glaciation comes in New South Wales in the Upper Kuttung Series, which is probably of Namurian age because of its *Rhacopteris-Lepidodendron* flora. K. Campbell (1961) has recently suggested that it may in part be Westphalian. The main glacial series is 600 m. thick, and includes several typical tillites up to 20 m. thick. Striated pavements are known, the striae being directed toward the north-northwest. Near Seaham, there is an excellent example of a varved shale showing slumping (Fairbridge).

Under this succession lies another "glacial series" into which a toscanite is intruded. This series does not, however, contain any true tillites, and its origin is therefore somewhat questionable (first glaciation of some authors).

The Kuttung glaciation was probably only of local significance; it may possibly have been related to the intra-Carboniferous, Kanimblan, folding and uplift of New South Wales.

The main glacial phase is represented by the Lochinvar Tillite, which is associated with a quite different flora, containing *Glossopteris* and *Gangamopteris*. In the Irwin River area of West Australia, the tillite is followed after an interval of about 300 m. by a marine horizon containing large numbers of the cephalopod *Metalegoceras jacksonii*. According to Teichert, this fauna is of Permian age, and it is therefore probable that the Lochinvar Tillite is also Lower Permian. In other localities, e.g. South Australia, where it is not possible to fix the stratigraphic position of the tillite accurately, it has sometimes been thought to be Cretaceous.

The Tillite Series attains a thickness of several hundred meters. In places it comprises a repeated succession of glacial and nonglacial sediments which, according to Bowen, may contain 51 cycles. Wanless (1960) deduced therefrom a repetition of glacial and interglacial phases similar to that of the Quaternary Ice Age, but this has not yet been proved.

Besides striated blocks, glacially-scored pavements (fig. 89) and U-shaped

FIG. 89. STRIATED PAVEMENT OF UPPER PALEOZOIC GLACIATION: INMAN VALLEY, SOUTH
AUSTRALIA (after Glaessner and Parkin, 1958).

valleys have been described from several localities. Traces of this continental
glaciation are scattered throughout all of Australia and Tasmania (fig. 90)
over a distance of more than 2,200 miles. In Permo-Carboniferous times, the
whole continent must have been "a veritable Antarctica" (David and
Süssmilch). The ice center probably lay at some little distance to the south,
beyond the present coast line, in what is now the Antarctic Ocean.

The Lochinvar seems to have been the only really widespread Younger
Paleozoic glaciation in Australia. Süssmilch and David propose two further
Permian glaciations but in these, as Teichert has pointed out, there are no

true tillites. Some of the tillite-like deposits are probably glacio-marine; other blocks occurring in coal seams are certainly not glacial. The Branxton Mudstone, with its many erratics, at the base of the Upper Marine Series of New South Wales, is usually regarded as a glacial deposit to be correlated with the Woodbridge Glacial Formation in Tasmania. Banks has shown in a diagram that many Permian sediments of Tasmania also carry erratics.

The evidence suggests that during the Permian Period, colder climates

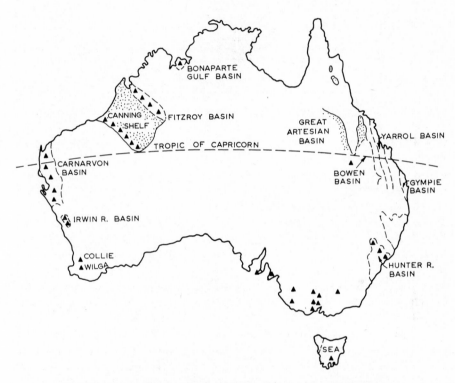

FIG. 90. DISTRIBUTION OF UPPER PALEOZOIC TILLITES IN AUSTRALIA

--- Marine area, ⠿ terrestrial deposits, ▲ glacial deposits (after D. Hill, 1958).

prevailed briefly from time to time; these were interspersed with periods of more active coal formation, and with transgressions of somewhat warmer seas. The island of Timor not far from the northwest coast of Australia has a rich Permian marine fauna of a type characteristic of a warm climate. Gerth has pointed out that this conflicts with the supposed glaciation of Australia. Since, however, the main glacial phase is clearly earlier than the Permian strata of Timor, this contrast presents no particular problem despite the proximity of the two areas. The time sequence of the Australian glaciations is shown in detail in Table 25.

TABLE 25

UPPER PALEOZOIC STRATIGRAPHY OF AUSTRALIA
(MAINLY NEW SOUTH WALES)

?ARTINSKIAN		Upper Coal Measures Upper Marine Series Branxton Mudstone at base with glacial erratics (–Woodbridge Glacial Formation of Tasmania)
ARTINSKIAN		Lower (Greta) Coal Measures

SAKMARIAN	Lower
	Marine
	Series
		Farley Sandstone
		Allendale Sandstone; fossiliferous limestones (Callytharra) in
		   NW Australia
		Lochinvar Group; glacial beds overlain by strata with
		   Eurydesma (*Metalegoceras* in Western Australia)

CARBONIFEROUS		Kuttung Group with tillite/Burindi Group

Further reading: CALDENIUS, 1938; CAMPANA & WILSON, 1955; FAIRBRIDGE, 1953.

South America.—Permo-Carboniferous tillites were not recognized as long ago in South America as they were in the other southern continents. As early as 1888, Derby and White did in fact suppose that certain sediments such as the Orleans conglomerate in south Brazil were of glacial origin, but striated boulders were not discovered until 1908, by Woodworth, on the Harvard Expedition of that year. The glacial deposits of the Falkland Islands were described by Halle in 1912. More recently, detailed studies have been carried out by Beurlen, Leinz, Maack, Martin, Putzer, and others (fig. 91).

The main outcrops are in south Brazil, where they extend in a narrow strip through the states of São Paulo, Parana, Santa Catarina and Rio Grande do Sul, and on into Uruguay and Paraguay, i.e. from 20° S to 35° S, a distance of some 900 miles. The tillite series also appears in the southern part of the Matto Grosso. In addition to typical morainic deposits, it also contains more normal clastic sediments, particularly sandstones, and some coal seams. Its thickness varies from 500 m. in Parana to 1000 m. in São Paula, suggesting sedimentation in a typical basin area.

The number of tillite horizons also varies: in São Paulo there are five, in Parana four, and in Santa Catarina only two; a southward decrease, though three glacial horizons are again recorded in Uruguay, and in the Matto Grosso. The tillites are sometimes associated with varved shales (Caster, 1952), which have been used to estimate the duration of each member. It was estimated that a single deposit took 10,000 years to form. Some of the moraines probably formed in part from floating ice. The glacial beds have been referred to as the Itararé Series (Oliveira). White has supposed the coal seams to be younger than the tillite series. A later suggestion, however, is that some of the coals represent interglacial or interstadial phases of the tillite series, while others are its lateral equivalents. The coal-bearing

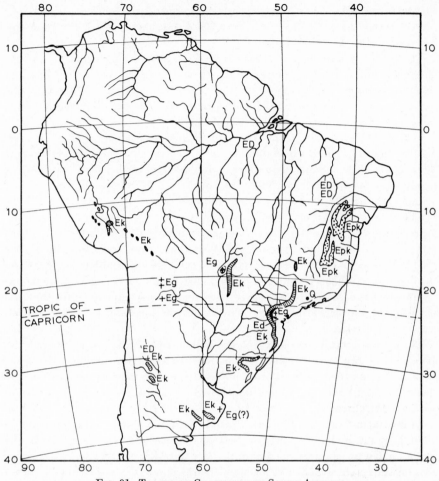

FIG. 91. TRACES OF GLACIATION IN SOUTH AMERICA
Epk—Precambrian to Early Paleozoic. Eg—Silurian. Ed—Lower Devonian. ED—
Upper Devonian. EK—Upper Paleozoic. Q—Quaternary. The age of the occurrences is
sometimes very uncertain (after R. Maack, 1957).

Tubarão series may thus be no younger than the Itararé Series, but simply
a different facies of the same age.

Striated pavements are known to occur at the 62nd km. post of the
São Bento to Mafra highway, where the grooves trend northwest to southeast (Barbosa), in São Paulo (Gutmans; grooves northwest to southeast),
and in Uruguay (Walter; northwest to southeast and east to west). Leinz
also deduced a north-northeast to northeast trend of flow in south Brazil,
from measurement of the long-axis orientation of boulders. Despite all these
measurements, we are still not certain of the direction of ice movement.
Leinz, Maack, and Martin, after thorough study, all place the ice center to

the northeast (Maack, in the present position of the Atlantic). Beurlen and Putzer think it lay to the south over the Precambrian Rio Grande shield, between Porto Alegre and Uruguay.

The former group suggest that the greater thickness and greater number of moraines would occur adjacent to the ice center; the latter, just the reverse, because of erosion near the ice center such as is found in the Canadian or Scandinavian Shields during the Pleistocene or in South Africa during the Permo-Carboniferous period itself.

The boulders of the South American tillites consist partly of quartzites. Maack found similar quartzites *in situ* in South Africa and therefore deduced that the South American boulders had come from there. But quartzites are too common to be very characteristic of a given area, so they are of little use for such source determination.

The Pasinho-Taio Formation is a marine deposit in the upper part of the Itararé Series; in Paraña, it intervenes between the fourth and fifth tillites (Maack). Its dominantly pelecypod fauna has been regarded as Upper Carboniferous (e.g. Beurlen, 1953), but this age determination is by no means as certain as is often supposed, for many of the genera are non-diagnostic, and some are unknown elsewhere; it is quite possible that the beds are of Lower Permian age. The strata of the Tubarão series contain a typical *Glossopteris* flora.

The bituminous Irati shales of the Passo Dois Series, that overlie the Itararé-Tubarão Series, have yielded reptilian remains, especially *Mesosaurus*. These attest to the Permian age of the beds, and as yet provide the most important evidence indicating the age of the tillites and the correlation with South Africa.

Tillites also occur in Argentina. In Harrington's latest classification in 1956, they are included partly in the Upper Carboniferous and partly in the Permian. On the western margin of the Pre-Cordillera in San Juan Province, several tillites lie within a succession several hundred meters thick. Besides *Glossopteris*, some Carboniferous plants have been recorded; Carboniferous brachiopods have also been found near Barreal—*Spirifer cf. supramosquensis, Linoproductus lineatus*, etc. Tillites are also known to occur on the eastern side of the Pre-Cordillera near Los Jejenes and Jachal (Keidel), where they rest on a striated Devonian pavement, and in the Sierra Bonaeronses (Sierra de la Ventana) south of Buenos Aires, where they underlie beds carrying either a *Glossopteris* flora or a marine fauna with *Eurydesma*.

Finally, even further to the south, lie the typical glacial deposits of the Falkland Islands (Lafonian Tillites). These are again associated with *Glossopteris* and with *Dadoxylon* trunks bearing distinct annual rings. The partially striated boulders cannot all have been derived from the Falkland Islands. Adie thinks that the tillites are probably largely of glacio-marine origin; yet in West Falkland, striated pavements are beautifully developed.

This account of the areal distribution of the tillites is not yet complete, for in the sub-Andean zone of southern Bolivia, as far north as lat. 21° S, the "Permian" Tarija Group contains a grey clay with striated boulders, mainly of red granite, derived from the Brazilian shield (Rod, 1960).

In retrospect, it appears that the South American tillites are widely distributed and of similar age everywhere. That they formed during a fairly wide span of time is suggested by the series of tillite horizons present in Brazil. In Argentina, too, glacial deposits of differing age probably occur. The exact age of the South American glaciation has not been decided. Brazilian geologists consider it to be Carboniferous, yet there is nothing to show definitely that it is not Lower Permian.

Antarctica.—The presence of a *Glossopteris* flora in the Beacon Series of Antarctica, has been recognized for many years—hence Mount Glossopteris, lat. 85° S, long. 114° W (Long; also Adie). W. E. Long (1961) has recently found tillites as well. L. C. King's assumption that conglomerates overlying an undated red bed series in Dronning-Maud Land (73° S, 30° W; Reece, Roots) are the equivalents of the Dwyka Tillite, is not very convincing. Roots never once discusses the possibility that the conglomerates may be of glacial origin.

Correlation of the Gondwana glaciations.—Disregarding the fact that the exact age of the Permo-Carboniferous tillites is not yet certain, we may reasonably assume that the main glacial phase is approximately the same age everywhere. This yields the correlation given in Table 26. It is also possible, however, that the main glaciation is not synchronous, but started in America and occurred subsequently in South Africa, India, and finally in Australia. This hypothesis has recently been advocated by L. C. King, and could be explained on the basis of migration of an Arctic climate belt through these areas, equivalent to the shifting of the coal belts and the arid belt in the Northern Hemisphere.

TABLE 26
CORRELATION OF THE PERMO-CARBONIFEROUS TILLITES

	SOUTH AMERICA	SOUTH AFRICA	INDIA	AUSTRALIA
Permian, (partly U. Carb.?)	L. Passo-Dois Series with *Glossopteris;* *Mesosaurus* at base	Ecca with coals and *Glossopteris* flora; *Mesosaurus* at base *Eurydesma* Bed	Damuda Series coals and *Glossopteris* flora *Eurydesma* Bed	Glacial horizon. Greta Coal Measures with *Glossopteris* *Eurydesma* Bed
	Tubarao Series coal seams, *Glossopteris*, and glacial Itararé Fm.	Dwyka Tillite	Talchir Tillite	Lochinvar Tillite
Carb.	Older Glacial deposits in Argentina?			Kuttung with tillite

SUMMARY

The climatic picture of the Younger Paleozoic is dominated, from Upper Carboniferous times onward, by the contrast between the Southern and Northern Hemispheres. South America, South Africa, and Australia, together with India, by their thick and widespread glacial deposits, bear witness to a very cold climate at a time when Europe, North America and Northern Asia enjoyed subtropical to tropical climates (fig. 85). During the Lower Carboniferous epoch, on the other hand, climatic conditions were apparently fairly warm and equable throughout the world. The extent of the glacial deposits is indicated in Table 27; but the data are still extraordinarily uncertain. Maximum development of ice did, however, take place at the end of the Carboniferous and beginning of the Permian Period, though in Australia at least, the first glaciers formed well within the Carboniferous, the last much later in the Permian. We have already observed a similar recurrence of glacial phases while dealing with the Older Paleozoic glaciers of South Africa and South America. The glaciers alternated with coal swamps, in which developed a *Glossopteris* flora indicative of a cool climate. In North America and Europe, the climate is assumed to have been warm; during the Carboniferous period, the rainfall was heavy, but Permian conditions appear to have been distinctly arid. Eastern and northern Asia experienced a humid climate, especially during the Permian Period.

TABLE 27

EXTENT OF UPPER PALEOZOIC GLACIAL DEPOSITS

	NORTHERN LIMIT	SOUTHERN LIMIT	AREA OF ICE (SQ. MILES) AFTER SALOMON-CALVI
South America	15°S	53°S	1,500,000
South Africa	6°S	33°S	1,000,000
Australia	18°S	44°S	1,500,000–2,000,000
India	32°N	17°N	1,150,000
Present Antarctic			5,000,000

C. E. P. Brooks has attempted to explain the problem of the distribution of climatic zones on a paleogeographic basis (Chapter 23, fig. 92). The result is, however, very unnatural. It is hard to see why Gondwanaland, in a position near the equator, should have been the site of ice sheets. It therefore seems better, in spite of the doubts of many geophysicists, to consider the position of the poles and the equator, at that time, to have been quite different from their present positions. Even this is not enough. A satis-

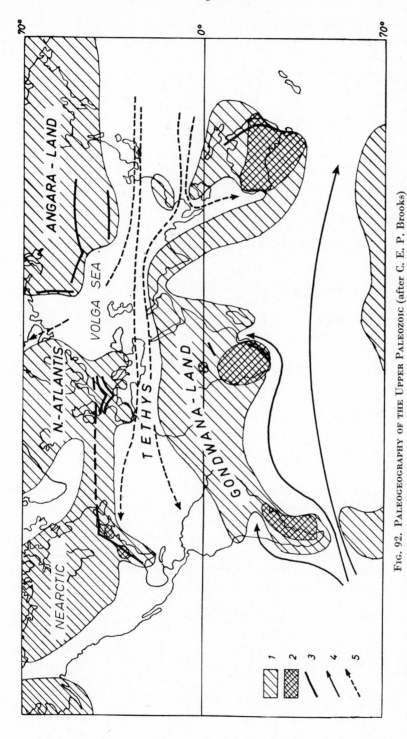

FIG. 92. PALEOGEOGRAPHY OF THE UPPER PALEOZOIC (after C. E. P. Brooks)

1 = Land; 2 = Glaciated Areas; 3 = Mountains; 4 = Cold ocean currents; 5 = Warm currents. Interpretation discounting continental drift.

factory solution, like Wegener's (fig. 93) requires in addition a relative displacement of the continents. Indeed, the climatic conditions of the Younger Paleozoic provide a powerful argument in favor of this hypothesis. Of course, many other objections to Wegener's theory have not yet been met. None the less, we have already seen much evidence in favor of polar wandering in the Older Paleozoic; and it now seems that a lesser amount of continental drift than Wegener assumed would greatly simplify the interpretation of the Permo-Carboniferous climatic evidence (see Salomon-Calvi's reconstruction).

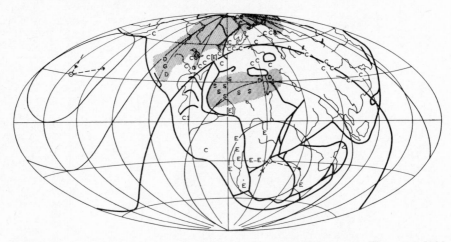

FIG. 93. PALEOGEOGRAPHY OF THE UPPER PALEOZOIC AFTER KÖPPEN AND WEGENER, 1924 E = glaciated areas; K = coal; S = evaporites; W = desert sandstones; ▦ = arid regions; ⊙ = north and south poles. Interpretation based on the hypothesis of continental drift.

The continents may then have occupied the following positions with respect to the earth's climatic belts; the Southern Continents near the South Pole, North America and Europe in the equatorial region or at least nearer the equator than they are now. In the course of the Permian, North America and Europe reached the desert belt of the Northern Hemisphere. The great extension of arid areas in Permian times is also due, in part, to the Variscan and Appalachian fold movements, which were largely responsible for producing continental conditions. A great part of Asia, on the other hand, entered a humid zone during the Permian Period. Schove, Nairn and Opdyke have recently demonstrated that these ideas agree quite well with paleomagnetic researches and with the admittedly few observations on wind direction. Schmucker has also proposed a similar reconstruction.

17

Mesozoic

The Mesozoic Era, comprising the Trias, Jurassic, and Cretaceous Periods, provides evidence of climatic conditions which, while rather variable, were yet sufficiently uniform in character to allow us to consider the era as a whole. The main features of the paleogeography were the relatively great extent of land areas at the beginning of the era, the low relief, and the existence of a sea connection between the Atlantic and the Pacific, the ancient "Mediterranean" of Tethys extending across southern Asia. All of these features influenced the Mesozoic climate.

TEMPERATURE AND PRECIPITATION

Reef Belt

In Europe, thick reefs were abundant, particularly in the Alpine geosyncline. The huge limestone and dolomite masses of the Trias, to which the South Tyrol Dolomites owe their imposing scenery, belong in this category. These masses were recognized as coral reefs a hundred years ago by Richthofen and Mojsisovics. Calcareous algae (Dasycladaceae) also play a considerable part in the formation of reefs; according to Pia, the number of their species is unusually high in the Middle Trias (see Table 13). Rhaetic coral reefs are best developed in the northern Calcareous Alps at Achensee and Osterhorn. There also appear in the Trias of the rest of the Alps, and in the Balkan Peninsula, limestone deposits which in places are many hundreds of meters thick; even in extra-Alpine areas, limestones predominate at times, e.g. in the Muschelkalk of Germany, the south of France, Spain, and Sardinia.

The Lower Jurassic is rather lime-deficient, but thick limestones are developed in the Apennines and North Africa. The remainder of the Jurassic carries abundant limestones. Reefs, some of coral, others of sponges, are widely distributed in such places as the Jura Mountains—whose reefs were mapped long ago by Gressly (see Heer, 1865)—the south of France, Spain, Portugal, England (map by Arkell, 1933, p. 559), the Alps—as at Berchtesgaden—and Czechoslovakia where Tithonian reef limestones form the Beskids (fig. 94).

Arkell (1935) showed that even at that time the number of reef-building corals increased significantly towards the equator (Table 10). Thus, in Europe, only six species are known from lat. $54\frac{1}{2}°$ N, while 184 are present at 47° N, some 450 miles to the south. During the Cretaceous Period, warm seas were characterized mainly by reef-building Rudistids; these thick-shelled pelecypods, similar in form to corals, were widespread in the Lower Cretaceous of the Mediterranean area. Nevertheless, on the whole, development of reefs was unimportant by comparison with the Jurassic. Ma (1957) has indicated this diagrammatically. Figure 122 shows the position of the reef belt in each of the three Mesozoic periods.

Limestones were much less important in the North American geosynclines than in Europe, but they did develop thickly in places, especially during the Trias. The coral reefs of Nevada (Muller), and the several hundreds of

FIG. 94. REEF LIMESTONE IN THE UPPER JURASSIC (TITHON-
IAN), STRAMBERK, MORAVIA, CZECHOSLOVAKIA. (Photograph:
M. Schwarzbach).

meters of limestone widely distributed further north in the Upper Trias of the Alaska range (Moffit) provide examples. The limestone deficiency in the Cordilleras would astonish an Alpine geologist; in fact, the Swiss geologist, A. Heim, considered just this contrast between the Alps and the Cordilleras (1924); he thought that a cold "Californian current" already existed in the Mesozoic.

Just as in Europe, calcareous sediments characterize the Tethys region of southern Asia and Indonesia. A strip of reefs extended almost the whole length of the Japanese islands in Middle and Upper Jurassic times. It was "perhaps comparable to the Great Barrier Reef of today" (Kobayashi, 1942), though there were fewer corals and many more Stromatoporids in its structure. Kobayashi believed that a warmer Kuro-Shio current was already in existence in the Mesozoic. The warmth-loving Tethys fauna of the Cretaceous Period is also present in the "guyots" of the northwest Pacific (Hamilton).

Other Evidence of a Warm Climate

The acme of reptile development was attained during the Mesozoic Era. The giant reptiles undoubtedly signify a warm climate. In the Trias, the localities where they have been recorded lie as far north as Spitzbergen; in the Jurassic and Cretaceous, they are found all the way from the Amur district of Northern Siberia to Australia and Patagonia. Other evidence also indicates that at this time temperatures in high latitudes were greater than at present; *Lingula*, for example, occurs in the Keuper of Spitzbergen.

TABLE 28

MESOZOIC SEA TEMPERATURES BY O[18] METHOD (AFTER UREY, LOWENSTAM, EPSTEIN, MCKINNEY, BOWEN, NAJDIN, TEJS, AND TCHUPACHIN)

LOCALITY	HORIZON	TEMPERATURE °C	PRESENT SEA TEMP. °C
France	Lias	24–25	
France	Bajocian	20–21	10–15
Alberta	Callovian	24	
British Columbia	Callovian	32	10
Alaska	Callovian	17	5 or less
France	Oxfordian	23	10–15
Switzerland	Oxfordian	26–27	
New Guinea	Oxfordian	16	25
Kutch, India	Kimmeridgian	19–25	
Skye, Scotland	Jurassic	17–23	7–13
Crimea	Hauteriv.-Aptian	13	2–24
Crimea	U. Alb-Cenomanian	19–24	2–24
Germany and Poland	Albian	24	
Germany and Poland	Cenomanian	16	
Germany and Poland	Senonian	20	
England	U. Cret.	16–23	5–15
Crimea	Campanian	17·6	2–24
Volga and Emba District	Campanian	15–21	
Tennessee	Maastrichtian	20–27	

Temperature values worked out by the O[18] method show that, in places, the sea temperature was 10° C higher than it is now (Table 28). During the Jurassic period, temperatures were uniformly high—as they probably had been throughout the Trias. Observations on belemnoids from Western Europe suggest a sea temperature of about 21° C during the Lias. This temperature was maintained, or even slightly increased in the course of the Jurassic period, and Bowen (1961) records temperatures of between 21° C and 28° C in the Upper Jurassic. After a slight cooling in the Aptian, the first Cretaceous maximum occurred in the Albian when the temperature reached 24° C.

This was followed by a sharp decline in the Cenomanian, for which temperatures below 16° C have been recorded in Denmark by Lowenstam and Epstein (1954). All studies have shown that there was a second maximum in the Coniacian-Santonian, when sea temperatures rose to almost 22° C. Thereafter, slight cooling led to temperatures of a little under 20° C at the end of the Cretaceous.

Those localities near the pole where rich floras have been found are of the greatest significance. Such a locality (described by Scoresby in 1822) occurs in the Rhaeto-Lias[1] of Jameson Land on the east coast of Greenland; here there are 200 plant species (T. M. Harris). A similar flora has been observed in Sweden, Germany, and Japan. In the Dogger[2] of Graham Land, near Cape Flora (lat. 63° 15′ N), the Swedish expedition of 1902–3 discovered a flora, containing numerous Cycadophytes ferns and conifers, which bears an amazing similarity to that of Yorkshire but is also closely related to those of Australia and India. The plant localities nearest to the poles are probably of Middle Jurassic age. The Byrd expedition found stems 45 cm. in diameter, and also remains of ferns and *Araucarites*, on the 10,000-foot high Mount Weaver in Antarctica (lat. 87° S).

Several well-known sites with abundant plant remains are to be found in the Lower Cretaceous of the Arctic; and in Alaska, Kome—west Greenland, Spitzbergen, and King Charles Land. Heer described 100 species from Kome; among them were cycads and ferns. Wood from King Charles Land— described by Gothan (1908) as Jurassic—shows distinct annual growth rings. In the Upper Cretaceous, a great many species have been recorded from Atane and Patoot in west Greenland. From these localities, Nathorst has described the leaves and fruit of the now tropical breadfruit tree (*Artocarpus dicksonii*, fig. 95). According to Seward, we must suppose that the climate was similar to that of Southern Europe at the present day.

The Jurassic and Lower Cretaceous floras indicate that at that time, the climate of the earth must have been fairly uniform. "In no other geological period", writes Gothan (in Gothan-Weyland, p. 474), "have we . . . had a more uniform flora throughout the world than at this time."

Boreal Province

Although at this time the climate varied little throughout the world, there was yet, in contrast to the very warm climatic belt, a cooler zone further north forming a boreal province (Neumayr, 1883, Uhlig, 1911). This province is characterized by the paucity of reef corals and calcareous sediments in general, while glauconitic sediments are often very prominent. Its southern boundary runs through North America and Central Europe; hence the Gault (Albian) forams in England denote a temperate climate (M. H. Khan). Other typical boreal elements of the fauna include the lamellibranch *Aucella* and the ammonite *Virgatites* in the Jurassic, and *Belemnitella* in the Cretaceous. In Japan, the presence of certain ammonites in the Lias and Upper Dogger may be attributed to temporary cold currents (Sato) that have been compared with the present-day Oya Shio current. Moreover, Handlirsch has interpreted the small wing-span of the Lias insects of Mecklenburg—11 mm. as compared with 22 mm. in the Malm—as a sign of a relatively cold climate. During the Mesozoic Era, however, the boreal province was very much warmer than it is today. In Jurassic times, the

1–2. Rhaeto-Lias=Upper Triassic to Lower Jurassic; Dogger=Middle Jurassic; Malm=Upper Jurassic. Ed.

poleward limit of reef corals lay over England, some 1800 miles north of the present limit (fig. 122). The O^{18} method has likewise yielded results indicating relatively high temperatures.

The Southern Hemisphere also contains evidence of a boreal zone—at least in the Cretaceous—in the southern Andes (Zeil) and in Graham Land and Seymour Island (Snow Hill Beds; Taylor, 1940).

FIG. 95. LEAF OF A BREAD-FRUIT TREE (*Artocarpus dicksonii*) FROM THE UPPER CRETACEOUS OF WEST GREENLAND

Modified after Nathorst, 1890. Original in the Geological Museum, Stockholm. The 26 cm. leaf remains were discovered by an Eskimo in latitude 70° N and "its discovery was immediately rewarded by the present of a knife".

Evidence of Glaciation

At no time in the earth's history is evidence of glaciation so scarce as during the Mesozoic Era. Undoubted tillites are completely unknown. Middle Triassic "moraines" near Gorki, to the east of Moscow (Tichvinskaya) are probably not of glacial origin; the same may be said of the Upper Jurassic and Upper Cretaceous conglomerates of the southern Andes (Zeil). Other tillites in the Congo and in Australia, that have long been regarded as Mesozoic, probably resulted from the Permo-Carboniferous glaciation. The "ice crystals" described by Pfannenstiel from the Lower Muschelkalk of

Baden, Germany, may have no climatological significance; neither may the needle-shaped structures described by Udden (1918) from the Upper Cretaceous sandstones and limestones of Dakota, and by Schuchert from Eaglefjord.

Evidence of Arid Climates

In many parts of the world, the Trias resembles the Permian so closely that we speak of the "Permo-Trias". The red beds that are so often the characteristic sediments of the Permian Period also occur in the Trias, and the two systems are often more or less indistinguishable, either petrographically or stratigraphically. In Germany, the type formations of the "Rotliegendes" in the Lower Permian, and "Buntsandstein" in the Lower Trias, are similar facies; both indicate a climate which at times was exceptionally arid. However, although both Permian and Trias represent unusually dry periods in the earth's history, they are not to be regarded as times when deserts continually covered the greater part of the world. The Upper Jurassic was another notably arid phase.

The Buntsandstein sediments of the "New Red" of Europe are typical. They consist of clastic deposits, often red in colour, and containing virtually no fossils, save only tracks and trails. Cross-bedding, ripple marks, and sun cracks are the most common sedimentary structures; clay-galls are also abundant. The sediments consist of sandy and clayey detritus carried into basins of internal drainage, partly by the wind, and partly by periodic floods. Bornemann, Fraas, Walther, and Strigel have all suggested this mode of origin for the sediments in Germany. H. H. Thomas, Shotton, and others have done likewise in England.

It is quite certain that the area was occasionally flooded not only by shallow seas but also by large pools and shallow saline lakes. Beds containing Apodids and *Estheria* in the middle of the Bunter sandstones of Germany were clearly described by Soergel (1928) as the results of desiccation of temporary lakes. Rain pits are infrequently preserved. Silicification and beds of carnelian, both produced by percolating silicic acid, are characteristic of this arid type of climate. Remains of the lung fish *Ceratodus* (fig. 54) are also common.

The facies, represented in Germany by the Buntsandstein, is widely developed in England, where it is known as the "Bunter" or "New Red" (Scrivenor), in the south of France, in west Sardinia, in the Balearic Islands and in eastern Spain. It is also to be found further south in the Moroccan Atlas, and east to the foothills of the Urals and the shores of the White Sea.

Evaporites are commonly associated with the red beds, and while sometimes nothing now remains but salt pseudomorphs, in many localities there are deposits of gypsum and halite. In central Europe, such beds continue from the Upper Permian to Lower Bunter—the "Haselgebirge" of the eastern Alps—and become common again in the Upper Bunter and Middle

Muschelkalk, once the most important salt-producing formation in Germany. Further deposits occur in the middle of the Keuper (Gipskeuper). In the British Isles, the Keuper also contains thick evaporites in Cheshire, Shropshire, Staffordshire, Lancashire, and Ireland. There, saliferous and gypsiferous marls attain a thickness of 900 m. The Keuper is also gypsiferous in the Alps and Apennines; in the foothills of the French Pyrenees, there are even potash deposits. Lotze has recorded thick salt domes in Spain and in the Moroccan Atlas. These are formed from Keuper salt.

Evaporites disappeared from Europe at the beginning of the Jurassic Period, only to reappear widely in the Upper Jurassic sediments of northwest Germany, the Swiss Juras, and the Crimea. The only later appearance of salt deposits in this continent is in the gypsiferous Upper Cretaceous strata of the north of Spain.

In North America, the Trias again exhibits much evidence of aridity. In the Rocky Mountains, continental red-bed deposits attain a thickness of several 1000 m. Typical of such formations are the Moenkopi Formation of Lower Trias age, which outcrops in Utah, Colorado, and Arizona, and the Triassic Newark Series extending from Virginia to New York State in Eastern U.S.A. Rain pits were described from the red shales of New Jersey more than 100 years ago by Redfield, who firmly believed that the rain-bearing winds blew from the west.

A similar red-bed facies covered much of the western United States in Lower Jurassic times. It is represented by the Navajo Sandstone of Arizona and New Mexico, and by the Nugget Sandstone of Utah and other states. Gypsum is not at all uncommon in the Triassic strata of the U.S.A., Alberta, and British Columbia. The same mineral, together with halite, is also widely distributed throughout the Jurassic sediments of the western and southern parts of North America, but is much less common in the Cretaceous, where it is best developed in the lower part of the system in Arkansas and Louisiana.

In Asia, evaporites are particularly prominent in the Upper Jurassic— e.g. the economically important rock salt and sylvite in the Hissar Range, and sylvite in eastern Turkmenia and Uzbekistan—they are also to be found in many localities among Cretaceous strata (fig. 96). In Japan, the Inkstone Group of Lower Cretaceous age contains red sediments.

Red beds also appear frequently in the Mesozoic rocks of the Southern Hemisphere. The areas where coals had developed in the Upper Paleozoic were gradually converted into at least semiarid regions. In South America, the Botucatu Sandstone, of possible Keuper age, formed in such an area as an eolian deposit containing numerous ventifacts (De Almeida). Covering as it does an area of some 500,000 square miles, this sandstone constitutes one of the most important eolian deposits in the world. From the structure of its dunes, De Almeida has deduced that the prevailing wind blew from the N.N.E. Gypsum and sometimes halite are also present in the Jurassic and more especially the Cretaceous sediments of the Andes; evaporites also appear in both systems in Africa.

To sum up we may say that the arid belt of the Northern Hemisphere covered more of Europe and North America and lay much further north than at present. The northern limit of the belt passed through southern Canada and Scotland. At times during the Jurassic Period, it extended equally far north to cover almost the whole of the U.S.A. and Europe; only in the Cretaceous did it recede southward nearly to its present position, when only the southern half of the United States, and a narrow strip in the south of Europe continued to experience arid conditions.

Further reading: SHERLOCK, 1947.

Humid Regions

The most important indicators of heavy rainfall are coals and other carbonaceous sediments. Their distribution in time and space may be summarized in the following manner, though it must be borne in mind that, in many cases, the exact stratigraphic position is very uncertain.

Lower Trias coals are developed in northern central Siberia as indicated in Sheynman and Vachrameyev's maps of the Mesozoic of Asia. The Leigh Creek Coal of South Australia, and the Ipswich Group of Queensland may also be of Triassic age. Keuper coals are to be found in Germany and in Virginia and North Carolina, the site of the oldest coal workings in the United States. Rhaeto-Liassic seams occur in Scania (south Sweden), Bornholm, western Poland, along the length of the Alps, in the Balkans, in the Caucasus Mountains, and in Spitzbergen and east Greenland. In "Angaraland", which stretches from east of the Urals and Turkestan, via Irkutsk and the Trans-Baikal region to China, Indochina, and Japan, there are important deposits of coal with, according to Bubnoff, reserves of 150–200 thousand million tons. Sheynman considers the main deposits to be Middle Jurassic. Coals of this age also occur in Yorkshire, in Scotland, and in Norway. Humid conditions in the Southern Hemisphere during the Jurassic Period gave rise to the Walloon Series of Queensland, and to carbonaceous strata in Victoria.

Lower Cretaceous occurrences are widespread throughout Germany, northeast and east Asia (fig. 96), Spitzbergen, west Greenland, the western part of North America, and Queensland (Burrum and Styx River Series).

Humid lowland areas covered much of Silesia, the Alps, Serbia, Bulgaria, Japan, Sakhalin, Spitzbergen and Greenland at times during the Upper Cretaceous. In North America, valuable coal seams extend from Mexico to Alberta (e.g. Montana Group). Bubnoff has calculated that reserves of Cretaceous coal in this continent run to 2.4 million million tons.

The more humid climate of the areas of coal formation sometimes resulted in extensive kaolinization; as in Scania, where the Lias rests on a kaolinized basement complex, and where fire clays are included in the Rhaeto-Lias

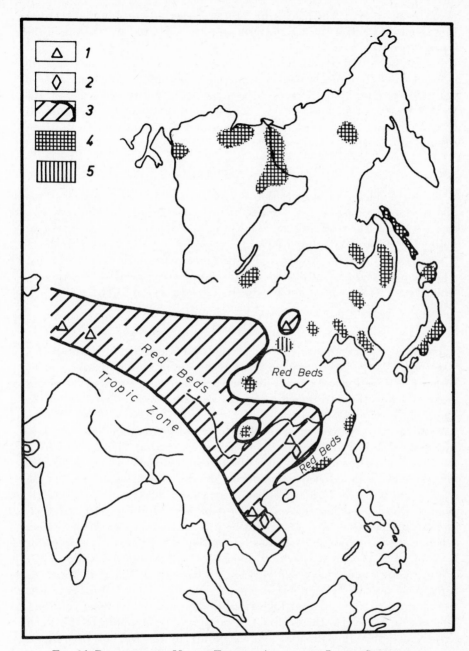

FIG. 96. PALEOCLIMATIC MAP OF EASTERN ASIA IN THE LOWER CRETACEOUS
1 = Gypsum; 2 = rock salt; 3 = arid regions; 4 = coal; 5 = lignitic shales. The arid zone is followed to the north by a humid zone (after J. M. Sheynman, 1954).

(Troedsson, Voigt). The decidedly clayey facies of the Lias and Lower Cretaceous in Central Europe suggests intensive chemical weathering of the source areas.

Formation of laterites may also be included here, though they tend to develop quite close to arid regions and are responsible for the coloration of the red-bed facies. Bauxite is best developed in the Lower Cretaceous of the Urals (Krotov and Sotova), in the foothills of the Altai Mountains (Bogolepov and Popov), in the Harz foreland (Valeton), in the south of France, and in Hungary (Bardoschi).

OCEAN CURRENTS

There is evidence to suggest that a warm Kuro-Shio, and cold Oya-Shio and California currents were already in existence during the Mesozoic Era (pp. 154, 156). The Gulf Stream, too, had probably formed, for the northern limit of the warmth-loving Rudistids lies a few degrees further north in Europe than in North America. This displacement of the climatic belts, which corresponds exactly with the displacement caused by the present Gulf Stream, was pointed out by Roemer as long ago as 1847.

SUMMARY

The whole of the Mesozoic Era represented a warm phase in the earth's history. Glaciation was unknown, and the polar regions were warm areas with a rich vegetation. Lateral climatic variation was particularly slight in Jurassic times. Definite Boreal provinces appeared for the first time in the Upper Jurassic and Cretaceous.

Some climatic changes are known to have occurred throughout this era. In Europe, the Lias stands out as a cooler epoch. Eristavi has inferred from the faunal variation in the Lower Cretaceous sediments of Transcaucasia that there was a climatic optimum during the Barremian stage, and that the cooling which set in during the Aptian reached a maximum in the Cenomanian. Bowen, and Lowenstam and Epstein, have also shown from oxygen isotope studies that the Cenomanian was a cool phase. Since boreal belemnites advanced as far south as Kopet-Dag, on the northern borders of Iran, in what H. and G. Termier describe as a "transgression arctique", eastern Europe must have experienced a relatively cool climate from the Santonian to the Maastrichtian epoch (Najdin, 1959). Further west, temperatures were somewhat higher, especially in the Santonian (Bowen). The extent to which these climatic variations were produced by such palaeogeographic changes as a sea extending to the pole in Lias times, remains undecided.

Other climatic changes took place on a more world-wide scale. The reef belt migrated gradually southward, the northern limit moving from about 55° N in the Trias and Jurassic, to about 45° N in the Cretaceous (fig. 122).

In the same way, the evaporite belt of the Northern Hemisphere shifted southward, from the European and North American area in the Trias, to almost its present position in the Cretaceous. The extent of arid regions was unusually great in the Lower Trias and again in the Upper Jurassic. On the other hand, the Rhaeto-Lias of Europe and Asia, and the Cretaceous of the same areas and the western parts of North America were much more humid. Throughout all of the Mesozoic strata of Australia, there is much more evidence of humid than of arid conditions.

18

Tertiary

When, genial, a lost Alaska grew brood-blossomed tree,
and the magnolia stole warm-scented to the Pole.
Cited in SEWARD, Plant Life, 1931.

Up to the end of the Mesozoic Era, the picture of the earth's climate can only be reconstructed in broad outline; from the beginning of the Tertiary Period onward, it becomes possible to fill in an ever-increasing amount of detail. This is largely due to the fact that the flora and fauna now very often lend themselves to direct comparison with Recent forms. With the appearance of the Angiosperms, plants become the most important indicators of climatic conditions.

Throughout the Tertiary, the climate was still warmer than it is at the present day, but in the course of the 70 million years or so occupied by this period, a gradual but noticeable drop in temperature took place until, by its close about a million years ago, climatic conditions were very similar to what they are at present. Precise dating of all these beds from which climatic evidence is derived, at least into their correct stage (Eocene, Oligocene, etc., Table 29), is therefore of particular importance.

During the Tertiary, those of the great Mesozoic geosynclines which had not come to an end in the Cretaceous, were compressed into chains of fold mountains. The resultant paleogeographic changes had a critical effect on climatic conditions.

TEMPERATURE AND PRECIPITATION

The Warm Zone

Throughout the world, Older Tertiary temperatures were higher than corresponding temperatures at present (fig. 105). Evidence for this is afforded by the subtropical character of the rich flora recorded from many localities now lying within the temperate zone. Palms provide a good example; in the Older Tertiary, their poleward limit lay in Alaska (lat. 62° N) and East Prussia (lat. 55° N), and even the Miocene strata of Germany carry palms. A classic locality for Miocene floras and faunas is Oeningen, on Lake Constance, whence O. Heer described, in the *Urwelt der Schweiz*, 465 species of plants, and 844 of insects (for the most recent

TABLE 29
SUBDIVISIONS OF THE TERTIARY

	MAJOR SUB-DIVISIONS	COMMONLY USED MINOR DIVISIONS	
		EUROPE	NORTH AMERICA
YOUNGER TERTIARY (NEOGENE)	Pliocene	Pontian	
	Miocene	Sarmatian Tortonian Helvetian Burdigalian Aquitanian*	
OLDER TERTIARY (PALEOGENE)	Oligocene	Chattian Rupelian Lattorfian	
	Eocene	Lutetian Ypresian	Uinta, Bridger, Wasatch (Wilcox)
	Paleocene		Fort Union

* Alternatively, upper Oligocene.

account, see Hantke). According to Czeczott, the present flora of the eastern Mediterranean area extended in mid-Miocene times at least as far as eastern Poland.

On account of its smaller land area, the Southern Hemisphere offers fewer fossil localities, and therefore fewer possibilities of comparison with the present flora, but it too supported a flora typical of a warm, humid climate in such places as New Zealand and Chile. Other similar examples have already been discussed (Chapter 4).

Hanzawa points out that the apparently rather cool Oligocene climate of Northern Japan is exceptional; even there, the Miocene was once again warmer than now. Dorman and Gill's (1959) oxygen isotope studies have indicated that the Tertiary climates of Australia and New Zealand were relatively warm.

Unfortunately, little information is available concerning the Tertiary vegetation of the present tropical zone. Dolianiti has mentioned that the fruits of the coconut palm (*Nipa*) occur in the Paleocene beds at Recife in Brazil, but they could, of course, have drifted to their present position. The Upper Miocene-Lower Pliocene flora of south Sumatra (Kräusel) and Rusinga Island, Lake Victoria (Chesters), differs in no essential respect from the present flora. Hammen's pollen spectra from Maastrichtian, Paleogene and Miocene sediments of Columbia closely resemble today's spectra.

Slight climatic variation is indicated by changes in distribution of such plants as palms. Hammen believes that these variations occur over regular intervals of 6 million and 2 million years, but this is still completely hypothetical.

C.P.—12

Crocodiles infested the Older Tertiary waterways as far north as New Jersey, England, and Mongolia, and as far south as Patagonia. Today they do not occur north of Florida and North Africa. Eocene beds near Halle contain many such tropical beetles as large Buprestids, Tenebrionids, and Pyrophorinids, while termites are present in Lower Oligocene amber in East Prussia.

Warm land areas are also characterized by red weathering products. As well as the "Bohnerze" of south Germany and Switzerland (fig. 97), bauxites which are, in part, of Older Tertiary age occur in Arkansas, Istria, Dalmatia,

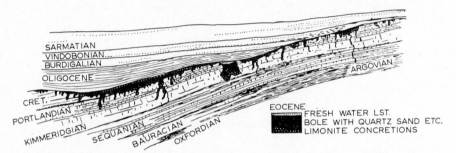

FIG. 97. RED BEDS (BOHNERZE) IN THE LOWER TERTIARY OF THE SWISS JURA MOUNTAINS
The red beds rest on the Cretaceous and are overlain by Oligocene sediments (from Heim, 1919).

and Northern Ireland. Neogene red beds are present in the Yenesei district of Siberia. Lateritization, in present tropical areas can, in places, be traced back to the Tertiary and probably even further, e.g. Guiana (van Kersen).

The warm Older Tertiary seas contained numerous larger forams (*Nummulites*) which were important as limestone-formers; they flourished throughout the length of Tethys, as far east as Indonesia. The Sphinx, near Cairo, is a famous example of a nummulitic limestone. Nummulites are also found all along the East African coast as far south as Cape Town. They probably could survive there because of the effects of an Older Tertiary Agulhas current.

Coral reefs of modest size still formed in Europe, and the coastal waters of the Miocene (Vindobonian) sea were strewn with coral reefs from Morocco to Catalonia, and the south of France to the Near East (Chevalier). Reefs also flourished in the Sarmatian sea covering southern Russia (Vznuzdaev).

The extension of the warm zone, with respect to its present size, was generally greater in Europe than in North America. It is true, as Durham has deduced from the Mollusca, that in the Older Tertiary, the 20° C February isotherm on the west coast of North America ran north of the 49th parallel, whereas now it lies in lat. 24° N (fig. 98); and the Alaskan flora also differed quite distinctly from the present flora. On the eastern seaboard, however, the coral reefs extended only a little further than now (Forman

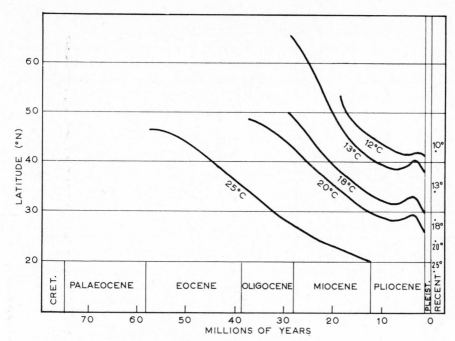

FIG. 98. FEBRUARY MARINE ISOTHERMS ALONG THE PACIFIC COAST OF NORTH AMERICA
THROUGHOUT THE TERTIARY
Showing the gradual southward displacement (after Durham, 1950).

and Schlanger), and the surface temperature of the Oligocene sea north of
the Bahamas, has been calculated by Emiliani, using the O^{18} method, as
$28.3°$ C. This corresponds, if the calculation is accurate, to the present
August temperature. The Miocene temperature dropped as low as $24.1°$ C.

The favorable climate which prevailed in Europe in the early part of the
Tertiary Period was probably due, in no small measure, to the presence, at
that time, of a broad sea connection joining the Mediterranean to the warm
Indian Ocean.

In the Southern Hemisphere, poleward displacement of the coral reef belt
is less pronounced, though reef-building corals have been found in the Older
Tertiaries of South Island, New Zealand, and in the Miocene Forrest Reef of
the Nullarbor Plain in South Australia, lat. $31°$ S (Fairbridge, 1953).

The symmetrical arrangement of the climatic belts with respect to the
present position of the equator may also show itself in the bipolarity of the
glauconite zones (Shatski) though, whether this is caused by climatic control
is by no means certain (Chapter 5).

Tertiary Climatic Deterioration and the Pliocene Climate

The gradual decrease in temperature throughout the Tertiary Period can
readily be detected in the flora, and sometimes also in the fauna. At first,

genera now found nearer to the equator predominate. These, however, are gradually replaced by genera which are still indigenous to Europe.

The fish faunas of West Germany (Chapter 4, fig. 99) and the floras of northwest Europe (Table 30, after E. M. Reid), afford good examples. Mean annual temperatures calculated for northwest and for central Europe are shown in Table 31.

TABLE 30

PROPORTION OF MODERN GENERA IN FOSSIL FLORAS OF NORTH-WEST EUROPE (AFTER REID)

Lower Pleistocene (Cromer) 97%
Lower Pleistocene (Tegelen) 78%
Upper Pliocene (Reuver). 53%
Lower Oligocene 34%
Upper Eocene (Hordle Beds) 23%
Lower Eocene (London Clay) 2%

The Pliocene climate was also warmer than that of the present day. Thus, at Frankfurt, the beds contain a rich flora comprising nearly 150 species of a whole number of subtropical genera (e.g. *Engelhardtia*) described by Mädler. Similar conditions must have existed in Holland to give rise to the abundant *Sequoia* and *Symplocus* (Zagwijn).

According to Bourdier and Sittler, the Pliocene flora of La Raza, in the Jura Mountains of France, contains many examples of *Taxodium*, *Nyssa*, and *Sequoia*. Szafer determined the following climatic data from the Lower

TABLE 31

MEAN ANNUAL TERTIARY TEMPERATURES IN EUROPE

STAGE	LOCALITY	AUTHOR	ANNUAL MEAN (°C)	
			TERTIARY	PRESENT
Pliocene	Frankfurt	Estimated from Mädler, 1939	14	about 9
Miocene	Oeningen	R. Hantke, 1954	16	about 9
Upper Oligocene	Rott, near Cologne	Weyland; Schwarzbach, 1952	18	about 9
Eocene	London Basin	Reid and Chandler, 1933	21	about 10

Pliocene of Kroscienko, in the Polish Carpathians; annual mean 17°–18° C, July temperature 29° C, January temperature 4°–5° C, and rainfall 60 inches. These temperatures appear rather high when compared with values from slightly older strata at Oeningen. *Heterobranchus* still flourished in the Vienna Basin during the Pannonian epoch. In eastern Europe, too, the flora and the deep lateritic weathering at Batum on the Black Sea denote temperatures higher than at present. The Middle Pliocene Kinelj Beds in the catchment area of the Volga carry *Juglans, Carya, Taxodium, Sequoia,* etc. (Grishchenko and Glushchenko). Walnuts were still thriving in Kamchatka as late as the Upper Pliocene (Vasikovski).

Climatic variations of the type experienced in the Quaternary were fore-shadowed by similar Pliocene changes. This is revealed not only by the presence of glaciations, alternating with warmer phases in circumpolar areas, but also by the Pliocene marine fauna of Iceland (Bárdarson), and by the pollen assemblage of the Wallensen lignite in the Harz foreland (Altehenger). In the latter case other factors such as variations in rainfall may also have played a decisive role.

Durham has produced some very informative temperature curves for the Pacific coast; Dorf has given us a comprehensive review of climatic changes in the middle latitudes of western North America during the Younger Tertiary. His figures for temperature and rainfall, given in Table 32, are not claimed to be absolutely accurate. The discovery of alligators in the Lower Pliocene of Oklahoma (Woodburn) shows that even then, the climate was still favorable for them.

In Australia and New Zealand, echinoids provide an indication that at the start of the Tertiary

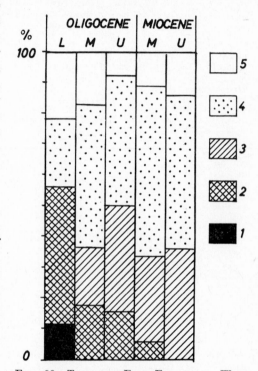

FIG. 99. TERTIARY FISH FAUNAS IN WEST GERMANY

The climatic habitat of the various supposed species is indicated. 1 = tropical; 2 = tropical and subtropical; 3 = tropical, subtropical and cooler; 4 = subtropical and temperate; 5 = temperate to cold. The gradual lowering of the temperature during the Tertiary is clearly shown (after W. Weiler, 1942).

Period, sea temperatures were fairly high, and that a progressive temperature decrease then took place. As a result, by mid-Pliocene times, a particularly cool phase had developed, when *Notocidaris*, a genus of sea urchin now living in sub-Antarctic regions, flourished (Fell).

Very recently, the O^{18}/O^{16} method has also been applied to deep oceanic sediments. Emiliani has suggested that bottom temperatures in the eastern equatorial sector of the Pacific dropped from 10° C in mid-Oligocene,

TABLE 32

CLIMATIC CHANGES IN THE YOUNGER TERTIARY OF WESTERN U.S.A. (AFTER E. DORF)

	LOWER MIOCENE BRIDGE CREEK FLORA	M. TO U. MIOCENE MASCALL PAYETTE FLORA	U. MIOCENE TO L. PLIOCENE WEISER FLORA	M. TO U. PLIOCENE ALTURA FLORA	PRESENT
Mean annual temperature (°C)	14·2	14·2	14·2	10	10
Mean temperature of six warmest weeks	18	18	18	20	22
Mean temperature of two coldest weeks	10·8	8·6	8·6	3·1	−2·5
Frost-free days	254	230	215	180	141
Mean annual rainfall (inches)	50	35	25	17·5	12

through 7° C in the Miocene, to 2° C in the Late Pliocene. The present bottom temperature is 2° C.

Further reading: KOENIGSWALD, 1930.

Rainfall in Europe

Lignite beds are especially extensive in Germany, where reserves total 13,000,000,000 tons in the Eocene and 45,000,000,000 tons in the Oligocene and Miocene. Such vast deposits must betoken considerable rainfall during great parts of the Tertiary. From time to time, though, some areas experienced conditions more arid than those which prevail at present. In this connection, certain areas of Europe merit special mention. Aridity during the Upper Eocene to Lower Oligocene is indicated in the Paris basin, and the northern Pyrenees foreland by beds of gypsum, and in the Ebro basin and Upper Rhine valley by beds of potash salts. Rock salt is present in the Lower Miocene strata of Hesse and in the northern Carpathian foreland where potash salts also occur. The Upper Miocene (Sarmatian) climate of the Tertiary basins of Spain, Italy and Sicily must have been dry, for halite and potash salts developed. The Vienna basin, with its steppe flora and fauna (Berger and Thenius) was another arid region. In Bessarabia, between Dniester and Pruth, the Lower Sarmatian was still fairly humid, the annual rainfall being about 40 inches. In the Middle Sarmatian, precipitation dropped to about 25 inches (Jakubovskaya). According to Crouzel, the Pliocene of the Aquitaine basin was drier than the Miocene (*cf.* the Aegean dunes; Mistardis). On the other hand, silicified pebbles in Pliocene strata of

Germany are not proof of arid conditions, for the silicification occurred earlier.

It seems therefore that, at times, there was a fairly general and widespread tendency toward aridity, particularly in the Upper Eocene and Sarmatian epochs. Such conditions could be explained on the basis of a slight north-ward shift of the present desert belt of North Africa. Regression of the sea may also have had some effect. If we combine the evidence of aridity with the evidence of humid conditions, given by the German lignites, we may suggest that the Middle Eocene, with its coals, was a period of high humidity, that the Upper Eocene and Lower Oligocene were generally arid, and that rainfall was again considerable in the Lower Miocene, when there are more lignites. The Upper Miocene was another period of marked aridity.

Local orographic factors must be taken into account as well as general shifting of the arid belt, for rising mountains must have produced rain-shadow areas. Such influences may readily be supposed to have affected the Rhine Graben (because of the Vosges). The leeward sides of the Carpathians and Pyrenees would also be rain-shadow areas and so would the Vienna basin (because of the Alps).

The climatic development in Russia differs from that of the rest of Europe; there, the Tertiary Period was often more humid than today, and the Ukraine was not, as it is now, covered largely by treeless steppes. This is clearly shown by the vegetation maps produced by Pokrovskaya (see also Klotz, 1955). Evergreen "tropical" and subtropical woodland predominated in Eocene times. In the Oligocene, the mixed coniferous and deciduous woods contained many subtropical evergreen genera and *Taxodium* swamps. At the start of the Miocene (fig. 100), there were deciduous forests which gave way later to mixed pinewoods and deciduous woods. Steppe floras were not established until the latter part of the Miocene, when the change is obviously closely related to the paleogeographic development of eastern Europe. During the Eocene, an east Ural seaway connected the extensive Tethys to the Arctic, but, as the Tertiary Period progressed, the seas gradually regressed to produce more or less the present extent of the continents, although the temperature was clearly higher than at present.

Further reading: MABESOONE, 1959.

Rainfall in North America

The effects of a mountain range on rainfall are displayed in classic manner in the western part of North America (Chaney, Dorf, Axelrod; Table 32). The present intermontane desert areas of the Great Basin and the Mohave Desert have yielded rich Cretaceous and Cenozoic floras which indicate that lush forests flourished in the Upper Cretaceous, and during the greater part of the Tertiary. At first, the climate was hot and humid. The first indication of a lower rainfall is afforded by the mid-Eocene Green

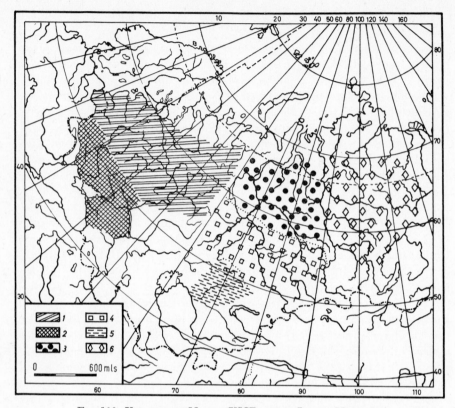

FIG. 100. VEGETATION MAP OF USSR IN THE LOWER MIOCENE
1 = Mixed coniferous and deciduous forest with abundant *Sciadopitys;* 2 = Deciduous
hardwoods with proportion of subtropical evergreens and Taxodium moors; 3 = Mixed
pine and deciduous hardwood; 4 = Deciduous forest; 5 = Very dense deciduous forest,
steppe flora on the watersheds; 6 = Pine and spruce forest with *Tsuga* and some deciduous
trees (after J. M. Pokrovskaya from G. Klotz, 1955).

River flora of the central Rockies; another, by the somewhat younger
(Lower Miocene) Florissant flora of Colorado. In the Miocene (fig. 101), the
Great Basin contained an arcto-Tertiary flora with deciduous hardwoods
and conifers. At this time, the rainfall of some 40–50 inches was distributed
evenly throughout the year. The Mohave Basin supported a Madro-Tertiary[1]
vegetation with evergreen oak, thorn scrub and chaparral. Here the climate
was semiarid, the 16–26 inches of rain falling in the winter. At this time,
some slight mountain uplift took place to the west, and the coastal slopes
carried a flora characteristic of a more markedly humid zone. A semiarid
climate prevailed in the mid-Pliocene; grassland and shrubland predominated. It is estimated that the annual rainfall was about 16 inches in
the north and 12–14 inches in the south. The main uplift of the Sierra

1. Madro-Tertiary: After Sierra Madre of Mexico.

Nevada and the Coast Range followed still later, and resulted finally in conditions like those of today, with only 4–8 inches of rainfall in the Great Basin area. These conditions were attained step by step as a result of Pleistocene events.

How precise is our knowledge of rainfall conditions, especially in the Younger Tertiary, is shown by the fact that rainfall maps have been produced to cover large areas such as the southwestern U.S.A. (Axelrod), even if they are not quite accurate. Axelrod (1956, fig. 12) jokingly gives as

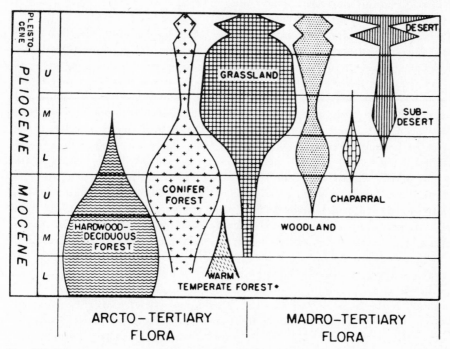

Fig. 101. Development of Vegetation in the Younger Tertiary of the Northern Part of the Great Basin, Utah

Increasing aridity (after Axelrod, 1956).

the Lower Pliocene weather forecast for a summer's day at Middlegate Nevada, "Continued clear with afternoon showers."

Rainfall in Other Areas

Widespread salt deposits indicate that those areas of North Africa and Asia which are now arid already experienced such conditions in the Tertiary Period. According to Lotze, the formation of evaporites in Asia was most intensive in the Lower Miocene and in the Sarmatian, which were also the periods of greatest development of European evaporites.

In Kazakhstan, the Eocene flora is of xerophilic evergreens, while the mid-Oligocene climate must have been humid and semitropical with a distinct seasonal rainfall (Lavrov).

Mid-Oligocene coals occur widely between the Aral Sea and the Altai Mountains, and also further north in western Siberia. They are followed, in the Lower Miocene, by saliferous beds, signifying arid conditions. The Angara region of the Yenisei highlands in northeast Siberia enjoyed, says Bogolepov, a warm humid climate at the start of the Oligocene, and supported the "Turgai" flora of oak, chestnuts, etc. Later, however, the climate became more arid. The Younger Tertiary is also relatively dry and cooler, although red bed weathering is still in evidence.

Evidently the character of the climate varied both in time and from place to place in Eastern Asia. In many parts of Southeast Asia, from Burma and Assam northward to Japan, the nature of the early Eocene flora suggests that it accumulated in subtropical swamps. At times, however, the climate may have been more arid for there are red beds of Eocene age in China and Japan. Floral variation indicates that the gradual fall in temperatures which has been mentioned as occurring in the Tertiary of the remainder of the Northern Hemisphere also affected this area. There was, though, a general mid-Miocene amelioration with a temporary return from temperate to subtropical vegetation. Temperatures dropped sharply in late Miocene times and, despite a slight improvement in the Pliocene, the climate of the late Tertiary appears to have been cooler than that of the present day. Rainfall at this time was very variable. Coniferous woodlands in Japan suggest a considerable rainfall, but in the north of China, both the flora and the presence of red beds are indicative of semiaridity. Teichert considers that there was a late Pliocene pluvial phase in China.

Little is as yet known about the Tertiary climates of South Africa, though both the Kalahari and the Namib regions were arid. Gypsiferous clays also occur further north in the Congo. A mammalian fauna indicative of a steppe climate, has been described from mid-Tertiary sediments in southwest Africa.

In South America there are isolated outcrops of gypsum and sometimes also of halite in the Older Tertiaries of Peru, Colombia, Bolivia, and further north, in Jamaica. Younger Tertiary evaporites are also present in Peru. The climate of the western part of South America was greatly affected by the progressive uplift of the Andes. To the east of the mountains, the climate was probably wetter. The fruits of palm trees have been recorded from Equador and the plants of Brazil all appear to have been tropical.

Oddly enough, salt deposits are missing from Australia. Only in the Eocene of New Caledonia are there beds of gypsum. Lateritic "duricrusts" occur widely, particularly in Western Australia. They are probably of Miocene age and indicate fairly heavy rainfall. Bauxite is developed as far south as Tasmania. In the same island, lat. 43° S, *Araucaria* flourished in the Tertiary. At present, the genus is found only where the temperature never drops below 12° C. The climate was generally warmer than at present, but temperate floras of beech and conifers were developed, especially in the Younger Tertiary.

Seasonal Climatic Variations

The very finely banded oil shales of the Green River Formation of Colorado, Utah, and Wyoming, investigated by Bradley (1929), deserve mention as evidence of a distinct seasonal variation in climate (Chapter 9). European examples include the Oligocene leaf-coal of Rott near Cologne (Schwarzbach, 1952; Chapter 9, fig. 68), and the Oligocene molasse of Switzerland (Bersier; Chapter 9). In every case, changes in the amount of rainfall may well have been the decisive factor. His research on the lamination of Eocene otoliths from Geiseltal near Halle, led Voigt to propose that there were two wet seasons in each year, but his evidence is rather inconclusive.

Evidence of Glaciation in Low Latitudes

While extensive ice sheets may have spread over the polar regions in the Younger Tertiary, and also appeared in Iceland and Alaska, few undoubted morainic deposits are known from elsewhere. W. W. and W. R. Atwood have described the Ridgeway and Gunnison tillites from the San Juan Mountains in Colorado, but van Houten has shown that they can also be interpreted as volcanic mudflows. In the same way, certain conglomerates in the Big Horn Mountains which Hares interpreted as glacial, may well be explained as Early Tertiary fanglomerates (Sharp). Scott, however, has also found tillites in Montana containing striated boulders. These he equates with an Eocene "glaciation", though their age cannot be accurately determined by any direct stratigraphic methods. The Lower Austrian deposits, interpreted by Mohr as Tertiary moraines, are even more problematical than these North American "tillites". In the Caucasus Mountains, Milanovski (1960) has observed tillites which he regards as Pliocene.

The Polar Regions in the Tertiary Period

The rich floras of the Arctic, described more than 200 years ago, are particularly impressive because they are found in areas which now lie north of the poleward limit of trees. O. Heer, the pioneer in this research, reported his findings in *Flora Fossilis Arctica* (1866–1883). These have been revised many times especially by Berry. Important fossil localities are also to be found in Iceland, Greenland, Spitzbergen (fig. 102), and Grinnell Land (lat. 81° 45′ N), the nearest Tertiary plant locality to the pole. According to Berry, 15 genera are known to occur in Grinnell Land; among them *Equisetum, Taxodium, Pinus, Abies, Populus, Betula,* and *Corylus* are prominent. Schloemer-Jäger (1958) mentions as the main elements of the Spitzbergen flora (lat. 78° N), *Sequoia langsdorfi* (fig. 23), *Metasequoia occidentalis*, and *Cercidiphyllum arcticum*. These inhabited the "lower wooded slopes of mountains" where the humidity was high, the summer rainfall heavy, and the January temperature never below freezing point. Pollen analyses have also been carried out in Spitzbergen, and in Iceland, by Manum and Pflug. Dominant among the rich flora of Greenland are the leaves of willow, poplar, birch, and hazel (Berry). *Liquidambar*, *Ulmus*, *Platanus*, *Sassafras*, *Fraxinus*, *Liriodendron*, *Acer*, and *Vitis* are all represented there. On the other hand, records of *Castanea*, *Juglans*, *Pterocarya*, *Laurus*, *Colutea*, *Diospyros*, and *Sapindus* are all very debatable. With the exception of some Recent relicts, the floras contain no plant that is not still thriving in the cooler parts of Europe and North America. In 1868, Heer gave the following as the annual mean temperatures based on Tertiary floras: Iceland, at least 9° C, Greenland 9° C, Spitzbergen $5\frac{1}{2}$°–6° C. Our present knowledge suggests that these estimates may be very close to the truth.

Fig. 102. Leaf of a Hazel (*Corylus m'quarrii*) from the Lower Tertiary of Spitzbergen (x$\frac{1}{2}$) (from Schwarzbach, 1946).

Most of the plants have probably come from Older Tertiary sediments, although their exact stratigraphic position is uncertain.

Since it is apparent from other observations that no substantial shift of the poles may be considered for the Tertiary, the additional problem arises here in the north of whether such unusual light conditions as the polar night and photoperiodism (H. A. Allard) have had any effect. The successes of Icelandic gardeners show immediately that, for many plants, these problems are not critical.

The Pliocene Period was so much cooler than the Early Tertiary, that Iceland was probably glaciated at that time (Jónsson, Schwarzbach and Pflug, fig. 103). D. J. Miller has presumed that glaciers also covered parts of Alaska in the Younger Tertiary. Disregarding Greenland, where no Pliocene sediments are known, and where extensive glaciers may possibly have existed, the north polar region must have been free of continental ice sheets throughout the Tertiary.

Little can be seen in Antarctica. Tertiary tree floras have been shown to be present in the now glaciated, sub-Antarctic islands of Kerguelen (lat.

49° S) and Seymour, near Graham Land (64° S). Dusen has pointed out that the flora of Seymour Island includes species indicative of a temperate (e.g. *Nothofagus*) and subtropical climate (*Araucaria, Dryopteris, Polypodium*); marine strata contain both vertebrates and *Lingula*.

Post-Miocene (Pliocene?) conglomerates in Cockburn Island, near Graham Land, have been taken to be glacio-marine deposits, yet the accompanying fauna contains, as well as a *Pecten* of doubtful cold-water type, species, especially of Bryozoa, that are indicators of marine temperatures probably

FIG. 103. UPPER TERTIARY TILLITE FROM SOUTHEAST ICELAND

(Hoffell) (Photograph: M. Schwarzbach).

2°–10° C in excess of present temperatures. Other Antarctic "tillites" are probably better regarded as volcanic breccias (Nichols, 1960). These facts led Griffith Taylor to conclude, in his *Geology of Antarctica* (1940): "The outstanding fact is that no clear indication of a former Ice Age—and certainly none of continental dimensions—is apparent in all the formations so far examined." He did, however, take into account the possibility that high level corries on Mount Lister, South Victoria Land, were of Pliocene age (fig. 104).

Further reading: FURON, 1950; HOLLICK, 1936.

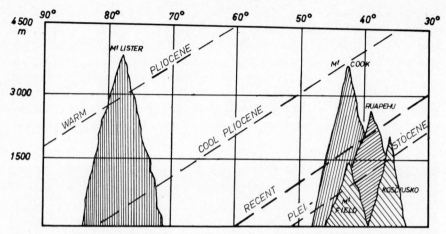

FIG. 104. DISPLACEMENT OF SNOW LINE IN ANTARCTICA, NEW ZEALAND, AND AUSTRALIA
DURING THE PLIOCENE AND QUATERNARY (after G. Taylor, 1940).

OCEAN CURRENTS AND WIND DIRECTIONS

Forerunners of our major ocean currents can be detected in the Tertiary as well as in the Cretaceous (fig. 105). The climate of Europe was influenced by a Gulf Stream, while a Kuro Shio, reaching the Pacific coast of North America, enabled palms to thrive in Alaska. The peculiar distribution of Nummulites in Africa may be attributed to the presence of a warm Agulhas and a cold Benguela Current.

Semper has pointed out that, in the early part of the Tertiary Period, a warm current from the Indian Ocean penetrated into the Mediterranean. It was probably produced by the northeast Trade Winds whose sphere of influence then extended further north, because the high-pressure belt of the horse latitudes was shifted nearer the North Pole at that time. Some isolated observations also make it clear that Central Europe already lay in the belt of the Westerlies. Voigt records that pollen concentrated on the eastern margins of Eocene pools near Halle; Hintze suggests that trees in the Oligocene lignites of Bitterfeld were blown over eastward.

SUMMARY

The climatic picture afforded by the Tertiary is relatively easy to assemble (fig. 105). In the early part of this Period, more or less all of the world enjoyed a climate considerably warmer than that which we experience now. The warm zone appears to have extended some 10°–15° further north and 10° further south than it does at present, while the polar limit of trees shifted poleward even more; by some 20°–30° in the Northern Hemisphere, and 10° in the Southern Hemisphere. Many types of trees flourished in the polar regions and polar icecaps did not exist. The temperature difference between

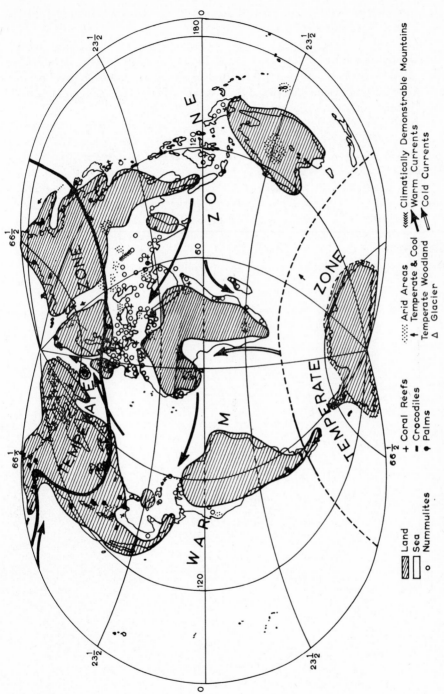

FIG. 105. CLIMATIC MAP OF THE LOWER TERTIARY (after Schwarzbach, 1946).

the poles and the equator was less than that at present; the overall climate of the earth was more uniform.

In the course of the Tertiary Period a gradual general cooling was super-imposed on the climatic fluctuations, so that, by the Pliocene, conditions were almost as they are now. The first glaciers appeared in the Arctic region, and probably also in the high mountain chains, in the latter part of the Tertiary.

Part of the climatic variation was due to changing paleogeographic conditions. The increasing aridity of western North America, for instance, was due to mountain building. Generally speaking, the desert belt of the Northern Hemisphere reached slightly nearer to the pole than it does now.

The symmetrical distribution of the climatic belts with respect to the equator, and also the manifest similarity of the ocean currents with those of the present day, make it very improbable that there was any great displacement of the poles. Chaney arrived at this same conclusion by reconstructing Tertiary "isoflors". It therefore follows that Köppen and Wegener's paleogeographic map of this period can hardly be correct.

19

Quaternary

"You may shake your head incredulously, when I
suggest that you should consider the garden of Switzerland, the whole wide range of hills between Lake
Geneva and the river Reuss, to have been once covered
by glaciers. Yet there are many factors which support
the probability of such an assumption."
B. Cotta, Geologische Briefe aus den Alpen, 1850.

DELIMITATION OF THE QUATERNARY

Although the Quaternary Period, lasting only about 1 million years so far
is much the shortest of all the major divisions of geologic time, it is
unparalleled climatologically in its development of Ice Ages. Moraines were
first discovered about 1800 in the Swiss Alps, but for a long time, most of
the Quaternary deposits were regarded as products of the Flood. In 1823,
Buckland coined the term Diluvium—Latin for Flood—for the Pleistocene.

Since then, particularly in Europe and North America, the main glaciated
regions, the study of the "Ice Ages" has become a separate branch of
geology, with its own societies, congresses, and periodicals. Hence, only
a small part of all our present knowledge can be dealt with here. It is
recommended that for further information the reader should consult the
excellent general texts recently produced by J. K. Charlesworth, R. F. Flint,
R. von Klebelsberg, P. Woldstedt, and F. E. Zeuner, or the Soviet writers
Gerassimov, Markov, Neystadt (summarized very well by B. Frenzel).

The 1948 International Geological Congress in London decided that the
appearance of the peculiarities of a "glacial climate" should be taken as
the upper limit of the Tertiary. Obviously, in areas as well known as Europe
and North America, this leads to ambiguity, for Tertiary glaciations have
been recognized in the northernmost parts of these continents. In standard
sections in Italy, the boundary is taken at the point where cold-water marine
species, especially *Cyprina islandica*, appear for the first time. This has
meant that two stages formerly regarded as Pliocene, the Villafranchian and
Calabrian, are now included in the Pleistocene. At present the Quaternary
is divided into the Pleistocene—formerly known as the Diluvium, the time
of the real Ice Age—and the Holocene or Recent, which represents the
postglacial period, formerly known in Germany as the Alluvium.

A slightly different and, in many ways, well-founded division has been proposed by the Russians (Gromov, Krasnov, Nikiforova, 1959, and Moskzitin). They recognize three subdivisions: the Eopleistocene, Q_1, the Pleistocene, Q_2, and the Holocene or Epipleistocene, Q_3, in the Quaternary or Anthropogene.

The Pleistocene can also be divided into Glacial and Interglacial phases. The Holocene covers only the last 10,000 years.

Further reading: MOSKVITIN, 1954; NIKIFOROVA & ALEXEYEVA, 1959.

CLIMATE DURING GLACIAL PHASES

Glaciated Areas

Huge ice sheets formed several times during the Pleistocene, particularly in Europe and North America, but also in Northern Asia, South America, and in many of the world's mountain chains (fig. 106, Table 33). Those areas

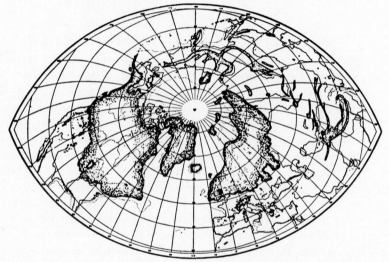

FIG. 106. MAXIMUM EXTENT OF THE PLEISTOCENE ICE IN THE NORTHERN HEMISPHERE
(From R. A. Daly, 1934).

of the world formerly covered by ice sheets and their marginal deposits constitute the true glaciated areas. Their climate will be considered first.

The extraordinary spread of the Pleistocene continental ice sheets must have needed a fundamental change in climatic conditions. It is now accepted that the critical factor was a decrease in temperature, not an increase in precipitation. Climatic conditions altered in the course of individual Ice Ages; naturally, they were also quite different in different latitudes. In general, advance of the glaciers was linked with the appearance of a cold, damp climate; a cold dry climate was then developed over the expanse of the ice sheet itself.

TABLE 33
EXTENT OF RECENT AND PLEISTOCENE ICE-SHEETS AFTER FLINT

PRESENT	PLEISTOCENE	MAXIMUM EXTENT	
		SQ. MILES	SQ. KILOMETRES
Antarctica		5,019,300	12,600,000
Greenland		637,050	1,700,000
	Antarctic	5,511,000	13,200,000
	Greenland	935,000	2,200,000
	Laurentian Ice	5,071,000	13,100,000
	Cordilleran Ice	957,000	2,500,000
	Scandinavian Ice	2,145,000	5,500,000
	British Ice	176,000	450,000
	Alps	14,750	38,500
	West Siberia	1,628,000	4,200,000
	East Siberia	440,000	1,100,000
	Central Asia	440,000	1,100,000
	S. South America	297,000	750,000
	Australia	25,700	70,000
Whole earth		5,830,120	15,000,000
	Whole earth	18,363,400	45,000,000

Boulder clay with erratic blocks (fig. 107), and the land-forms associated with its deposition—such as end moraines, striated pavements, roches moutonées, drumlins, and glacial run-off channels—provide the most significant evidence of former glaciation. These all help to create the typical flat, glacial landscape of northern Europe, North America, and northern Asia. In formerly glaciated mountain chains, such features of glacial erosion as roches moutonnées, U-shaped valleys, and corries, are much in evidence. It should, however, be remembered that these land forms are largely the result of the Last Glaciation. Regions affected by the Penultimate Glaciation exhibit only fragmentary end moraines, a very few glacial lake deposits, and drainage channels modified by later weathering (Chapter 5).

Around the perimeter of the glaciers, in what are known as the *periglacial areas*, there appear various permafrost phenomena—including ice wedges, cryoturbation, etc.—eolian deposits of loess, and asymmetrical valleys. France, for example, formed part of the periglacial area of Europe, as Tricart's map shows.

FIG. 107. ERRATIC BLOCK NEAR BRESLAU (WROCLAW), POLAND, which has been carried at least 600 Km. by the Scandinavian ice-sheets (Photograph: M. Schwarzbach).

To these inorganic indications may be added organic evidence. Floras, including *Dryas*, etc. (fig. 45), that are very suitable for pollen analysis, and such vertebrates as musk ox, reindeer, mammoth, and woolly rhinoceros, are all adapted to life in a cold climate. In addition to the terrestrial fauna, there were also marine organisms inhabiting the neighboring seas. These included *Yoldia* (*Portlandia*) *arctica*, found in the late glacial phase of the Baltic, and the arctic whale *Balaena mysticetus*, in the late glacial sediments of the Lower Rhine (Jux and Rosenbauer).

Some examples of the fall in temperature during the Pleistocene period are collected together in Table 34. It can be seen from these that we must suppose a *maximum* fall in temperature of 8°–13° C in temperate latitudes of the Northern Hemisphere. More recently, however, Kaiser (1960) has proposed a higher value of 15°–16° C. All these estimates apply to the latest (Würm) glaciation. Since the extent of the ice sheets was even greater in the preceding glacial phase, the drop in temperature at that time can hardly have been less (fig. 108). The decrease in summer temperatures may have been different from the decrease in winter temperatures. The poleward limit of trees gives us a clue to the summer difference as it generally coincides with the 10° C July isotherm. Now, Poser has recently pointed out that the western parts of central Europe were covered by a treeless tundra, and that the ground was permanently frozen, whereas in the permafrost area of Hungary, there was woodland. The presence of permanently frozen ground requires a mean annual temperature below −2° C. Thus, where the tree limit cuts the permafrost limit, in the foreland of the Eastern Alps, it may be assumed that the July isotherm was just about 10° C, and the annual

TABLE 34

DROP IN TEMPERATURE DURING THE ICE AGE

TEMPERATURE INDICATOR	PLEISTOCENE TEMPERATURE LOWERING (°C)	AUTHOR
Dryas octopetala in Central Europe	10	C. Gagel, 1923 P. Range, 1923 E. Werth, 1925
Picea glauca and *P. marianna* in Texas	8 in July	J. E. Potzger and B. C. Tharp, 1947
Picea and *Abies* in Florida	7–8 in July	J. Davies, 1946
Pinus koraiensis in Japan	7½	S. Miki, 1956
Tundra polygons in England	13½	F. W. Shotton, 1960
Frost fissures in central Germany	11	W. Soergel, 1936
Frost fissures in Montana	> 8	J. P. Schafer, 1949
Lowering of snow line in Alps	> 6	A. Penck, 1938
Lowering of snow line in Colorado	5·5	E. Antevs, 1954
Lowering of snow line in central Japan	4½–6½ in summer	M. Hoshiai and K. Kobayashi, 1957

mean was −2° C. Monthly temperatures can then be estimated as shown in Table 35. These show that July temperatures were about 8° cooler than they are today, and January temperatures 12° cooler. Further east, the summer was warmer, the winter colder, as the climatic type became more continental. On the other hand, in the west of France, the temperature decrease in summer and winter amounted to about 7° C and 0°–3° C respectively.

TABLE 35

MONTHLY TEMPERATURES IN THE EASTERN ALPINE FOOTHILLS, DURING THE WÜRM GLACIATION. AFTER POSER

J	F	M	A	M	J	J	A	S	O	N	D
−14	−12	−8	−2	4	8	10	8	4	−2	−8	−12·C.

According to Poser, those temperatures controlled the depth to which the permanently frozen ground thawed in summer. Where summer temperatures were high, e.g. in Hungary, the depth of thaw was particularly great and trees could flourish. These statements are, however, still in need of further supplementation before the above temperature values can be regarded as completely reliable.

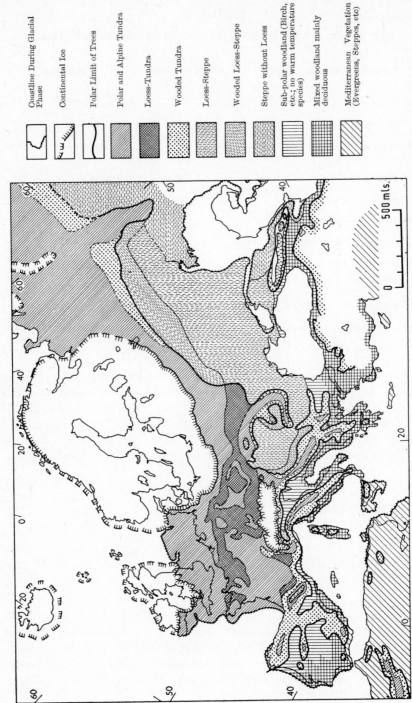

Coastline During Glacial Phase

Continental Ice

Polar Limit of Trees

Polar and Alpine Tundra

Loess-Tundra

Wooded Tundra

Loess-Steppe

Wooded Loess-Steppe

Steppe without Loess

Sub-polar woodland (Birch, etc.; no warm temperature species)

Mixed woodland mainly deciduous

Mediterranean Vegetation (Evergreens, Steppes, etc)

500 mls.

Fig. 108. Climatic Zones in Europe during the Würm Glaciation (after Budel and Woldstedt, 1954).

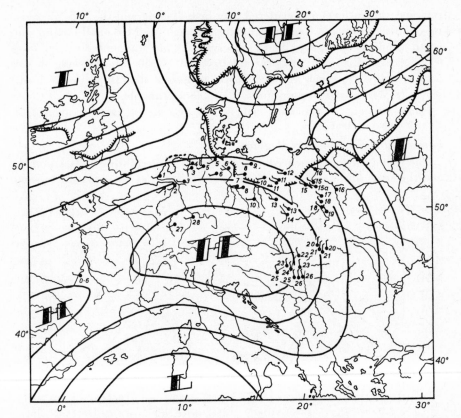

FIG. 109. WINDS AND ATMOSPHERIC PRESSURE IN EUROPE IN SUMMER DURING THE LATE
GLACIAL PHASES

The numbers indicate individual localities; the arrows, wind direction (from dune bedding) and the hatched lines, the ice margin at the beginning and end of the Late Glacials.
(From Poser, 1948).

Precipitation in the glaciated areas was probably not high; indeed, it was
perhaps even less than at present. This is evident from the fact that the
lowering of the snow line was not so great as ought to have resulted from
about a 10° C drop in temperature. Nowadays, a decrease in temperature of
0.5° C corresponds to a 100 m. depression of the snow line, so that a 10° C
decrease should have produced a 2,000 m. depression; about double the
actual observed value. This too small drop in the snow line may also be
related, as Mortensen showed, to the fact that the fall in temperature was
greater at low altitudes.

During the late glacial phase in particular, i.e. during the latter part of
the Würm Ice Age, dune bedding indicates the direction of the *prevailing
winds* in several parts of Europe. Poser has attempted thereby to reconstruct
the position of high and low-pressure areas in central Europe (fig. 109). In

summer, the anticyclones centered over Scandinavia and the Alps gave rise
to west winds in north Germany, northwest winds in Silesia and Poland, and
north winds in Hungary. These observations are undoubtedly somewhat
fragmentary. Moreover, it is certain that not all the dunes belong to this
period; many are much younger. Lotze considers that those in the Lippe
valley in Westphalia are not more than 2,000 years old.

 Further reading: S. T. ANDERSON, 1961; DILLON, 1956; KLUTE, 1951; RATHJENS, 1954;
H. E. WRIGHT, jr., 1961.

Lower Latitudes and Arid Regions

The whole earth experienced a drop in temperature during a glacial phase,
and the *snow line* was depressed everywhere, even at the equator, to some

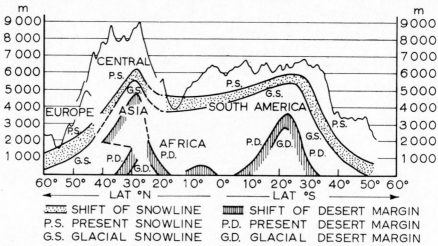

FIG. 110. PRESENT-DAY AND PLEISTOCENE SNOW LINES ALONG A MERIDIAN

 The migration of arid areas is also indicated. The snow line shows a constant world-wide
depression. (From Penck, 1937.)

500–1500 m. below its present level (fig. 110). According to Flint, the
difference on Mount Kilimanjaro amounted to some 1300 m. while, in the
Andes, it ranged up to 1400 m. (Wilhelmy). Flohn has proposed that, in the
tropics, the temperature was 4° C less than it is just now, which would mean
that the annual mean at the equator was 23° C. At the same time *marine
temperatures* in the warmest parts of the oceans cannot have dropped below
20° C, otherwise reef corals would not have survived the glacial phases so
readily. During such phases their distribution was naturally restricted (see
Daly, 1934, and his glacial control theory). O^{18} estimates also indicate a
marine temperature of about 21° C in the equatorial zone (Chapter 11). The
smaller decrease in temperature of the tropics as compared with higher
latitudes is indicated by the fact that, at least in the tropical lowlands, it
had little or no effect on the flora, fauna, or sedimentation.

On the other hand, the climates of present desert areas were greatly affected. During the great glaciations, especially in the Northern Hemisphere, the West Wind Belt was forced equatorward; consequently, at least the poleward limits of the deserts received a more abundant rainfall. Thus a glacial phase in the polar regions corresponds to a "pluvial" with reduced temperatures nearer the equator. The influence of pluvials can also be detected quite clearly in semiarid regions.

Pluvial effects are known from every present desert area. In North America, the Great Basin is a well-known example of an area which, during the last glacial period, was flooded by such extensive lakes as Lake Bonneville (figs. 55–56). The old lake terraces indicate the former high levels of water. The classic description of these terraces is that given by Gilbert in 1890, but Ives (1948) has shown that they were recognized by the Franciscan monk Silvestre Velez de Escalante as long ago as 1776. Arid and pluvial phases can also be detected, though not very clearly, in the sediments of the Great Salt Lake (Eardley and Gvosdetsky). Flint and Gale have recognized in Searles Lake a pluvial dating from 10,000–23,000 years ago, and represented by a bed of mud between two layers of salt. In the Great Plains, the increased rainfall manifests itself in the greater abundance of aquatic snails (Frye and Leonard). Sears and Clisby have shown that pollen diagrams from Mexico indicate a repeated change between wetter and drier phases, but the correlation with events further north is still uncertain.

In the Mediterranean coastlands of Spain, pluvial phases, i.e. periods of warm humid climate, are distinguished by red coloration; the warm dry interpluvial phases, when the present type of climate prevailed, are represented by caliche deposits (calcareous duricrusts).

In Asia, the Caspian Sea was at times connected with the Aral Sea, 300 miles away, and with the Black Sea, through the Manytch Depression. The Dead Sea stood 400 m. higher than now; 15 raised beaches are developed.

The fauna and traces of Prehistoric Man (Schwarzbach, 1953) bear witness to the once higher rainfall of the Sahara. In the lakes of the East African Rift Valley, the water level was higher than at present (Flint, 1959). Yet there are also examples of increased Pleistocene aridity, as in the intensification of dune formation in the Kalahari (Flint, Leakey, *et al.*, 1959, p. 364).

Figure 111 gives Budel's idea of the distribution of the climatic belts as they were in the Pleistocene and as they are now. It is assumed that the northern and southern margins of the desert belt of the Northern Hemisphere approached each other during a pluvial. This need not mean, however, that the "north" and "south" pluvials occurred simultaneously. The northern limit of the Sahara probably retreated during the glacial phases, while the southern margin, by analogy with present meteorological conditions, would have received its increased precipitation—resulting in the advance of the tropical rain-forest belt during warm phases (Balout) and also during the postglacial Climatic Optimum.

Further reading: BUTZER, 1958; TONGIORGI & TREVISAN, 1942.

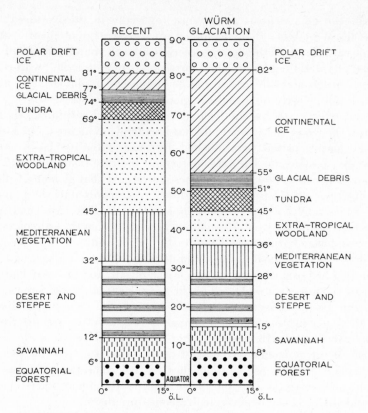

RECENT   WÜRM
GLACIATION

POLAR DRIFT
ICE

CONTINENTAL
ICE
GLACIAL DEBRIS

TUNDRA

EXTRA-TROPICAL
WOODLAND

MEDITERRANEAN
VEGETATION

DESERT AND
STEPPE

SAVANNAH

EQUATORIAL
FOREST

POLAR DRIFT
ICE

CONTINENTAL
ICE

GLACIAL DEBRIS

TUNDRA

EXTRA-TROPICAL
WOODLAND

MEDITERRANEAN
VEGETATION

DESERT AND
STEPPE

SAVANNAH

EQUATORIAL
FOREST

Fig. 111. Displacement of the Climatic Belts of the Northern
Hemisphere during the Würm Glaciation (after Büdel, 1951).

CLIMATE DURING INTERGLACIAL PHASES

Numerous observations have shown that the climate of the interglacial periods was similar to today's, or at times even slightly warmer. Where cooler conditions did prevail, as during the formation of many of the Swiss shale coals of the last interglacial (Ludi), we may assume that they represented only a relatively cool phase of the whole interglacial.

In Europe, the much-discussed scree-breccia deposits of the Mindel-Riss interglacial at Hötting, near Innsbruck, contain the Pontian Alpine rose, *Rhododendron ponticum*, and the vine *Vitis sylvestris*, plants that can no longer flourish in this region.

Since the marsh turtle, *Emys orbicularis*, still lived in the Weimar district of central Germany during the last interglacial, the mean temperature of the warmest month must have been at least 19° C and the summer rainfall must have been low (H. Ullrich). The July temperature today is 17° C; the rainfall distribution shows a summer maximum. Marls formed during the same interglacial, near Lehringen in Lower Saxony, contain the gastropod *Belgrandia marginata* (C. R. Boettger), now to be found only in southeast Europe. The gastropod *Helicigona banatica*, present at other fossil localities in central Europe in beds of the same age, now lives somewhat further south in the south Carpathians (V. Ložek).

Interglacial strata in England have yielded the brackish water pondweed, *Najas minor*, which requires a higher summer temperature than now occurs in England (H. Godwin, 1956). Marine beds belonging to the Last, Eem, Interglacial in the North Sea area are characterized by such southern "Lusitanian" species as *Tapes aureus*.

Where pollen analyses have been carried out on interglacial strata, they have indicated certain stratigraphically characteristic vegetation changes resulting from climatic variation (Firbas *et al*). Thus the widespread distribution of spruce, fir, and heather, in central Europe, during the latter part of the Last Interglacial, suggests that, at that time, the climate was fairly wet. This humidity was obviously the result of a readvance of the ice. During the postglacial period, on the other hand, the areal distribution of these plants extended only belatedly. Beech disappeared almost completely during the Last Interglacial, to be replaced by the hornbeam, *Carpinus*. It is not, however, certain that this replacement was due to climatic changes. Gerassimov and Markov have given us a lucid account of pollen analysis variation in the U.S.S.R. during the Interglacials.

In North America, it is considered that temperatures around Toronto throughout the time of deposition of the Don Beds of the Sangamon Interglacial were 2°–3° C higher than today's. The marine lamellibranch, *Rangia cuneata*, now living in the Gulf of Mexico, occurs frequently in interglacial (Aftonian) strata in Maryland (Blake). Hibbard has ascertained from the vertebrates of the Jinglebob (Sangamon Interglacial?) of Kansas that, at times, the climate was humid, with an annual rainfall of some 40 inches, and that the summers were cooler, and the winters warmer than they are at present.

In central Chile, red-bed weathering is very common in one of the early interglacials; at present, this type of weathering is first developed over 150 miles further north (Illies).

Interglacial beds at Stöd in Iceland contain the alder, *Alnus viridus*, which no longer flourishes there (Askelsson, see Schwarzbach's review, 1955).

The climate of the early interglacials was probably even slightly warmer than that of the later. Indeed, an ape, *Macaca florentina*, has been identified in the Tegelen Beds of Holland. The only part of Europe where modern representatives of the family continue to thrive is Gibraltar. Plants such as *Tsuga, Carya, Pterocarya*, etc., which have all since disappeared from Europe, and the water fern, *Azolla tegelensis*, were also represented. *Pterocarya* survived, in places, as late as the Mindel-Riss Interglacial. (For Japan, see Miki.)

COURSE OF THE ICE AGE

Europe

During the Quaternary, there were *three great ice centers* in Europe; one in Scandinavia, one in the British Isles, and one in the Alps. There were also countless smaller glaciers in other mountain ranges.

The Scandinavian and British ice sheets sometimes formed one extensive and more or less continuous ice sheet. The Scandinavian Ice thrust forward through the Baltic Basin, onward for more than 1250 miles into the heart of central and eastern Europe, but the British Ice was more or less confined to the British Isles, and, in fact, even the south of England remained free of ice. The ice center in Scandinavia lay slightly to the east of the present mountain watershed, in a position asymmetric to the ice sheet as a whole. At its center, the ice was about 3000 m. thick.

In the Alps, the valleys and some of the passes were submerged under an interconnected network of glaciers, with the higher peaks towering above. The snow line lay some 1200 m. lower than now. Several mighty glaciers surged out of the mountains as piedmont (Malaspina type) glaciers; most of them flowed northward into southern Germany. Their length was remarkable by comparison with the 16 miles of the present largest Aletsch Glacier. The Rhone Glacier was 225 miles long, the Inn Glacier 210 miles, and the Rhine Glacier 125 miles (Klebelsberg, 1949).

The maximum extent of southward penetration of the Scandinavian Ice, usually marked by the southern limit of erratic blocks of Scandinavian type, was clearly influenced by the pre-existing topography; the limit bulges far to the south along river valleys. This same control can also be observed in North America. The boundary runs through Holland and central Germany, and on along the northern edge of the Carpathians to the basins of the Dnieper and the Don.

It was in Europe that it was first realized that there were *several* glacial phases during the Pleistocene Period. This was firmly established by Penck and Brückner, when they were working on the glaciated areas of the Alps between 1901 and 1909 (see fig. 43). They were able to distinguish four ice ages which they named after Alpine rivers (fig. 112). Of these, the earliest was the Günz Glaciation, followed by the Mindel, by the Riss, and finally by the Würm. The glacial phases were separated by interglacials.

It later became apparent that it was possible to divide each glacial into a number of cold periods (stadials) separated by shorter warm periods (interstadials). Studies of the river gravels of central Germany and the Alps (Soergel, Eberl) have resulted in very detailed subdivisions whereby deposition of gravel is equated with a glacial phase, erosion with an interglacial or interstadial. Almost all of the finer subdivisions are, however, still uncertain. Similarly, all of the widely spread loess can be interpreted as an eolian sediment forming during glacial phases, while the interbedded loams

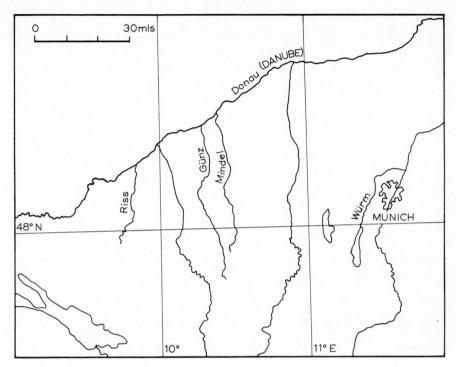

FIG. 112. THE BAVARIAN RIVERS WHICH GIVE THEIR NAMES TO PHASES OF THE ALPINE
GLACIATION

represent the products of interglacial weathering. In this way, climatic
variation in the periglacial area can also be worked out in detail. The
interpretation and correlation of different sections is still very problematical;
the same may be said of all the finer subdivisions of the Pleistocene Period.
In Europe, even the divisions of the comparatively well-known Last
Glaciation are still hotly disputed. Woldstedt, the authority on conditions
in central Europe, at present recognizes two major stadials separated by
a distinct interstadial (Göttweiger Horizon). Moreover, the subdivisions of
the Alps and northern Europe cannot readily be correlated, and so local
names have been chosen for each. It also seems certain that before Penck's
earliest glaciation (Günz), we must recognize an earlier, if less extensive cold
phase, the Donau Glaciation. These observations result in the scheme shown
in Table 36.

Only the Last Glaciation is at all well known, and only in the case of the
last three glacials can we estimate the extent of the Scandinavian Ice. In
places, the maximum spread of ice occurred during the Elster Glaciation;
and elsewhere during the Saale Glaciation (as in the U.S.S.R.). After the
Last Glaciation, the ice retreated in stages, with pauses between when the
position of the ice margin remained constant for a time. These pauses, or

retreat stadials, are marked by end moraines, outwash sands, and abandoned glacial melt-water channels.

In the Alps, too, the Würm glaciers did not extend as far as those of the earlier glaciations. No Donau moraines appear to have been preserved but,

TABLE 36
DIVISIONS OF THE QUATERNARY IN EUROPE

	ALPS	NORTH GERMANY AND HOLLAND
Last Glacial	Würm	Weichsel
Last Interglacial . . .	Riss-Würm	Eem
Glacial	Riss	Saale { Warthe / Drenthe
Interglacial	Mindel-Riss "Great Interglacial"	Holstein
Glacial	Mindel	Elster
Interglacial	Günz-Mindel	Cromer
Glacial	Günz	Weybourne
Interglacial	Donau-Günz	Tegelen
Glacial	Donau	Pre-Tegelen

in the Southern Alps, pollen analyses have revealed a considerable climatic change which took place in the early part of the Quaternary Period. This, Venzo considers to be at least partly the result of the Donau glaciation, and Zagwijn equates it with the Pre-Tegelen phase in Holland. According to Bout, considerable early Quaternary (Villafranchian) climatic variation can also be detected at Velay in central France.

In other mountain ranges which now support only a few small glaciers, e.g. Pyrenees or Abruzzi, little other than valley and corrie glaciers are known (fig. 31). The amount of glaciation decreased eastward because of the increasingly continental nature of the climate. In central Europe, this decrease is clearly revealed by the maximum length of the Pleistocene glaciers; in the Vosges they stretch for up to 25 miles, but in the Riesengebirge, further east, are only a little over 3 miles long. The Pleistocene snow line also rose in this direction (Table 37). Only in some exceptional cases has it proved possible to assign these mountain glaciations to their correct stratigraphical positions. Those corries, U-shaped valleys, terminal moraines, etc., which form distinct morphological features all originated during the Last Glaciation.

Further reading: VAN DER VLERK & FLORSCHÜTZ, 1953.

TABLE 37

PLEISTOCENE SNOW LINE IN SOME EUROPEAN MOUNTAINS

MOUNTAINS	LONGITUDE	HEIGHT OF PLEISTOCENE SNOW LINE
British Isles	0–10° W	600 m.
Vosges-Black Forest	7–8° E	900 m.
Riesengebirge (Silesia)	15–16° E	1200 m.
Tatra (Carpathians)	20° E	1500–1600 m.
Transylvanian Alps	23–26° E	1900 m.

North America

In America, too, there were several separate ice centers. The North American ice sheets differed from those of Europe in that the center of the main "Laurentian Ice" lay over the relatively low-lying area of the eastern part of the Canadian Shield. Further dissimilarities are that the large Cordilleran ice complex was connected to the Laurentian ice sheet, and that the area of plains covered by the ice was much greater than in Europe.

R. F. Flint considers that the *Laurentian ice center* originated in the highlands of northeastern North America, i.e. in northern Quebec, Labrador, Newfoundland, Baffin Land, Devon Island, Bylot Island, and Ellesmere Island, etc. Valley glaciers and small icecaps gradually built up until piedmont glaciers began to thrust outward to the south and west. The drop in temperature required to cause this ice formation need only have been relatively small for, even today, Arctic North America is extensively glaciated, while the other areas mentioned lie just below the snow line. Most precipitation was confined to the area of the piedmont glaciers with the result that they grew more quickly than the mountain glaciers. Eventually the thickness of ice over the piedmont area exceeded that of the mountains, which then disappeared under one vast continuous ice cap.

Just as in Europe, the Last (Wisconsin) Glaciation was not as extensive as its two forerunners which had penetrated from the Laurentian center almost as far south as St. Louis. The degree to which advance of the ice was affected by relief is revealed in the very *sinuous* southern boundary of the glaciated areas, and by the fact that southwest Wisconsin, the "driftless area", remained free of ice while morainic deposits built up all around. Yet, during the Wisconsin Glaciation, the ice in New York State must have been at least 1000–1300 m. thick, as it covered all of the Catskill and Adirondack Mountains.

Westward, the Laurentian Ice linked up with the *Cordilleran Ice* which, although considerably less extensive, nevertheless stretched unbroken from the Columbia River to the Aleutian Islands, a distance of some 2200 miles. It embraced not only a network of valley glaciers and piedmont glaciers, such as existed in the Alps, but also a continental icecap 2500 or more meters thick, centered on British Columbia.

Glacier formation began in the high rainfall areas of the Coast Range, and gradually migrated eastward to the Rockies, where topographic conditions were more favorable for the accumulation of ice. Apart from the Cordilleran Ice itself, there existed innumerable glacier complexes, the largest of which lay in the Sierra Nevada of eastern California.

Southward limitation of the ice sheets resulted from increased temperatures; in parts of the far north, it was caused by decreased precipitation. Thus, with the exception of the Brooks Range, northern and central Alaska were never glaciated; a corresponding example today is obviously afforded by the frigid, ice-free wastes of northern Greenland.

Four major glaciations have long been recognized in North America; the Nebraskan, Kansan, Illinoian, and Wisconsin Glaciations separated by the Aftonian, Yarmouth and Sangamon Interglacials (Table 38). Here, too, the Last (Wisconsin) Glaciation has had the greatest effect in determining the form of the present landscape and the drainage system of the Great Lakes. Among the sediments of the interglacial phases, loams (gumbotils), resulting from the weathering of the ground moraines, are particularly important. As floral evidence of climate is much scarcer than in Europe, much less is known about the Pre-Nebraskan stages of the Quaternary in North America. Flint has correlated the Pleistocene stages of Europe and North America as shown in Table 38.

Further reading: DILLON, 1956.

TABLE 38

CORRELATION OF THE QUATERNARY OF EUROPE AND NORTH AMERICA

EUROPE	GLACIAL	INTERGLACIAL	NORTH AMERICA
Würm	W		Wisconsin
		R–W	Sangamon
Riss	R		Illinoian
		M–R	Yarmouth
Mindel	M		Kansan
		G–M	Aftonian
Günz	G		Nebraskan
		D–G	
Donau	D		

Asia and the Southern Continents

Much less is known about the Pleistocene stratigraphy of other areas. The only thing that is certain is that, in every locality where detailed studies have been carried out, it is likewise possible to recognize several distinct Ice Ages. From these, it has, at most, been possible to correlate only in very limited fashion with the standard successions of Europe and North America. Correlations of the standard pluvial subdivisions of Asia (Movius) and Africa (Flint), with the European glacial succession, are even more tentative.

The *Asian Ice* (Gromov, Moskvitin), a direct extension of the Scandinavian ice sheet, covered great parts of western Siberia, and drove eastward across the Yenesei. Though the mountains of eastern Siberia also bore a considerable ice cap, on the whole the vast spaces of Siberia were glaciated to a much lesser extent than the neighboring continents, because of the markedly continental nature of the climate, and thus a deficiency in precipitation. Many of the other mountain ranges of Asia also carried extensive glaciers.

Pleistocene glaciers were extremely small in *Africa* and restricted to small areas in *Australia*, as around Mount Kosciusko. There were rather more extensive glaciers in Tasmania and in South Island, New Zealand. A continuous ice sheet developed in the *South American Andes* south of latitude 26° S. This ice spread out eastward over the lowlands of Patagonia, eventually to reach the Atlantic south of 52° S. Recent research in this area has been carried out by V. Auer.

Further reading: GILL, 1953.

The Polar Regions

The *Polar regions* are of particular interest in the stratigraphy of the Ice Age for they still support numerous glaciers. Naturally, in these areas, the Pleistocene glaciation was very considerable. In spite of this, however, interglacials can be recognized in Alaska (Hopkins, MacNeil, Leopold), Arctic Canada (Terasmae *et al.*; see Craig and Fyles, 1961), Greenland (Bryan), Iceland (Pjeturss, Askelsson, see Schwarzbach, 1955), the southern part of the Kola Peninsula (Verzilin), and Antarctica (Péwé). This evidence suggests that the course of the Ice Age in high latitudes was largely similar to that of lower latitudes, and that, even here, the extent of the glaciers varied considerably during the Pleistocene. In Iceland and Alaska, at least two stratigraphically distinct interglacial phases can be recognized.

Oceanic Areas

The Quaternary climatic variations also affected marine areas; indeed, many people assume that, in a general way, the climatic events of the continental areas were controlled by the oceans. In any event, the change between glacial and interglacial phases is very clearly shown in two ways: by oscillation of the shore line resulting in raised beaches, and by changes

C.P.—14

in the character of abyssal sediments. Since both these phenomena are of world-wide distribution, they are of particularly great stratigraphic significance.

1. Sea Level Variations.—*Eustatic* changes of sea level resulted in considerable lowerings during glacial phases, and, during interglacials, in rises to above the present level. It is estimated that during the Last Glaciation, sea level was depressed by about 90 m. This rhythmic variation related to glacials and interglacials, is superimposed on a gradual lowering of sea level since the beginning of the Quaternary, so that the early Pleistocene wave-cut platforms lie much higher than the later ones.

In Europe, these platforms have been particularly closely studied around the Mediterranean by Blanc, Gignoux, Pfannenstiel, Zeuner and others. There, the terraces bear the names given in Table 39. The two lowest terraces are characterized by the presence of the warmth-loving gastropod, *Strombus bubonius*.

TABLE 39

ELEVATION OF THE MORE IMPORTANT MARINE TERRACES
OF THE MEDITERRANEAN AREA

NAME	ELEVATION ABOVE MEAN SEA LEVEL	POSSIBLE STRATIGRAPHIC HORIZON
Sicilian	90–100 m.	
Milazzian	55–60 m.	Günz-Mindel Interglacial
Tyrrhenian	28–32 m.	Mindel-Riss Interglacial
Monastirian	18–20 m.	Riss-Würm Interglacial
Nizza	2–3 m.	Postglacial Climatic Optimum

Unfortunately, since this area is one of great tectonic mobility, a simple comparison of the height of the terraces above the present sea level, in different localities, may easily lead to an incorrect correlation. Table 39 shows one way in which the individual terraces have been correlated with Ice Age chronology, but other stratigraphic interpretations have also been suggested. In particular, the assignment of the lowest Terrace to the postglacial Climatic Optimum, has recently been questioned (Flint, Graul, etc.).

The Bermudas might be cited as a North American example (Sayles). There, low sea level during the glacial phases led to the exposure of calcareous sands, from which dunes were formed. During the succeeding interglacials, these were either weathered or covered by marine sediments. Five dune phases or "eolianites" thus indicate five cold phases which, despite recent C[14] dating (Kulp, 1953), can still be correlated only tentatively with the succession on the mainland. Ruhe, Gomez, and Cady (1961) and Fairbridge and Teichert (1953) have shown that Sayles' interpretation may be incorrect.

In the actual glaciated areas, the weight of ice in the glacial phases and the relief of pressure during the interglacials set up *isostatic movements*. These movements, which led to a considerable migration of shore lines, were therefore also controlled by climate. They may best be studied in Scandinavia and North America, although they also affected such areas as Iceland.

2. Abyssal Sediments.—The importance of abyssal sediments is constantly increasing. Because of the very slow rate of sedimentation, *cores* a few meters long span a very long period of time which, in some cases, stretches

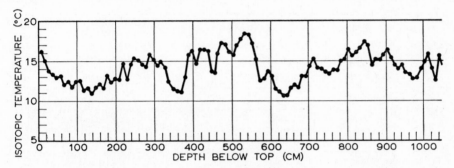

FIG. 113. TEMPERATURE CURVE OF THE SURFACE WATERS OF THE OCEAN DURING THE QUATERNARY

O^{18}/O^{16} data from the upper 10 m. of abyssal sediment in the Mid-Atlantic (core 280, depth 4256 m.). The time span of the section is not known (after Emiliani, 1958).

back to the Tertiary. Emiliani considers that in Pacific core 58 the whole of the Quaternary is represented by only 6·1 meters of sediment. We cannot of course be certain that sedimentation has continued without interruption throughout this period.

Research on cores from the Atlantic, Caribbean, and Pacific has yielded undoubted evidence of repeated alternations of normal (compared with the present) and colder phases (fig. 113). This fluctuation is indicated, among other things, by changes in the foram assemblage; thus Schott showed, in 1938, that the warmth-loving *Globorotalia menardii* only occurs at certain horizons which can be equated with interglacials or interstadials. (Similar research has been done by Bradley, Bramlette, Hamilton, Parker, Phleger, Ericson, Wiseman and others.)

Similarly, Emiliani found, by direct O^{18} temperature determinations, that the various beds formed under differing temperature conditions. The surface temperatures of the oceans fluctuated by some 6° C; as many as 7 cycles have been demonstrated in the Caribbean, and 15 in the Pacific.

During glacial phases, bottom temperatures in the eastern equatorial zone of the Atlantic were 2° C lower than they are now: in the Pacific, on the other hand, they were just about the same. It is therefore apparent that the

open connection between the Atlantic and Arctic Oceans, as opposed to the
narrow connection between the Pacific and Arctic, played some part in
determining the temperature. "Interglacial" bottom temperatures are the
same, in the Pacific, as "Glacials", but in the Atlantic, they are almost
4° C higher. Saks, Belov, and Lapina found that in Siberian Arctic waters,
the abyssal sediments could be subdivided as shown in Table 40.

TABLE 40

SUBDIVISION OF DEEP-SEA SEDIMENTS IN SIBERIAN
MARGINAL SEAS (AFTER SAKS, BELOV, AND LAPINA)

AGE IN YEARS	CLIMATE	EQUATION WITH CONTINENTAL SUBDIVISIONS
0–10,000	Recent	Recent
10,000–20,000	Cold	Sartian
20,000–30,000	"Warm"	Kargian
30,000–45,000	Cold	Zyrian II
45,000–50,000	Short warm phase	
Over 50,000	Cold	Zyrian I

The problem is to correlate the temperature curves derived in this way
with the stages of the Ice Age in neighboring continents. Up till now this has
only proved possible for about the last 10,000 years, since, for the remaining
part of the cores, there are neither key horizons, nor, except for the last
50,000 years, any reliable method of absolute dating. Emiliani has shown
that it is possible to extrapolate age determinations on the basis of rates of
sedimentation, but this method has as yet little firm foundation. The age of
about 270,000 years that he ascribes to the Günz Glaciation does not agree
at all with other estimates. Moreover, the curves afford little evidence of the
position of the Tertiary-Quaternary boundary as deduced from the forams,
because the amounts of temperature fluctuation, 6° C in the Quaternary,
3°–4° C in the Tertiary, are not unduly different.

Further reading: BROECKER, TUREKIAN & HEEZEN, 1958; HOPKINS, 1959 (Behring
Strait); WOODRING, 1957.

ABSOLUTE DATING

De Geer's studies of Swedish *varved clays* at the beginning of this century,
showed that the Weichsel (Vistula) Ice had reached its retreat stadial
position in Scania about 15,000 years ago. According to Sauramo, the ice
finally withdrew from the terminal moraine formed during this stadial at
Salpausselkä in Finland about 8,150 B.C. Similar investigations in North
America, by E. Antevs, resulted in less definite values, because there, the
succession of varved clays is not continuous.

The C[14] *method of dating,* invented by Libby (1946), corroborated De Geer's results, and enabled other key horizons to be dated. Unfortunately, this method can be used to date little more than the last 50,000 years; i.e. a period which does not quite extend back to the last interglacial. All attempts to date the remaining, much greater, part of the Quaternary have, as yet, yielded only uncertain or very dubious values. These attempts include Milankovitch's solar radiation curves, measurements on deep-sea cores using assumed rates of sedimentation (Emiliani, see above), rates of sedimentation in the Great Salt Lake (Eardley and Gvosdetsky), comparisons of depths of weathering (Penck, Kay, reviewed critically by Hunt and Sokoleff), and the Ionium-Radium content of abyssal sediments (see Rosholt, Emiliani, Geiss, Koczy, and Wangersky, 1961). We may look forward, however, to the discovery in the moderately near future of a completely reliable method of dating the Quaternary. Then all those now open questions regarding correlation of Pleistocene strata in different areas, particularly between the Northern and Southern Hemispheres, will be resolved.

THE LATE GLACIAL AND POSTGLACIAL PERIODS

Only some 15,000 years have elapsed since the Würm glaciers began to retreat. This late glacial and postglacial period is interesting because of the existence of a great number of continuous pollen profiles, and also of a method of absolute dating. It also includes historical times whose climatic variations, though they appear to have been very slight compared with the great events of the Ice Ages themselves, are most precisely known through direct meteorological observations.

Europe

In Europe, with the retreat of the Würm glaciers, the climate did not attain a general uniformity, but was subject to greater and smaller fluctuations. The following sequence of events has been worked out and dated, partly from varves, and partly by the C[14] method (figs. 114, 115); the closely related vegetational changes have been studied by Firbas, Godwin, Hyyppä, Nilsson, Overbeck, and others.

Firstly, there was a gradual retreat of the northern ice into Scandinavia, with the occurrence about 10,000–9,000 B.C. of the first Late Glacial climatic optimum, the *Allerød* phase. Manley's map (1949) shows that July temperatures in central Europe were 4° C cooler than now. This maximum was succeeded by a renewed climatic deterioration, the *Upper Dryas* phase (or Younger Tundra phase), about 9,000–8,000 B.C. At this time, temperatures in Germany dropped to some 7–8° C below the present level. Terminal moraines were formed by the Scandinavian Ice (at Salpausselkä in Finland, and in central Sweden, south of Stockholm), and also by the Alpine Ice (the Gschnitz and Daun Stadials). Thereafter, the ice retreated finally, and more rapidly into the mountains of Scandinavia; the pike perch *Lucioperca*

lucioperca was living near Upsala in 7,500 B.C. (Horner). The temperature rose till the annual mean was 2–3° C higher than today's and rainfall

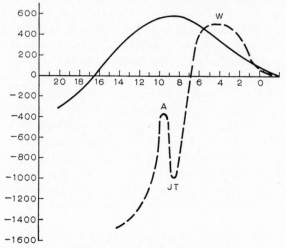

FIG. 114. CLIMATIC CURVE OF THE LATE GLACIAL AND
POSTGLACIAL PHASES IN EUROPE
Ordinate = displacement of the tree line in metres;
Abscissa = age in thousands of years; A = Allerød
Fluctuation; JT = Younger Dryas; W = Postglacial
Climatic Optimum; Solid line = Milankovitch's radiation
curve: it does not coincide with the climatic curve (after
Firbas, 1947).

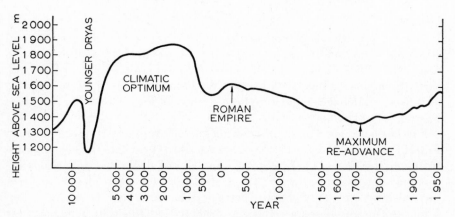

FIG. 115. SNOW LINE IN NORWAY DURING THE LAST 12,000 YEARS
(after O. Liestöl) (in O. Holtedahl, 1960).

increased. This was the postglacial *Climatic Optimum*, which occurred about 5,000–3,000 B.C. Hazel (*Corylus*, Andersson), the water chestnut (*Trapa natans*), and the marsh turtle (*Emys orbicularis*, Degerböl and Krog), etc., were all more widespread than they are now; the tree line was some 100 m. higher and treeless tundra almost disappeared from northern Eurasia (Neystadt; see Frenzel, 1960).

A lesser drop in temperature led to the present conditions. That the periods around 2,300, 1,200, and 600 B.C. were relatively dry is indicated by the presence of recurrence surfaces in peat deposits. In the last 2,000 years, the following dates stand out (after Brooks *et al.*; see also Schove).

A.D. 500–700	Unusually arid.
A.D. 800–1200	Rainfall heavier than now, mild winters, little ice, Vikings colonized Greenland.
16th–late 19th century	Little Ice Age including:
1st half of 17th century	Glaciers advanced.
1810–1820	Glaciers advanced.
1850–1860	Glaciers advanced.
1680–1740	"Interglacial" with dry, mild winters.

Since the end of the 19th century, there has been a retreat of glaciers, and milder winters. Brooks has pointed out that a close correlation exists in England between retreat and advance of the ice, and direction of the prevailing wind. When the glaciers advanced, the prevailing wind was easterly; when they retreated, the wind direction often changed, and westerlies prevailed. This is related to the fact that, when the glaciers advance, the Polar front is driven further south.

North America

In North America, the general ice retreat is also characterized by terminal moraines, which owe their origin either to brief standstills, or even to slight readvances. One such readvance in about 10,500 B.C. brought the ice margin southward once more to Port Huron, at the southern end of the lake of the same name. It was followed, a thousand years later, by a retreat to the position of the Straits of Mackinac joining Lake Huron to Lake Michigan. Peat formed at this time near Two Creeks, Wisconsin. Thereafter, during the more extensive Valders readvance, the ice thrust forward to the northern shores of Lake Erie, before retreating for the last time (8,700–8,600 B.C.).

There is obviously a strong correspondence between late Glacial events in Europe and North America (Table 41).

The postglacial Climatic Optimum, "Hypsithermal" of Deevey and Flint, can again be recognized, although not so distinctly as in Europe. Here, too, it shows up in pollen spectra with, in Maine, a maximum in oak vegetation accompanied by a minimum development of hemlock and birch (Deevey). The 8° C increase in temperature suggested by Moore from studies in caves in western U.S.A. seems to be considerably too high (Chapter 4).

TABLE 41
LATE GLACIAL PHASES OF EUROPE AND NORTH AMERICA

EUROPE	NORTH AMERICA	DATE
Younger Dryas phase	Valders	9000–8000 B.C.
Allerød fluctuation	Two Creeks	10,000–9000 B.C.
Older Dryas phase	Port Huron-Mankato	Before 10,000 B.C.

Arctic Regions

The Climatic Optimum is clearly revealed at many places in the Arctic, through the presence of shore-line deposits, e.g. in Spitzbergen and Greenland, carrying the edible mussel (*Mytilus edulis*) which is no longer indigenous to these latitudes.

In Iceland, postglacial climatic variations are not so prominent as in Europe, though they are still demonstrable (Einarsson, 1961). It can be

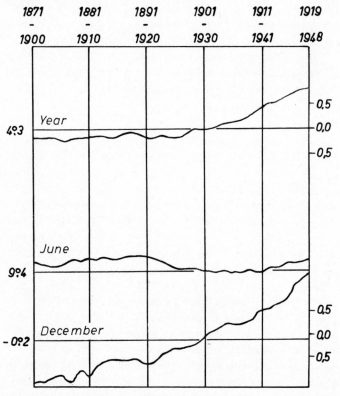

Fig. 116. Temperature Variation in Reykjavik, 1871–1948, showing an Increase in Annual Mean and Winter Temperatures (after J. Eythorsson, 1949).

shown that glacial advances occurred between 1750–1760 and 1840–1850, since 1890, the glaciers have become much reduced (Thorarinsson). These events correspond in part with those of Europe. The latest phase of glacial retreat is related to an increase in winter and annual mean temperatures, though the summer temperature has remained more or less constant (fig. 116, see also Lysgaard's diagrams).

Other Areas

Climatic fluctuation has also been observed in historic times from other continents. Variations in rainfall are particularly noticeable, and are best known in Africa, partly from records of Nile floods, and also in Asia (fig. 117). Fig. 118 shows an example of very recent retreat of a glacier in the Caucasus Mountains. Before the Climatic Optimum, both the Sahara and

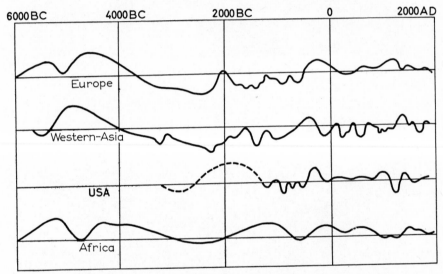

FIG. 117. RAINFALL VARIATION IN THE PAST 8,000 YEARS
The curves are partly hypothetical (after C. E. P. Brooks, 1949).

the Trans-Caucasus region had a climate somewhat similar to that of central Europe today, because of the greater extent of the northern ice sheets. About 8,000 years ago, however, as the ice retreated, the climate became too arid for agriculture, the early inhabitants of these areas were forced to migrate, and their great urban communities fell into ruin.

The Climatic Optimum is the most important of earlier events. Its effects are apparent in pollen spectra (fig. 119) from Hawaii, New Zealand (Cranwell and von Post), Tierra del Fuego (von Post and Auer), and recently from the Eastern Cordillera of Colombia (van der Hammen and Gonzalez). It cannot, of course, be dated directly in each locality, and, naturally, expresses itself

FIG. 118. RETREAT OF THE BOLSHOI-ASAU GLACIERS ON MOUNT ELBRUS (CAUCASUS MTS.)

Above—September, 1878; the glaciers traverse a pine forest. Below—from the same view-point in August, 1958; the glaciers have retreated more than 2 Km. up the valley. (From G. K. Tushinski, 1958.)

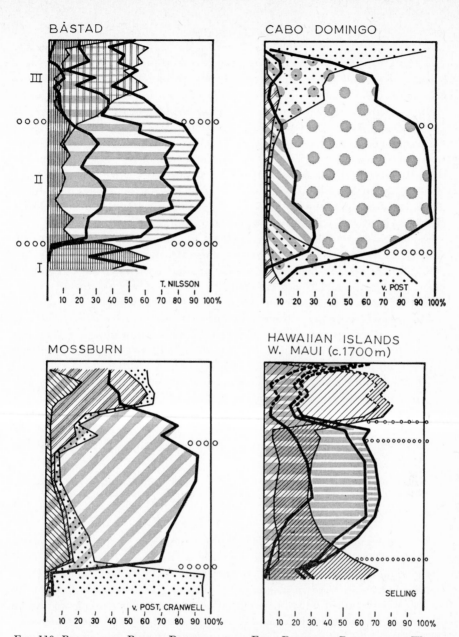

FIG. 119. POSTGLACIAL POLLEN DIAGRAMS FROM FOUR DIFFERENT PARTS OF THE WORLD

Båstad (Sweden), Cabo Domingo (Tierra del Fuego), Mossburn (New Zealand), Hawaii.
II = Postglacial Climatic Optimum; III = Recent. The thick lines represent, in diagram A,
mixed oak woodland, *Alnus* and *Betula*; in B, Caryophyllaceae and grasses; in C,
Dacrydium + *Phyllocladus* + *Podocarpus* (tropical mountain flora = rainforest in low-
lands); in D, predominant *Metrosideros* + *Myrsine* + *Cheirodendron* + *Coprosma* and
Pritchardia. The thin lines indicate in A, *Pinus* + *Picea* + *Fagus* + *Carpinus*; in B,
Nothofagus, and Cyperaceae; in C, *Metrosideros*, *Nothofagus*, and Cyperaceae + grasses; in
D, *Chenopodium* and *Dodonaea* + *Myoporium* + *Sophora* + *Acacia*. The Postglacial
Climatic Optimum was clearly characterized by vegetation requiring either a warm or
a humid climate (after Nilsson, v. Post, Cranwell, modified from Selling, 1948).

differently in different places. For example, in Hawaii, tropical rain forest became more widespread at this time (Selling); increased rainfall is also its most important feature in New Zealand. Auer has recognized climatic variations in Tierra del Fuego, preceding deposition of the first bed of volcanic ash, and therefore dating back more than 9,000 years. These variations can be equated with the Older and Younger Dryas periods and with the Allerød fluctuation. In the Behring Straits, the Climatic Optimum seems to have occurred somewhat earlier, about 8,000–6,000 B.C. (Hopkins, MacNeil, Leopold). The foram assemblage of abyssal sediments also shows a change corresponding to this warm phase, e.g. Ovey (mid-Atlantic), Hough (Antarctic); O^{18}/O^{16} values fluctuate too (Emiliani).

The *correlation* of late and postglacial events still leaves much to be desired; in very few cases is it yet sufficiently secure. But where precise equation has already been done as, for example, between the late glacial events of Europe and North America, the result is very significant. These climatic fluctuations lasting for the order of several thousand years, follow a similar course in both continents, and are not therefore due to local factors. Brooks's rainfall curves (fig. 117) are of lesser significance, for they are necessarily partly hypothetical. In part, their similarity has been presumed rather than proved.

Another definite world-wide phenomenon, to which there are very few exceptions, is the retreat of glaciers and pack ice in recent years. This is clearly related to a definite amelioration of winter temperatures.

R. W. Fairbridge (1960), more than any other, has demonstrated the relationship between postglacial climatic fluctuations and changes of sea level.

Further reading: AARIO, 1944; AHLMANN, 1953; DUBIEF, 1956; GROSS, 1958; MANLEY, 1949; REGEL, 1957; A. WAGNER, 1940.

SUMMARY

The Quaternary, or Ice Age, lasted about 1 million years, and is characterized everywhere by temperatures which were, at times, lower than today's; on average, by about 4° C. In temperate latitudes of the Northern Hemisphere, they were, in places, 8–12° C lower. This cooling is linked with the development of mighty continental glaciers, particularly in North America and northern Eurasia. At its maximum extent, the ice covered more than 17 million square miles, as compared with less than 6 million nowadays.

There were at least three major glaciations of similar extent (Mindel, Riss, and Würm) preceded by two or more cold phases (Donau and Günz). As the glaciers advanced, pluvials were experienced in the present desert areas.

Between Ice Ages, in the interglacials, the climate was either similar to, or slightly warmer than, it is today. It is, however, probable that there has been a small progressive drop in interglacial temperatures from the start of the Pleistocene to the present day. Since the Last Glaciation drew to a close some 10,000 years ago, slight climatic fluctuations have occurred especially during the Climatic Optimum, dating back to about 5,000–3,000 B.C., when temperatures in Europe were 2–3° C higher than they are now.

20

The Earth's
Climatic History

ALTERNATION OF COLD AND WARM PHASES

We have seen that cold and warm phases alternated repeatedly throughout the earth's history. This applies not only to particular small areas, but
to the whole world, not only to the short Quaternary Era, but to all the
parts of the stratigraphic column for which we possess fragmentary climatic
evidence, i.e. for the last 1,000 million years.

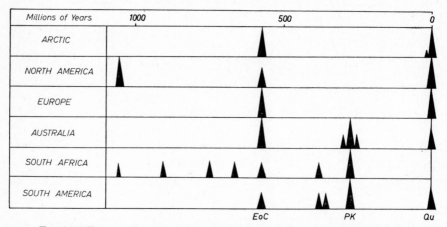

FIG. 120. TIME OF OCCURRENCE OF GLACIATIONS IN DIFFERENT CONTINENTS

Qu = Quaternary; PK = Permo-Carboniferous; Eo-C = Eo-Cambrian. The exact age, by
absolute dating, particularly of the Precambrian glaciations is still very uncertain.

Warm phases, when the poles were free from ice, have been much more
common than Ice Ages, i.e. the present familiar condition of the earth with
polar icecaps is unusual and indicates that we are living in an Ice Age. It
remains to be discovered whether we are in an interglacial or really, as we
usually assume, in a postglacial period.

At least *three* epochs may be regarded as really major Ice Ages (fig. 120);
the Eo-Cambrian about 600 million years ago, the latter part of the
Carboniferous and early Permian, dating back some 275 million years, and
the Pleistocene, which began only about 1 million years ago. The span of

time between major glaciations has therefore amounted to about 300 million years in each case. Lungershausen (1956) assumed a rhythm of 190–200 million years, using a somewhat different time scale and inserting an alleged "Ordovician" glaciation. He made the interesting suggestion that there existed a relationship between glaciations and the galactic year (or period of rotation of the Milky Way) which is about the same order of length.

Over 17 million square miles of the earth's surface were ice-covered during the period of maximum extent of the Pleistocene ice; probably considerably more than 4 million square miles were covered in the Permo-Carboniferous; but we can make no estimate of the extent of the Eo-Cambrian ice. Except for the Pleistocene, the duration of each Ice Age is as yet unknown, but it may be suggested, at least in the case of the Permo-Carboniferous Glaciation, that its duration was much longer than the Quaternary. This applies even more when early and late glacial phases are considered.

So long as we remain in ignorance of the length of the cold phases, it will not, unfortunately, be possible to use climatic events as fairly precise time planes. Only for the relatively well-known Quaternary does this possibility exist; in fact, climatic correlation forms the basis of almost the whole of Quaternary stratigraphy.

We must exclude the actual Precambrian almost completely from our general observations, as our knowledge of that era is still very fragmentary. However, the presence of Huronian tillites, probably 1,000 million years old, obviously denotes the existence of a continental glaciation as long ago as this.

In so far as we can tell, there were no major glaciations during the periods between the three Ice Ages mentioned above, though there are enough indications of limited regional glaciations and generally colder phases. For example, the main Permo-Carboniferous glaciation of Australia was obviously preceded by at least one smaller glaciation in the Carboniferous, and followed in the Permian by another. In the Lower Paleozoic of the Southern Hemisphere, there are several tillites, e.g. in South America and South Africa.

In contrast to this, no definite tillites have been recorded from the Mesozoic, and in the Tertiary, there are only small Pliocene occurrences in the Arctic. Other sediments, however, tend to indicate that cooler climatic conditions prevailed during the Lias, at the very end of the Cretaceous, and within the Tertiary.

As yet it appears that these lesser cold phases followed no regular time cycle. Taking the Siluro-Devonian and Permo-Carboniferous junctions, the Lias, the late Cretaceous, and the Pleistocene as cold phases, the intervening time spans work out at about 130, 95, 120, and 60 million years respectively, while the span back from the late Silurian to the Eo-Cambrian is probably some 200 million years. Absolute age determinations are as yet very uncertain, and there is still much to be learned about the earth's climatic changes.

OTHER CLIMATIC DEVELOPMENTS AND
PALEOGEOGRAPHY

Evaporites provide us with a clear indication of aridity, the degree
varying from extreme in the Permian and Trias, to slight in the Upper

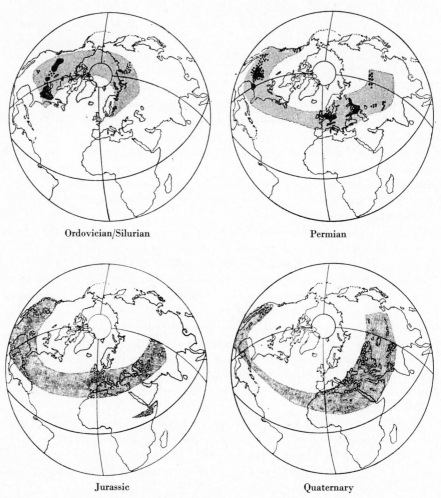

Ordovician/Silurian   Permian

Jurassic   Quaternary

FIG. 121. MIGRATION OF THE EVAPORITE BELT IN THE NORTHERN HEMISPHERE SINCE THE
ORDOVICIAN (after Lotze, 1957).

Carboniferous, Lias and Lower Cretaceous. It is also very noteworthy that
the position of the "evaporite belt" has gradually shifted through time
(Lotze). The northern evaporite belt, at least, has migrated from the polar
region to its present position in the desert belt (fig. 121). The reef facies
(fig. 122, 123) has moved in like manner.

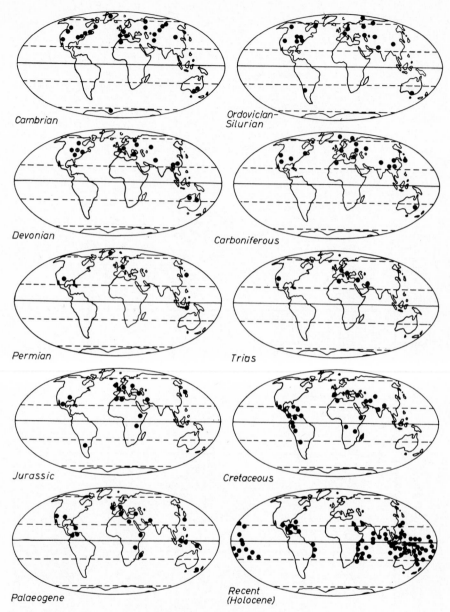

Cambrian

Ordovician-
Silurian

Devonian

Carboniferous

Permian

Trias

Jurassic

Cretaceous

Palaeogene

Recent
(Holocene)

FIG. 122. MIGRATION OF THE REEF BELT SINCE CAMBRIAN TIMES (after Schwarzbach, 1949).

The climatic development of central Europe is shown in Table 42, while Table 43 indicates the overall development in each continent.

World paleogeography has also changed with time and it seems reasonable to postulate a causal relationship with climatic variations. How far the two

TABLE 42
CLIMATIC HISTORY OF CENTRAL EUROPE

PERIOD	TEMPERATURE	RAINFALL
Holocene	3000–5000 B.C. slightly warmer than present	Not very different
Pleistocene	Repeated alternation of glacials and interglacials	Not very different
Tertiary	Very warm (subtropical) at first, becoming cooler	Arid in places at times
Cretaceous	Warm	Humid, especially Lower Cretaceous
Jurassic	U. Jurassic very warm L. Jurassic cooler	Lower Jurassic humid
Trias	Hot	Dominantly arid, locally very arid, U. Keuper more humid
Permian	Hot	Humid in places at first, then arid and very arid
Carboniferous	Hot	Humid
Devonian	Hot, at least in Middle Devonian	
Silurian	Hot	
Ordovician		
Cambrian	Hot	

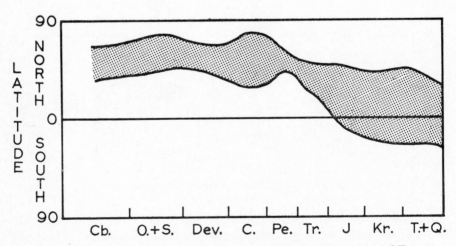

FIG. 123. DISPLACEMENT OF THE REEF BELT ALONG THE MERIDIAN 40° E

Systems shown along horizontal axis, latitude vertically (after Schwarzbach, 1949).

TABLE 43   CLIMATIC HISTORY OF THE CONTINENTS

	ARCTIC	NORTH AMERICA	EUROPE	ASIA	AUSTRALIA	AFRICA	SOUTH AMERICA	ANTARCTICA
Quaternary	Glaciations	Extensive glaciations	Extensive glaciations	Extensive glaciation in places	Glaciations in South	Pluvials	Glaciation especially in South	Glaciation
Tertiary and Mesozoic	Temperate to warm	Warm, arid in places	Warm, arid in places	Warm, arid in places	Warm	Warm, partly arid	Warm, partly arid	Warm at times
Younger Paleozoic	Warm	Warm, partly wet, partly arid	Warm, partly wet, partly arid	Partly wet, glaciations in India	Glaciations	Glaciations in South	Glaciations	?
Older Paleozoic	Warm	Warm	Warm	Partly warm	Partly warm	Cool at times at least in S.	Partly cool	?
Eo-Cambrian	Glaciations	Glaciations in East	Glaciations in North	Glaciations in East	Glaciations	Glaciations in South	Glaciations?	?

are in fact bound up one with the other will be discussed in the last chapters.
Here, only some of the major factors can be dealt with.

Since the Cambrian, the great periods of *mountain building* or orogenesis
have been concentrated, in Europe at least, in the late Silurian-Early
Devonian (Caledonian folding), in the latter part of the Carboniferous

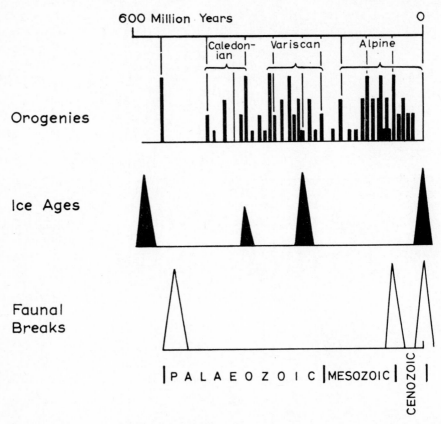

FIG. 124. TIME RELATIONSHIP BETWEEN OROGENESIS, GLACIATION AND ORGANIC EVOLUTION
(orogeneses after Brinkmann, 1959).

Recent age determinations suggest that the duration of the Mesozoic and Paleozoic was
somewhat greater than indicated.

(Variscan folding), and in the Cretaceous-Tertiary (Alpine folding) (fig. 124).
In North America, there were the corresponding Acadian, Appalachian, and
Laramide Revolutions. These movements led each time to the folding and
uplift of long mountain chains which were then gradually worn down by
erosion. As well as these orogenies, there were a great many more periods of
movement which had a quite different regional effect. The Cambrian and
Trias stand out as periods when major tectonic movements were absent
throughout the world.

Transgression and *regression* are sometimes closely related to orogenies and vary very greatly from place to place. There were many periods when low cratonic blocks were widespread, e.g. Trias, and many transgressions of world-wide significance, e.g. Middle Cretaceous.

Vulcanicity is also closely related to orogenesis; its intensity certainly varies very considerably with time.

Many workers have stressed the rhythmic development of these processes and the consequent cyclical nature of the earth's history (v. Bubnoff, Umbgrove). That they are to some extent closely linked is certain, and we will consider the matter further in a later chapter.

21

Climate and
Organic Evolution

Je dus constater que la chaleur agit sur les ailes d'une
mouche tout autrement que sur le cerveau d'un
archiviste paléographé.
ANATOLE FRANCE, Le Crime de Sylvestre Bonnard.

Not only the climate has changed in the course of time, not only the
position of land and sea, but also animals and plants. We must therefore
discuss whether the sort of causal relationship between climate and organic
evolution, which Matthew tried to establish, does in fact exist.

We shall not consider here those displacements of zoogeographic and
phytogeographic zones which are largely dependent on climate and which,
in fact, serve as an important source of paleoclimatic information. Neither
shall we go into the question of the far-reaching effects of climate on the
history of Man, though migration of races, wars, changes in economic
structure, etc., might all be mentioned (see Le Danois).

We may first consider whether there appears to have been a connection
between *extinction of species* and *climatic deterioration*, but of course, the
great climatic changes proceeded so slowly that even the slowest moving
organisms could have migrated to areas of more favorable climate. It does
not, therefore, appear likely that the destruction of the great saurians at the
end of the Cretaceous Period, to take just one example, was due to such
changes (Audova). Nevertheless, the impoverishment of the Quaternary
flora of Europe compared with that of the Tertiary, shows that in this area,
the Ice Age succeeded in killing off a great many species. It is a mere
accident that some have not been completely exterminated, but still survive
locally (e.g. *Sequoia*) in other continents as "living fossils". It is also
conceivable that decrease in temperature led to *selective destruction* of some
species and so steered organic evolution in a certain direction. This, Matthew
has assumed; accordingly, he considers that new faunas originate in the
polar regions, particularly in the Arctic because of its favorable land bridges.
He also maintains that increased aridity is an important factor in the
evolution of the vertebrates. Discoveries made so far have not been sufficient
to prove his assumption conclusively. Too great an *increase in temperature*

may also be noted as a decisive factor with regard to vertebrate evolution. Indeed, none of the higher animals can tolerate excessive heat, and it is possible that in lower latitudes these optimum temperature conditions were, at times, exceeded.

B. Rensch attributes the gradual increase in *size* of the mammals, as shown by classic work on fossil horses and elephants, to the gradual decrease in temperature throughout the Tertiary, and he points to "Bergmann's Rule" that mammals living in cold climates are generally bigger than those which inhabit warmer areas (see Chapter 4). The development of other animals began quite differently, however; small forms appeared first. Change in size must therefore be considered to owe less to climatic than to general evolutionary causes.

Seasonal or daily climatic rhythms have their greatest effect on plants, e.g. short and long-day plants. In this connection, we should remember that days and years may once have been shorter than they are now.

J. Wilser (1931) considered in detail whether secular variation in electromagnetic radiation (light) influences evolutionary trends (paleophotobiology). He considers that the intensity of light reaching the earth in the Upper Trias, Upper Jurassic and Upper Cretaceous epochs was critical, and that light-sensitive organisms such as the Echinoids, Cephalopods, Teleosts, and Reptiles therefore evolved unusually quickly. Modern genetic studies do indeed suggest that this is possible. Many workers, latterly Schindewolf and Krasovski and Shklovski, have also considered the effect of cosmic radiation, originating from, say, a supernova. Such radiation certainly need not have produced simultaneous climatic effects and so does not fall within the province of paleoclimatology. Nevertheless, it is easily possible that variation in solar radiation, at least, would influence the earth's climatic history and that a certain parallelism between climate and evolution would be apparent.

Further reading: A. S. ROMER, 1961; YAKOVLEFF, 1922.

TIME RELATIONS

We can also try to establish, by inductive reasoning, purely empirical time relations between climatic changes and evolution (fig. 124), starting preferably with the climatologically outstanding periods of the Ice Ages. It certainly is not easy to establish objectively really major floral or faunal breaks from among the plexus of evolutionary changes in plants and animals. Opinions depend very largely on the very fragmentary fossil evidence available, and on the particular lines of research of different workers.

Nevertheless, it is evident that the Eo-Cambrian glaciation immediately preceded the greatest faunal break known to paleontologists; namely, the sudden appearance of rich Cambrian faunas. The Permo-Carboniferous glaciation is not known to have produced any consequent change in the organic world. The Paleozoic-Mesozoic boundary occurs much later; more-over, despite lively argument this junction is not characterized by any particular faunal break. The Pleistocene Ice Age is very closely related to the origin and development of man.

There are, therefore, *two significant coincidences between glaciation and evolution:* in the Cambrian and the Quaternary. The Permo-Carboniferous Glaciation shows *no* clear relation to evolution. If we consider faunal breaks and not climatic events, we can detect a very important one at the Cretaceous-Tertiary boundary, with the extinction of the saurians and ammonites and the beginning of the ascendancy of the mammals; *no climatic change* occurs at this horizon. More detailed and apparently definite curves, such as those put forward by Lull (1948) contain too many elements of doubt to be of any real value. A great deal remains to be done before we can establish any conclusive link between paleoclimates and major evolutionary developments.

Part 3

GENETIC PALEOCLIMATOLOGY

Climatic Hypotheses

22

Introduction

Sei ruhig—es war nur gedacht.
Thales, in GOETHE's Faust, II, 1830.

Ever since it has been known that climate has varied during the earth's history, the causes of that variation have been sought. Long ago, Hooke, Herder, and Buffon investigated this question thoroughly; Hooke considered the effects of polar wandering; Buffon thought that the gradual cooling of the earth was important. The real heyday of climatic hypotheses began, however, with the discovery of the Ice Age; more than 50 "theories of the Ice Age" were proposed to explain this unusually marked climatic change, but all of them are very insecurely founded. Nothing illustrates this better than the fantastic situation where occasionally the same cause has been used to explain opposite effects. Thus, Croll and Pilgrim think that cold winters favor the development of glaciers, while Köppen suggests that it is best if the winters are mild. Outbreaks of vulcanicity are regarded by Frech as the cause of warm phases, by Huntington as the cause of glacial phases. The onset of glaciation is considered to be due both to decreased solar radiation (Dubois *et al.*), and to increased radiation (Simpson); and while ice ages are almost always interpreted as being consequent upon mountain building, Phillippi and Schirmeisen have argued the reverse, and explain the upfolding of mountains as the effects of ice ages. The blocking-off of the Gulf Stream was given by Wundt, for example, as the reason for the Ice Age; Behrmann and others, however, are of the opinion that it was the humidity brought by the Gulf Stream that made ice ages possible. In fact, there are even investigators who deny the existence of ice ages at all, and regard all the relevant climatic evidence as misleading (Sandberg).

CLASSIFICATION

Many workers have attributed major climatic changes to events occurring on the earth itself, or to variations in its orbit; others relate them to extra-terrestrial happenings in the sun, or even in the universe. The first group consider that the incidence of radiation at the top of the atmosphere has always remained constant, regardless of cold and warm phases, and that secular variations in the inflow and distribution of heat in different parts of the earth were produced by terrestrial conditions. The second group, on the other hand, suppose that incident radiation may previously have varied, with the result that, over a long period of time, warmer and colder phases were produced; terrestrial factors had, at most, only a modifying effect. Many hypotheses also use a combination of both possibilities. The large number of causes which have been considered may be classified in the following manner:

Terrestrial Causes

1. Continents—extent, distribution, and topography; relief hypotheses *sensu stricto*.
2. Oceans
   (*a*) Distribution of oceans, ocean currents.
   (*b*) Salt content of ocean.
3. Interior of the earth and vulcanicity—cooling of the earth, volcanic and radioactive heat, volcanic ash.
4. Atmosphere
   (*a*) Cloudiness.
   (*b*) Carbon dioxide content.
5. Polar wandering and continental drift.

Variations of the Earth's Orbit (Planetary Hypotheses)

1. Periodic variation (radiation curves).
2. Aperiodic variation.

Extra-terrestrial causes

1. Absorption of solar radiation outside the earth's atmosphere.
2. Primary variations of solar radiation.

23

Relief Hypotheses

MIOTHERM AND PLIOTHERM PHASES

Charles Lyell, founder of the Principle of Uniformitarianism, was first to recognize the fundamental importance of *paleogeographic changes* in determining climatic history. In fact, historical geology shows that the distribution of land and sea, the position and height of mountains, and similar paleogeographic factors have all varied continuously, while meteorology and climatology have demonstrated the close causal relationship between the configuration of the earth's surface and the present climate (Chapter 2). The varying geography of the earth—relief in its wider sense— is, therefore, also doubtless of great paleoclimatic significance. Hypotheses which regard these relationships as being of prime importance, or even as the only major cause of climatic changes through time, may be designated *relief hypotheses*. Fundamental papers on this topic have been published by W. Ramsay (1910, 1924), and later by C. E. P. Brooks, and F. Kerner-Marilaun. Attempts have even been made to estimate quantitatively the effects of different paleogeographic factors, and hence to determine mathematically the character of past climates. We have already seen, however (Chapter 10), that these attempts, interesting though the method may be, have yielded no reliable results.

The starting point for relief hypotheses is the degree of parallelism between glaciation and mountain building. Ramsay has pointed out that extensive areas have been greatly uplifted by crustal movements to produce climatic conditions favorable to the formation of glaciers. Thus strong relief gives rise to less warm or miotherm epochs, while low relief creates warmer (pliotherm) periods.

EFFECTS OF UPLIFT OF LAND AREAS AND MOUNTAINS

Uplift of land affects climate in several different ways. Of these, the most obvious is the decrease in temperature with height. This is due to the fact that rising air expands and therefore cools. The associated condensation of water vapor is important, for clouds reflect solar radiation and thereby produce a considerable drop in temperature (except in high latitudes in winter). Once they have formed, surfaces of snow and ice on mountains cause further cooling. To these may be added indirect effects. Shallow shelf seas were dried up, with consequent increase in continentality, and at the same time ocean currents were restricted. Volcanic activity broke out during orogenic phases and the volcanic ash promoted cooling by cutting off part of the solar radiation. Many factors, therefore, worked together, and finally gave rise to polar icecaps and mountain glaciers, which then brought about further "self-induced" cooling.

The climatic effects of high mountains are not confined to decrease of temperature resulting in glacier formation; mountains also function as rain traps. Fossil examples of this are afforded by the Tarim Basin, whose gradually increasing aridity in the Tertiary Period was related, according to Norin, to the uplift of the Kuen-Lun, and by western North America, where the upfolding of the Rockies resulted in drier climates (Chapter 18). Puri records that a rich Lauracean flora still flourished in the Kashmir valley in Pleistocene times; it is now absent because late uplift of the Pir Panjat range cut off the southwest monsoon from the area.

Atmospheric circulation was completely upset by the formation of such mighty north-south mountain ranges as the Cordilleras (F. Albrecht), the massive rock barrier which cuts off the west wind and divides the earth into an oceanic half, the Indian and Pacific Oceans and their border lands, and a land half, the greater part of the continents and the Atlantic. The great continental masses derive their rainfall almost entirely from the Atlantic, and the cold winters of Canada and eastern Siberia are due to the lack of latent heat of condensation in the air, because of the absence of winter rainfall. Albrecht suggests that without the Cordilleras, North America, Europe, and Siberia would all have considerably more winter rainfall, and appreciably higher temperatures. He supposes that this state of affairs existed until the Younger Tertiary, when, for the first time, the degree of winter cold became so great that the Ice Age could originate.

The uplift of the Cordilleras did not, of course, take place as one single event, nor did it occur everywhere at the same time, so it is probably at most only one factor among the many which led to glaciation.

SELF-INDUCED COOLING

We have just mentioned that once snow and ice surfaces have formed, they themselves contribute to the temperature decrease, so that an ever-increasing reciprocal reaction may be set up. This process of *self-induced cooling* generally plays a part in discussions on the origin of the Ice Ages. By a sort of chain reaction, a small initial cooling can lead finally to a significant secondary lowering of temperature. Ice produces cooling in the surrounding area because it reflects the greater part of the sun's rays, i.e. its albedo is very high (Table 44; W. Wundt in particular has paid attention to the albedo effect). So the ice cap gradually grows from year to year, though only to a certain limit. C. E. P. Brooks attempted to work this out mathematically, and found that if the winter temperature at a sea-covered pole

TABLE 44

ALBEDO OF CERTAIN BODIES. (ALBEDO=RATIO OF REFLECTED TO INCIDENT LIGHT)

Absolutely white body	1
Cloud	0·36–0·78
Snow	0·52
Etna lava.	0·05
Forest, Ocean	0·04

was just above the freezing point of sea water (—2° C), and if there then occurred an initial drop in temperature of $\frac{1}{3}$° C, the final result, without assistance from any further cause, would be an icecap of 25° latitude (1,500 miles) radius and a final temperature at the pole of —27° C (fig. 125). Thus the differences in temperature between glacial and interglacial phases are not dependent entirely on a great initial cooling.

ICE-FREE POLES

At the present time, "glacial" conditions prevail at the poles, but we can readily envisage their gradual replacement by the "nonglacial" or "acryogenic" (Kerner-Marilaun) conditions represented in the upper curve of fig. 125. As Brooks showed, the process is closely bound up with the denudation of high mountain ranges, a development which the earth is undergoing at present. First of all, the mountain glaciers will vanish as the mountains are gradually worn down below the snow line. The Behring Strait will widen as a result of eustatic rise of sea level, an increasing volume of warm water will flow into the Arctic, and a "bridgehead" of continuously ice-free water may be established. At the same time the gap between Labrador and Newfoundland will become broader and into it will flow an increasing part of the cold Labrador Current; hence the remainder will be correspondingly less effective in cooling the Gulf Stream. So the Arctic Ice will dwindle, until finally—probably under the influence of unusually intense solar

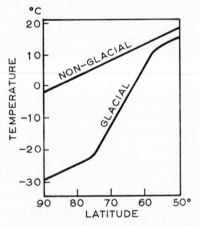

FIG. 125. TEMPERATURE DIFFERENCES BETWEEN NON-GLACIAL AND GLACIAL CLIMATES

When the annual temperature at the pole falls a little below the freezing point, a temperature drop of about 25° C takes place with the automatic formation of an icecap (after C. E. P. Brooks).

radiation—it will disappear completely in summer. Then the polar front will also vanish in summer, the Azores High will shift further north, and in mid-latitudes the summer months will be almost rainless. The Arctic

Ice will re-form later and later each year until at last the pole remains ice-free, even during the winter. The Greenland glacier ice will also gradually disappear, and the warm and arid climate of ice-free epochs will prevail.

This process does not proceed so readily as does the growth of ice sheets, for, in order to make such a previously-formed icecap disappear completely in summer, it is not enough that the summer temperature at the pole should once again correspond for a short time to that of the nonglacial maritime climate; it must be considerably higher. Under certain circumstances, therefore, a polar icecap may persist long after climatic conditions have become more favorable. It then represents a *glacial relic* that would not form anew under the prevailing temperature conditions. Besides, it is possible for the surface of a continental ice sheet, some thousands of meters thick, to lie above the snow line, so that conditions favoring glacial formation prevail, while the rock base remains far below the snow line. This state of affairs exists, for example, in central Greenland at the present time, and in this connection Cailleux has spoken of "autocatalyse d'altitude".

The ice-free polar sea can also be regarded, quite differently, as the initiator of a new glaciation (see Ewing and Donn's hypothesis).

H. Flohn and others have reflected on what present meteorological conditions would be if the pole were ice-free. He considers that the temperatures would be: equator 27° C (as at present), North Pole, winter 1° C, summer 8° C, mean temperature of earth 19° C (against 15° C now). He based his observations, of course, on Tertiary conditions, which have already been assessed as being above average. Under such conditions, the circulation would vary as follows: the subtropical high would shift poleward in winter, the average wind speed would decrease considerably in winter, and so would the number and intensity of depressions. The winter circulation would correspond with that of May or September at present. Brooks had already assumed that the present summer wind directions in the Pacific demonstrate the general conditions which would prevail during a warm phase (he gave clear pictures of these, and Lasareff also illustrates them experimentally).

OCEAN CURRENTS

Relief changes sometimes cause deflection or modification of climate-controlling ocean currents. If, say, the Gulf Stream were denied access to the Arctic Ocean, probably by uplift of the Faroes-Iceland ridge, this would have a considerable effect on climate, although it is difficult to imagine exactly what effect. In the opinion of many investigators (Wundt *et al.*) a glacial phase could be initiated thereby, yet Behrmann asserts "not in spite of, but because of the Gulf Stream, did the continental ice extend as it did over northern Europe during the Ice Age."

It may be assumed (with Brooks) from meteorological considerations that if the poles were ice-free, warm currents would flow poleward more strongly than at present, since, as we have already seen in the previous section, the winter winds would also blow from lower latitudes much further toward the poles.

It is therefore certain that the mild polar climate of the Early Tertiary, etc., was largely dependent on warm currents. Other views may, however, be advocated in regard to ocean currents, as we shall see in dealing with Chamberlin's hypothesis.

Frequent examples of the far-reaching effects of warm and cold ocean currents have been cited from the stratigraphic column, e.g. the warm "Indian Current" which still flowed into the present Mediterranean area in Early Tertiary times.

The present considerable intensity of the Gulf Stream is geographically controlled (the coast line of South America projecting to Cape Roque directs part of the South Equatorial Current into the Northern Hemisphere). This may not always have been so, but no more precise statement can be made. In the same way, the former strait between North and South America, in place of the present Isthmus of Panama, must have had an influence on ocean currents.

EWING AND DONN'S HYPOTHESIS

The configuration of the *Arctic Basin* is one of the special characteristics of terrestrial relief. While Antarctica consists of an extensive continent, there exists at the North Pole a deep sea, ringed about by continents, and having only restricted shallow connections with other oceans. Ewing and Donn attempt to explain the variation between glacial and interglacial phases on the basis of this geographical framework. It is their idea that an *ice-free* Arctic Ocean (fig. 126, 1) may have been the cause of increased precipitation, heavier snow, and consequently of the formation and growth of glaciers (fig. 126, 2). An open Arctic Ocean, then, was not characteristic of interglacial phases—as all other investigators assume—but resulted in the initiation of a glacial phase. The ocean remained ice-free while the great continental ice sheets formed and only then did it become covered with ice (fig. 126, 3), largely because the Faroes-Iceland ridge shallowed, as a result of the eustatic drop of sea level, and cut off the Gulf Stream. With the icing-over of the Arctic Ocean, the glacial phase came to an end, because the glaciers, no longer receiving enough rainfall, slowly disappeared. The polar ice sheet also melted gradually (fig. 126, 4) except over Greenland, and the cycle could begin anew.

Thus the driving force behind the alternation of glacial and interglacial phases is essentially the Arctic Ocean which, when ice-free, produces by evaporation, the water required to feed the glaciers and, when ice-covered, allows the glaciers to dwindle. Another absolute prerequisite, however, is the present geographical environment of the North Pole.

c.p.—16

FIG. 126. DIAGRAMMATIC OUTLINE OF THE GLACIAL THEORY OF EWING AND DONN

The north polar region is shown. 1 = beginning of glacial phase (Arctic Ocean ice-free); 2 = glacial phase (Arctic Ocean ice-free); 3 = maximum extent of glaciation—beginning of interglacial phase (Arctic Ocean covered with ice); 4 = interglacial phase (present condition; Arctic Ocean ice-covered). Black = Continental Ice; shaded = Floating Ice; arrow = Gulf Stream. The Davis Iceland-Faroes Ridge is also marked. (From Schwarzbach, 1960.)

The following objections, in particular, may be raised to this hypothesis (Livingstone, 1959; Schwarzbach, 1960):

(a) The mechanism would probably function too quickly, i.e. the Arctic Ocean might well become covered with ice much more rapidly than Ewing and Donn assume, long before the continental ice sheets attained their maximum development (Stokes, 1955, also suggested this in another connection).

(b) It is not obvious why the Greenland Ice persisted throughout the interglacials.

(c) It is not easy to see why Siberia was not glaciated to the same extent as Canada if, in fact, the open Arctic Ocean was the source of precipitation.

(d) The Faroes-Iceland ridge would indeed be covered to a lesser extent during glacial phases but the difference would not be great.

(e) Ewing and Donn also explain why the mechanism first started to function at the start of the Quaternary Period; the North Pole was previously situated elsewhere, and the exceptionally favorable conditions were only achieved at the start of the Quaternary. Yet there is no indication of marked polar wandering in the Cenozoic. This hypothesis does not explain the pre-Quaternary glaciations any better.

While the hypothesis leaves several questions to be answered it is valuable in that it draws attention to the very special geographical situation of the Arctic region at the present time, with its oceanographic and meteorological consequences.

EXPLANATION OF THE GONDWANA GLACIATIONS

It is readily apparent that small climatic changes can originate from paleogeographic effects. Attempts have also been made, however, to elucidate such puzzling phenomena as the Gondwana glaciations of the Upper Paleozoic entirely on a paleogeographic basis. The best reasoned reconstruction of this type is that given by Brooks (see fig. 92).

In view of the present proximity of the glaciated areas to the equator, one cannot help accepting that at that time, Gondwanaland must have been uncommonly high (provided there has been no polar wandering). Brooks assumes an altitude of 3,000–5,000 m., i.e. the present height of Tibet. This cannot be proved directly, but then it is always difficult to prove the existence of such former highland areas, and in any case, it is just as difficult to disprove it. Brooks cites widespread and vigorous volcanic activity in the Upper Carboniferous as one of the causes of glaciation. The fine volcanic dust must have reflected a considerable part of the sun's rays and thus produced a marked cooling.

Brooks regards Nearctis, North Atlantis, and Angaraland as the Permo-Carboniferous continents of the Northern Hemisphere. Nearctis (North America) was joined to North Atlantis (Europe and East Greenland) by a land bridge. Between the two lay an Arctic Gulf bounded to the south by this land bridge. Angaraland (Northeast Asia) was separated from North Atlantis by the broad Volga Sea. To the south lay the mighty Gondwana continent of South America, South Africa, India, and Australia. It was separated from the northern continental blocks by a mediterranean Tethys which encircled the globe. Brooks considers that the warm waters of both

North and South Equatorial Currents flowed from the Pacific into Tethys and the Volga Sea, to bring the warmth which gave rise to the coal forests and the fusulinid limestones of Spitzbergen.

On the other hand, the sea south of Gondwanaland was cut off from a supply of warm equatorial water. Consequently, the middle latitudes of the Northern Hemisphere were warmer than usual, and those of the Southern Hemisphere relatively cool. Brooks asserts that the resulting pressure distribution resulted in southerly winds, which, when forced to ascend over the Gondwana continent, gave rise to cloud and precipitation. Together these caused cooling and the development of ice fields which, once formed, constantly enlarged themselves because of self-induced cooling. The most favorable conditions for widespread glaciation undoubtedly occurred on the southern margin of Gondwanaland. Only where the topography was unusually high could glaciers have flowed, as they did at times in India, into Tethys. Brooks assumes that there was a small icecap in the Arctic, whence were derived the icebergs that deposited the Squantum Tillite near Boston. If, as all previous geological observations suggest, Antarctica remained ice-free, this may be attributed to a rainfall too low to support glaciers. These, then, are Brooks's ideas.

Arguments Against Relief Hypotheses

We will discuss only a few of the arguments against purely paleogeographic explanations of climatic variation.

Let us begin right away with the interpretation of the *Gondwana glaciations* which have just been outlined. That ice could occur in equatorial regions, or at least subtropical regions, while warm climates prevailed in high latitudes is, for a start, so paradoxical that one is compelled to think that the assumption of paleogeographic causes appears unlikely and the argument is forced. It may be difficult to dispute particular points in the argument, but it is very doubtful if we have correctly estimated the extent of the climatic factors or have taken all factors into account. For example, Huntington and Visher gave quite a different interpretation in 1922; see also J. Wolbach. The geologist must also point out that the paleogeographic assumptions are extremely uncertain; many geologists (e.g. Teichert) reconstruct Gondwanaland quite differently; this would vitiate an essential part of the reasoning. Furthermore, it seems probable, because of the marine intercalations, that the glaciated area was at a relatively low rather than a high level, and one can hardly find any abnormal volcanic activity outside Australia. Lastly, the paleogeographic conditions cannot have been sufficiently different immediately before and after the Ice Age for one to understand why the glaciers were exceptionally extensive at this time.

The oft-invoked succession of *mountain building and Ice Ages* is, in detail, not always so exact as Ramsay and others have shown in their schematic diagrams; especially if one equates mountain building with orogenic phases.

In the great mountain chains, the different parts are often of somewhat different age, and successive fold movements gave rise to a great many periods of mountain building which are distributed throughout great parts of the stratigraphic column, and are not associated with Ice Ages (fig. 124). Of course, folding need not always be related to uplift, but usually it is.

There is also a wide *spatial* discrepancy, for most of the Permo-Carboniferous mountain building occurred in the Northern Hemisphere while the glaciation was confined to the Gondwana continent. Hence, it appears that the formation of individual mountain ranges is not an essential factor in development of an Ice Age, although mountains may occasionally form the site of extensive icecaps (e.g. Cordilleras or Alps in the Quaternary). On the other hand, as Bederke rightly stressed, world-wide epeirogenic movements are of major importance, though we can only perceive this clearly in the Cenozoic. They are associated with orogenic cycles, and result everywhere in uplift of the continental blocks (and corresponding deepening of the ocean basins). The gradual climatic changes of the Tertiary Period clearly coincided with such movements.

The mild climate of the polar regions and "polar floras" have frequently been attributed to warm ocean currents. These are certainly an important climatic factor, but are unlikely to be the only one. Ocean currents cannot raise or lower the overall heat balance of the earth; they can only affect the distribution of heat. We can readily envisage that they are the cause of the present warming of the Arctic and will, in the foreseeable future, produce melting of the polar icecap. It is hardly conceivable, however, that conditions suitable for the growth of *Taxodium*, poplars, and spruce will then exist at the North Pole—as they did in Grinnell Land during the Tertiary Period—simply because of the action of ocean currents. Other factors are also involved here.

In this connection, G. S. Simpson has pointed out that, in spite of the obvious very great difference in distribution of land and sea, the Northern and Southern Hemispheres have strikingly similar annual mean temperatures for any given latitude (at least between 0° and 70° latitude, see Table 3). In general, the difference between the two hemispheres does not exceed 3° C. Of course, the comparison comes out rather unfavorably if, unlike Simpson, we consult more recent data for the polar regions themselves (according to Meinardus' table, the differences there amount to 6–7° C). On the whole, however, the similarity is remarkable; so the earth's overall temperature distribution obviously depends but little on the distribution of land and sea, and therefore must always have been more or less the same in past ages as it is now, as long as no other major factor was involved.

Simpson naturally concedes the very great influence of land and sea in controlling the climate of different areas, but only with reservations. The seasonal minimum temperatures of North America, in lat. 40°, 50°, and 60° N are 10°, 1°, and —8° C respectively; those of the much larger land mass of Asia are 10°, 0° and —8° C at the same latitudes. This shows that there is a limit to the influence of a continental land mass; even North America is large enough to produce the maximum possible temperature lowering. It therefore follows that paleoclimates at times when coastlines were quite different, cannot have differed in any essential respect from today's.

One important objection to Simpson's ideas is that when polar icecaps have formed, they undoubtedly have a decisive effect on climate. It is even difficult to reconstruct with any reasonable accuracy the climatic conditions that would prevail if there were no icecaps. Brooks believes that even the small difference of 3° C conceded by Simpson would, under favorable conditions, suffice to produce a complete rearrangement of climatic belts. Neither should we forget, as Sir Napier Shaw remarked in the discussion following a lecture by Simpson, that altitude can have a far-reaching effect; the modification involved because of this is probably only slight.

Lastly, *multiple glaciations* constitute a difficult problem for relief hypotheses, since it is very improbable that repeated uplifts or the like, could affect extensive areas more or less simultaneously. For this reason, many investigators combine relief hypotheses with other explanations such as radiation curves (Wundt, Zeuner) or variations in solar radiation (Flint).

Philippi's Opposed View

E. Philippi's (1910) explanation of the relationship between Ice Ages and mountain building is completely opposed to that of other investigators. Cooling produced by glaciation would have intensified the contraction of the earth, and would thus have produced crustal movements and folding! By this interpretation, coal formation in the fore-deeps of mountain chains, and volcanic activity, were *consequences*, rather than *causes*, of the Ice Ages. Cause and effect change places. Schirmeissen has likewise assumed that the burden of polar ice forced magma toward the equator, and thereby gave rise to great tectonic events. Apart from geophysical considerations, however, the chronological sequence of events refutes these hypotheses.

SUMMARY

We may be sure that the earth's climatic history is closely related to its paleogeographic history. Major Ice Ages occurred in times of strong relief, and many regional climatic characteristics may be explained on the basis of such paleogeographic conditions as the distribution of land, sea, and ocean currents.

On the other hand, it is either uncertain or improbable that the whole extent of climatic variations could have been caused by relief (in its widest sense). Other factors obviously played an important part.

24

Other Terrestrial Causes of Climatic Variation

> There were hot springs in the valley, and from these, he concluded that the subterranean fires were responsible for preventing the glaciers from flowing together to cover the whole valley.
>
> Icelandic saga of the 13th Century.

INTERIOR OF THE EARTH AND VOLCANIC HEAT

It has long been assumed that the gradual *cooling* of the earth has had a tremendous influence on the development of climates. Buffon expounded this in classical fashion as early as the 18th century (Chapter 1), and S. v. Waltershausen also considered it at least a hundred years ago. At first, the Quaternary Ice Age, the only one then known, appeared to be the end point of this development. Soon, thereafter, the earth would become a cold, dead planet. The discovery of pre-Quaternary glaciations, however, showed that no considerable cooling of the earth could be detected during the last few hundreds of millions of years. At the present time, only a very small proportion of the earth's internal heat goes to produce any climatic effects; according to Trabert, the increase in temperature caused in this way amounts to only 0.1° C. The earth's own heat was probably important only in the initial stages of the development of the planet.

Later *volcanic activity* can also have had, at most, a very local, short-lived effect on climate (disregarding, for the moment, the influence of volcanic ash). The reverse has sometimes been assumed though, and in 1823, no less a person than A. Humboldt himself thought it exceedingly important. Volcanic outbreaks are of little consequence as far as major climatic events are concerned, and in areas such as Iceland, postvolcanic heat can be used to explain only small local climatic anomalies, e.g. in the extent of the glaciers. Such ideas are to be found even in the old Icelandic sagas (see quotation at the beginning of this Chapter).

Krige (1929) proposed an involved mechanism whereby extrusion or intrusion of hot magma under the ocean basins caused increased evaporation of sea water, leading to extensive cloud formation and eventually to glaciation; but such an explanation is not in accordance with any geological observations.

The internal heat of the earth has again been regarded as important, in quite a different way in some modern theories of climatic variation (e.g. A. Wagner, 1940). Wagner, starting from Brockamp's observations in Greenland, points out the significance of the flow of heat from the interior to the surface of the earth, in regard to the growth of glaciers. The thermal conductivity of ice is about the same as that of consolidated rock (temperature increase 3° C for every 100 m. depth). If the heat flow were lower than at present, the ice would attain a greater thickness before melting occurred on the underside of the glaciers (i.e. the glaciers would grow). Now, a great part of this heat is produced by *radioactive decay*, and according to this theory, it increased continuously during times of tectonic stability and was instrumental in producing the warm climates of the early Tertiary, etc. Mountain building, however, exhausted the reserves of heat, and therefore resulted in a much reduced heat flow. Growth of glaciers and Ice Ages followed the formation of fold mountains. This mechanism would explain the connection between glaciation and orogenesis. Wagner also sought to explain the repeated alternation of glacial and interglacial phases.

Brockamp supplemented this theory by pointing out that the ice centers often lay over old shield areas, e.g. Canadian Shield, which are characterized by unusually low geothermal gradients, i.e. where the heat flow is small.

The physical basis of Wagner's hypothesis can hardly be assessed in quantitative fashion. There only remains the possibility of comparing its findings with geological observation, and thereby verifying its accuracy. In this case, even more than with relief hypotheses, one can point to the great spatial discrepancies between glaciation and mountain building, especially in the Upper Paleozoic, for here there should definitely be a close relationship between the two. Moreover, the difference in time between orogenesis and glaciation is sometimes small, sometimes great, and certainly very variable. Hence it seems that variable heat flow constitutes, at best, a trivial contributory factor, rather than a decisive one.

Contrariwise, others assume that the cooling produced by the Pleistocene glaciations affected the geothermal gradient which at present is still smaller than it should be from theoretical considerations (Koenigsberger, Mühlberg; see also Birch, 1948).

VOLCANIC ASH

Volcanoes can also influence the climate, by the ash which they eject (Sarasin and Sarasin, 1901; more recently Fuchs and Patterson). The amount of ash shot out can occasionally be tremendous; in 1883, Krakatoa hurled over 4 cubic miles of fragmental material into the heavens, and in 1912, Katmai in Alaska ejected 5 cubic miles of rock. In 1912, after the Katmai eruption, Abbot and Fowle observed that both at Mount Wilson, California, and at Bassour in Algeria, solar radiation was reduced by about 20%.

According to Brooks, the really cold years since 1700 have all followed volcanic eruptions.

1784–1786   Asama eruption, Japan, 1783.
1816   "The year without a summer"—Tomboro, 1815.
1884–1886   Krakatoa, 1883.
1912–1913   Katmai, 1912.

This may have been largely coincidental for there have been other great eruptions, such as that of Coseguina, Nicaragua in 1835, which blew out 12 cubic miles of ash (Sapper, Vulkankunde, 1927) without producing any particularly noticeable effect on climate.

Arctovski showed that relatively cool weather had prevailed for a month before the Katmai eruption, though naturally the volcanic outbreak may

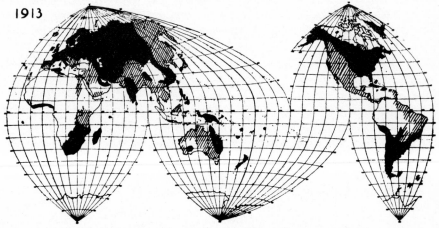

FIG. 127. VOLCANIC OUTBURSTS AND CLIMATE; TEMPERATURE CHART FOR 1913, THE YEAR
AFTER THE KATMAI ERUPTION (June, 1912)

Black = temperature higher than normal; shaded = lower than normal. No obvious relationship between the two phenomena (after Gentilli, 1948).

have intensified the drop in temperature. Gentilli's maps (fig. 127) likewise indicate that the *overall* temperature of the earth was not conspicuously low in the years 1884, 1913, and 1922 (after the eruptions in the southern Andes).

Brooks tried to assess numerically the effect of volcanic ash on paleo-climates (Chapter 10). He worked out the thickness of volcanic rocks in each formation and drew up the following relative values (on a scale from 1–10).

Holocene	2
Pleistocene	3
Pliocene	6
Miocene	3
Oligocene	3
Upper Eocene	4
Lower Eocene	8

and so on. These estimates are very uncertain, however, and in some cases it is possible to disagree with them. Besides, lavas predominate among the volcanic rocks, and in this connection they are of much less importance, for they need not be associated with considerable ejection of ash. On the whole, the influence of volcanic ash on climate is probably only slight, and at best, it is of no more than secondary importance. This is apparent since, for example, the Upper Paleozoic glaciations seemingly occurred before the maximum vulcanicity, while the volcanically active Early Tertiary enjoyed a decidedly warm climate.

CO_2 CONTENT OF THE ATMOSPHERE

There is yet a third way in which volcanoes can produce climatic changes; by emission of carbon dioxide. The "carbonic acid" hypothesis has been of particular significance in the last hundred years or so. Arrhenius propounded its physico-chemical basis, Frech and others, its geological importance, and Plass (1956) has re-examined it very closely.

The varying CO_2 content of the atmosphere has undoubtedly affected incident radiation; when the CO_2 content was high, a greater proportion of solar radiation penetrated to the earth, and besides, more of the rays reflected from the earth's surface were absorbed (greenhouse effect). Consequently, warm phases correspond to periods when the CO_2 content of the atmosphere was high. At first, volcanoes were regarded as the source of the CO_2, but other origins are possible.

Plass has carefully investigated the physical foundations of this hypothesis (Table 45) and has found that a temperature variation of about $3°$ C would

TABLE 45

CO_2 CONTENT OF THE ATMOSPHERE, AND MEAN TEMPERATURE OF THE EARTH'S SURFACE (AFTER PLASS)

CO₂ CONTENT OF ATMOSPHERE	TEMPERATURE OF EARTH'S SURFACE	
	WITH CLEAR SKIES	HALF CLOUDED
Double present content	3·6°C higher	2·5°C higher
Half present content	3·8°C lower	2·7°C lower

take place, if the CO_2 content were doubled or halved. The variation is dependent upon cloudiness, but water vapor is less influential than Brooks (1951) assumed.

Philippi and others have objected that the excess CO_2 would not have remained in the atmosphere, but would have been transferred to the "enormous reserve supply of the oceans". It does seem, though, that the atmosphere-hydrosphere system is, at present, more or less in equilibrium.

Theoretical considerations indicate that the following mechanisms could be initiated if the earth's CO_2 supply were somewhat reduced (possibly by 7 per cent), and then remained constant.

(a) The temperature would fall by about 4° C, till equilibrium conditions were achieved once more in the atmosphere-hydrosphere system. (G in fig. 128.) This would take some tens of thousands of years (probably 50,000) for water exchange in the ocean is very slow. Kulp (1952) estimated by C^{14}

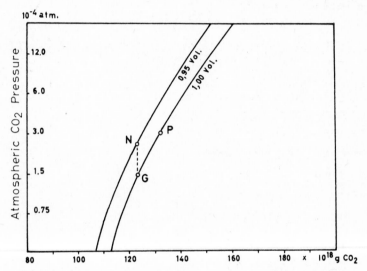

FIG. 128. CURVES OF CO_2 BALANCE IN ATMOSPHERE-HYDROSPHERE SYSTEM.

Ordinate-atmospheric CO_2 pressure. Abscissa-corresponding mass of CO_2 in atmosphere-hydrosphere; 1·00 vol. = present vol. of oceans; 0·95 vol. of ocean decreased by 5%. P = present CO_2 pressure; G = CO_2 pressure during glacial phase; N = CO_2 pressure on melting of glaciers (after Plass, 1956).

dating that water from the ocean deeps near Newfoundland had been at the surface 1,700 years earlier. Extensive glaciation would appear and the volume of the oceans would be reduced thereby by about 5%.

(b) Ice can contain only a very small amount of carbonates compared with sea water, so the concentration in the remaining sea water rises, and since its CO_2 content is now too high, CO_2 is transferred to the atmosphere until equilibrium is again achieved between the atmosphere and the 5 per cent smaller volume of sea water (N in fig. 128). The CO_2 partial pressure of the atmosphere, and the temperature, rise.

(c) The ice melts, the volume of the ocean increases, and so the equilibrium is upset once more. When balance is restored, conditions are once more as they were in (a) so the cycle begins anew, provided that the CO_2 content of the earth as a whole has not changed. A periodicity of the order of 50,000 years is plausible for this cycle. Only when the CO_2 content increases or decreases does the mechanism vary. Too little CO_2 would lead to permanent glacial conditions.

As with many other climatic hypotheses, the geologist is not in a position to pass judgement on the physico-chemical assumptions. His criticism must apply, above all, to the geological applications of the hypothesis; which raises, first of all, the question, "which geological events cause considerable differences in CO_2 content?"

TABLE 46

MAJOR FACTORS AFFECTING CO_2 BALANCE AT THE PRESENT TIME (AFTER PLASS)

	TONS/YEAR	
Photosynthesis	-60×10^9	Organic world
Decay, respiration	60×10^9	
Peat formation (and other organic sedimentation) . .	-0.01×10^9	
Weathering of lavas	-0.1×10^9	Inorganic world
Primary CO_2 (hot springs, volcanoes, etc.)	0.1×10^9	
Burning of coal, etc. Land cultivation, etc.	6.0×10^9	Agency of man

Table 46 shows that, apart from the effects of industry over the last few decades, volcanic activity, weathering of eruptive rocks, and coal formation all play a part. Primary CO_2 from the centre of the earth can certainly be produced in considerable quantities. Knetsch, for example, calculated that in the Eifel alone, an area where volcanic activity became extinct long ago, 200 tons of CO_2 are still emitted daily. Plass has rated the formation of carbonates from the silicates of eruptive rocks during weathering as being of particular importance. Lastly, the accumulation of coal and oil must doubtless have withdrawn much CO_2 from the atmosphere and the ocean at times. The earth's coal reserves alone have been estimated at almost 5 million million tons, and most coal seams are, in fact, concentrated at certain definite horizons in the stratigraphic column.

Callender, Chamberlin, Frech, Lozinski, Plass, and others have stressed the *time relations* between these processes and events in the earth's climatic history. There does indeed appear to be a possible connection over the last few decades, for CO_2 enrichment resulting from industry has been paralleled by a climatic amelioration; but otherwise, the relationship is not very clear. Warm phases, such as the Mesozoic, are often characterized by little volcanic activity. Intensive *coal formation* does indeed precede the Gondwana glaciations, but the interval between the period of maximum coal formation in the Westphalian and the main glacial phase is of the order of several millions of years, if that phase occurs at the Permo-Carboniferous boundary.

Nevertheless, this is the earliest period where a relationship can be thought possible. With the Quaternary Ice Ages, however, the discrepancy is much greater still, amounting to some tens of millions of years after the Miocene coals, and to much more after the early Tertiary and Cretaceous coals. Plass also considers that mountain building is important, since it encourages the weathering of eruptive rocks. However, large plutons are usually very gradually exposed at first, and the world's younger fold mountains still display a surface consisting, for the most part, of non-igneous rocks, i.e. it is impossible to explain the Quaternary glaciations as having succeeded the Tertiary mountain building, for this reason.

Plass saw, in plants, another interesting indication of a once higher CO_2 content; they grow considerably better when the atmosphere is rich in CO_2 (carbonic acid as a fertilizer!) and therefore, they probably first developed in such an environment.

On the whole, it can probably be said that a relationship does appear to exist between CO_2 content of the atmosphere and temperature. But at present, no geological factors are known which could have influenced the CO_2 balance so considerably as to provide a possible explanation of the fundamental characteristics of paleoclimates.

Further reading: REVELLE AND FAIRBRIDGE, 1957.

CLOUD

Clouds are an important factor in determining climate, for they reflect a considerable part of the sun's rays; 74–80% where they are 1000 m. or more thick. At the same time, there are considerable differences in cloud

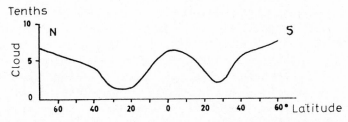

FIG. 129. MEAN ANNUAL CLOUDINESS ALONG THE GREENWICH MERIDIAN (0°) at the present time (after A. A. Miller, 1943).

cover, i.e. the proportion of the sky covered by cloud, at different latitudes. At the equator, the mean annual value amounts to six-tenths, in the deserts of the horse latitudes, two-tenths, and in higher latitudes, as much as seven-tenths (fig. 129). The extensive cloud of the equatorial zone is the reason why that area has lower mean annual temperatures than the almost cloudless desert belt. Clouds, of course, do also help to prevent loss of heat radiated from the earth, but this effect is not so great as that of reflection of solar radiation. Only in the polar regions does cloud cover during the polar night produce an appreciable rise in temperature; for then, all effective radiation is coming from the earth itself.

A mean annual cloud cover of five-tenths over the whole earth results in a $37\frac{1}{2}\%$ loss of solar radiation. Brooks has calculated that if this cover were reduced by only one tenth, then the mean annual temperature over the earth would rise by about 8° C.

Glaciations have therefore been attributed to increased water vapor content in the atmosphere (Tamarelli, 1888; Harboe; de Marchi). It was thought that volcanoes were the main source of water vapor, but the amounts resulting from volcanic activity are so small that they could, at most, have had only a slight, local significance.

From the geological point of view, the extinction of the saurians at the end of the Cretaceous Period has been explained by saying that then, for the first time in the earth's history, the previously thick cloud cover was rent asunder, so that seasonal temperature variation first occurred (Stechov, 1954). No other factors support this assumption. The periods of great, widespread aridity, that are known to have taken place long before this, must have required clear skies.

SALT CONTENT OF THE OCEAN

The present salt content of the ocean amounts, on average, to 3.5 per cent. Salt water is denser than fresh water, cold water is heavier than warm water. This is important in controlling deep oceanic circulation, and is the basis of T. R. Chamberlin's hypothesis that the currents in the deep ocean once ran in the *opposite* direction, and thus caused the strikingly uniform climates of many former epochs (1899; see Chamberlin and Salisbury, 1906).

The starting point for this hypothesis, as for Arrhenius's, is the varying CO_2 content of the atmosphere; a high CO_2 content leading to a slight temperature increase. Evaporation in low latitudes was thereby increased to such an extent that there, the surface waters of the ocean became relatively rich in salt. This enrichment caused their density to increase and they sank, to create a situation the reverse of today's, when cold water descends to the depths near the poles. This brings about a great exchange of polar and equatorial water, with strong bottom currents flowing toward the equator and producing low temperatures on the sea floor. According to Chamberlin, warm equatorial water flowed poleward along the bottom during warm phases. Its heat was therefore not lost to the atmosphere, but mostly retained in the oceans; cold polar water flowed along the surface to lower latitudes.

Chamberlin assumed that both glacial and interglacial phases were characterized by cold water sinking at the poles, though in the latter case, the circulation was on a smaller scale. The resulting exchange of water led to a constant decrease in amplitude of the climatic fluctuations.

Against Chamberlin's ingenious hypothesis, one can probably argue that it is doubtful whether small variations in CO_2 content, and the resulting slight fluctuations in the salt content of the oceans, would have produced an effect so revolutionary as the complete reversal of deep oceanic circulation. Moreover, his explanation of multiple glaciations is not really convincing, and naturally the arguments against the "carbonic acid" hypothesis can also be used against Chamberlin's.

The salt content of the oceans may not always have remained constant. It has generally been assumed that much of the salt was brought in by rivers, and that the salt content of the oceans has therefore increased with time (first by Halley, 1715). In fact, this can only be deduced theoretically. Faunas, and other geological data do not support it; indeed they suggest that there have been no, or at most only quite insignificant, variations in the salt content of the oceans during the later part of the earth's history, from Cambrian times onward.

A smaller salt concentration would result in a rise of freezing point; at present, with a 3.5% concentration, it is $-2°$ C. This means that the Precambrian seas, if they really were deficient in salts, would have become ice-covered more readily than today's. Oceanic circulation was also presumably more active at that time (Huntington and Visher, 1922) because the upwelling of cold waters in the equatorial zone would not have been hindered to the same extent by descending dense salt-rich waters. Increased circulation would have led to lower temperatures at the equator, and to higher temperatures at the poles. Reduced salinity would therefore have produced a more uniform climate. Such an effect cannot, of course, be demonstrated, because our knowledge of the Precambrian is too slight.

A last hypothesis dependent on salinity is A. H. Clark's (1924). Clark's idea is that increased salt concentration would have appreciably reduced the vapor pressure of water, and so would have led to much decreased evaporation. Hence, as time went on, the amount of water vapor in the atmosphere decreased, and so the climate became less uniform. A further effect was that, because of the reduced evaporation, the oceans contained more water; many of the present land bridges must therefore have been flooded.

Mencher showed that Clark's stimulating hypothesis cannot withstand any close inspection. At most, the variations in sea level caused in this way would have been only 30 cm.; and the vapor pressure decrease, during the conversion of a fresh-water ocean into one with the present salt content, would have amounted only to some 2%. So small a decrease can have had no important effect on climate.

25

Polar Wandering, Continental Drift, and Paleomagnetism

If the orientation of the earth in relation to the sun had been only slightly different, everything else would have differed too.

J. G. HERDER, Ideen zur Philosophie der Geschichte der Menschheit, 1784.

POLAR WANDERING

If the position of the poles varied, then the climatic belts would migrate. Thus, for example, Central Europe could easily arrive in either the polar or the equatorial zone. Hooke, Herder, and others explained the former "tropical climate" of Europe in this way more than 200 years ago. The Ice Ages and polar floras were soon interpreted in the same fashion, particularly by paleobotanists. At the same time, they related polar temperatures to the polar night, as Heer, Lyell, and others had already done.

At first, polar wandering was thought of as an actual shifting of the earth's axis of rotation; but certain physical considerations weighed against this idea, so now most investigators view it with disfavor, or consider it as having been possible only in the early stages of the earth's development (see Schwinner, 1936; Gold, 1955, gives the opposite view). At present, only slight, climatically insignificant, variations in position of the pole can be observed.

CONTINENTAL DRIFT

There remains, however, the second possibility of a *relative* displacement of the poles, whereby the distance between any given point on the earth's surface and the pole of rotation (constant) varies; and thus so does its latitude and longitude. For this reason, crustal shortening resulting from the formation of fold mountains may well have had some climatic effect. According to Cadisch, a strip 400 miles wide was compressed into 90 miles to form the Swiss Alps; in the Himalayas, the crustal shortening may have been much greater (Argand considers it to be of the order of 1,250 miles).

It is much more commonly assumed that the lighter continental blocks have moved over the denser basement (Kreichgauer, Taylor, especially Wegener, 1912). Wegener and Köppen assembled the paleoclimatic data, and represented it in many maps (fig. 93) that support the idea of extensive continental drift. Köppen and Milankovitch worked out the route traversed by the poles since Carboniferous times.

Whether or not the drift assumed by Wegener and others is physically possible, is still very controversial. We shall consider the possibility, in unbiased fashion, and see how it accords with paleoclimatic data.

Further reading: Du Toit, 1937; Salomon-Calvi, 1931, 1933.

Paleoclimatic Arguments Against Wegener's Drift Hypothesis

According to Wegener, there was also considerable continental drift in the relatively recent geological past. But it has now been established that, contrary to this theory, the position of the pole during the Pleistocene Period was no different from what it is now. The Quaternary glaciation of Scandinavia, for example, cannot be explained by polar wandering. The glacial snow line ran parallel to the present one in all areas (Klute; fig. 110). Hence a migration of the climatic belts cannot be recognized in the Quaternary or Younger Tertiary (Behrmann); or possibly even in the early Tertiary (Chaney, Schwarzbach; Chapter 18).

Paleoclimatic Evidence in Favor of Continental Drift.

In pre-Tertiary times, conditions were different. Lotze has shown that the evaporite belt of the Northern Hemisphere has been shifting continuously since the start of the Paleozoic Era; it gradually migrated from the polar zone to its present position (fig. 121). He interpreted this movement as a result of shift of the poles. The evidence would be more definite if we could also demonstrate movement of the arid belt of the Southern Hemisphere; but for this, not enough information is available.

The reef belt, however, behaved in exactly the same fashion (Schwarzbach; fig. 122), and we have seen that the north polar zone has yielded a great deal of evidence of warm climates during the Paleozoic and Mesozoic Eras. Paleoclimatology thus affords a strong argument in favor of extensive shift of the poles, and probably of considerable continental drift, especially in the Paleozoic. It at least supports the fundamental principles of Wegener's Hypothesis, even if it does not confirm particular points. Neither the extent nor the time of continental drifting need have corresponded with Wegener's concept of them; to some extent, at least, they certainly did not. By and large, we should probably think more of a shift of the earth's crust as a whole, than of drifting of individual continents.

The Upper Paleozoic Glaciations are of vital importance in this connection. Some traces of these glaciations are now to be found at the equator, and despite the efforts of Brooks and others to explain this on a purely paleogeographic basis (Chapters 16, 28, fig. 92), it seems impossible to avoid assuming a different position for the pole at that time, though Koken recognized, in 1907, that given a suitable position for the pole, the further-most traces of glaciation lie far outside the polar circle. Wegener's reconstruction, extended by Du Toit and others, shows a close grouping of the Gondwana continents, an imaginative solution which is undoubtedly a highlight of his hypothesis (fig. 93). It is also possible, though, to give an adequate explanation which requires only a moderate amount of drift, much less than Wegener assumed.

Many paleoclimatic facts can be explained then on the basis of a different position of the poles; but this theory does not provide a complete solution to all climatic problems, for it does not explain the alternation of ice-free and ice-covered poles during the earth's history.

PALEOMAGNETISM

Modern investigations of paleomagnetism have furnished unexpected arguments in favor of shift of the poles. Lavas exhibit a *remanent magnetism* whose direction was determined by the magnetic field at the time when the lavas cooled below their Curie point[1] (thermoremanance). The direction of the remanent magnetism can be measured exactly. This makes it possible to estimate the position of the magnetic pole at the time of the eruption. Comprehensive descriptions have been given by G. Angenheister, Blackett, Cox and Doell, Hospers, Irving, Nagata, Nairn, Runcorn, and Schmucker.

The following difficulties stand in the way of the geological application of this method:

(*a*) The measured values are always extremely small, and only relatively few rocks, mostly those containing magnetite, are suitable.

(*b*) The remanent magnetism may not have remained absolutely unaltered (see Schmucker, 1959).

(*c*) In many cases, the magnetic field has reversed, i.e. the north and south poles have changed places. The cause of this phenomenon is still uncertain. It appears to be stratigraphically useful, e.g. in investigations in Iceland (T. Einarsson, Hospers, Rutten).

(*d*) It is not certain that the magnetic pole always lay in the vicinity of the geographic pole as it does at present.

The present magnetic poles are situated at (*a*) lat. 73° N, long. 100° W (1948), and (*b*) lat. 69° S, long. 143° E (1952); but at times, the position changes rapidly. The declination at London *circa* 1600 was $+10°$; in 1823, on the other hand, it was $—25°$; now it is $—9\frac{1}{2}°$.

There are theoretical grounds for believing that the pole of rotation and the magnetic pole are causally related; the terrestrial magnetic field probably arises from currents in the interior of the earth, which will be symmetrically disposed with regard to the axis of rotation. Thus the earth represents a sort

1. The Curie point is the temperature above which the ferromagnetic minerals lose their magnetism; in magnetite, the ferromagnetic mineral of greatest geological importance, it is 575° C.

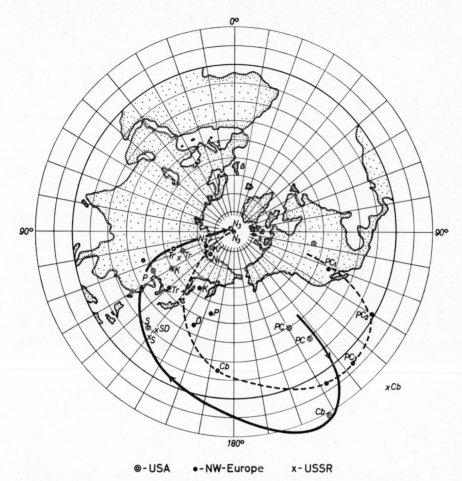

0°

90°

90°

180°

◎ - USA   ● - NW-Europe   x - USSR

FIG. 130. MIGRATION OF THE MAGNETIC POLES THROUGHOUT THE EARTH'S HISTORY

Solid line shows course as indicated by measurements in North America. Dotted line— from measurements in Europe. Further measurements in Russia are indicated by crosses. PC = Proterozoic (PC$_1$ = Lower Torridonian, PC$_2$ = Longmyndian, PC$_3$ = Upper Torridonian); Cb = Cambrian; S = Siluro-Ordovician; D = Devonian; Tr = Trias; Kr = Cretaceous; N$_1$ = Eocene; N$_2$ = Oligocene; N$_3$ = Upper Tertiary and Quaternary. The measurements in Europe and America suggest different routes (after a compilation by Komarov, 1960).

of gigantic dynamo. Conditions over the last few centuries, however, show that we must reckon with a deviation of at least 20°.

The paleomagnetic poles have lain in more or less their present position as far back as the Tertiary Period (disregarding the intermittent 180° reversals), but in pre-Tertiary times, they often occupied a quite different position. Fig. 130 indicates the paleomagnetically deduced migration of the northern pole. According to this map, it lay over North America or the northeast

Pacific in the Precambrian Era, in mid-Pacific in the Cambrian, and in the northwest Pacific and northeast Asia later in the Paleozoic, and in the Mesozoic.

Another important result is that pole positions, as estimated in different continents, are somewhat different. This can only be interpreted as showing that the position of the continents relative to one another has changed.

Paleomagnetism therefore affords evidence not only of an overall polar wandering, but also of continental drift. The paleomagnetic poles are entered in the climatic map of the Devonian Period (fig. 84); they are in agreement with the other paleoclimatic evidence, sometimes remarkably so. In Permian times, the paleomagnetic equator ran through North America and Europe; again in good agreement with other climatic evidence. It is to be hoped that the method may be developed still further, and that it will provide the paleoclimatologist with still more valuable results.

TREE TRUNKS AND POLE POSITION

The *longest* radius of tree trunks often lies in a direction away from the sun, i.e. facing the pole. Therefore, it is theoretically possible to recognize the former position of the pole, and hence how it has shifted (Kossovich, 1935, Krames). The method can hardly ever be applied with success, however, for there is only a very slight difference in length of the radius; other factors, particularly the wind, produce much greater asymmetries in growth (Assmann, 1959; see Chapter 8, and fig. 62). Moreover, at any given locality, there hardly ever remains enough material for such statistical investigations to be carried out.

Further reading: LIESE and DADSWELL, 1959.

26

Orbital Variations
(Radiation Curves)

> Cecily: That certainly seems a satisfactory explanation,
> does it not?
> Gwendolen: Yes, dear, if you can believe him.
> Cecily: I don't. But that doesn't affect the wonderful
> beauty of his answer.
> > Oscar Wilde, The Importance of Being Earnest,
> > Act III, 1895.

HISTORY

In 1842, the French mathematician J. F. Adhémar first explained the Ice
Age as having been caused by variations in the earth's orbit (rotation of the
perihelion). Around 1860, James Croll enlarged this theory by introducing
the idea of variable eccentricity of the orbit. Schmick, Ball, and Pilgrim
(1904), in particular, also considered the possibility of changes in obliquity
of the ecliptic, and in 1920, M. Milankovitch worked out a new "radiation
curve" which W. Köppen and A. Wegener (1924) related to Penck and
Brückner's subdivision of the Ice Age. This interpretation has since found
a great deal of fervent and unreserved approval, especially from W. Soergel
and F. E. Zeuner.

Hypotheses based on radiation curves enjoy two great advantages; they
explain multiple glaciations in simple fashion, and they permit the absolute
dating of Ice Ages.

Meteorological Data

While Adhémar, Croll, and Pilgrim stress the importance of severe winters
as a cause of Ice Ages, Köppen, Spitaler, and others regard mild winters and
cool summers as favoring glaciation. Milankovitch's and Spitaler's radiation
curves therefore represent the summer half of the year, and the periods of
cool summers are interpreted as glacial phases. In this connection, Köppen
and Wegener point to conditions in Greenland and Siberia at present
(Table 47). Greenland with its mild winters and cool summers is glaciated;
Siberia, despite its extremely severe winters, is not.

TABLE 47

TEMPERATURES OF GREENLAND AND SIBERIA. (AFTER KÖPPEN AND WEGENER)

	GREENLAND	SIBERIA
Coldest month	−10°C	−47°C
Warmest month	6°C	17°C
Annual mean	−2°C	−14°C

MILANKOVITCH'S RADIATION CURVES

Astronomical Basis

In constructing his curves, Milankovitch made use of the inclination of the earth's axis (obliquity of the ecliptic), the eccentricity of the earth's orbit, and the precession of the equinoxes (rotation of the perihelion).

The *inclination of the axis* is responsible for seasons (Chapter 2). The degree of tilt at present amounts to 23° 27', but varies between 24° 36' and 21° 59', over a period of 40,000 years (20,000 years between the extreme positions). When the tilt was small, i.e. when the seasons were less marked, glaciation may have arisen provided other factors were also favorable. First of these, the *eccentricity of the orbit*, varies between two extremes in 92,000 years; the orbit itself is at times more circular, at times more ellipsoidal. *Precession of the equinoxes* causes the day on which the earth approaches nearest to the sun to alter. At present, the perihelion is reached during the Northern Hemisphere's winter; hence the winters here are milder, while those of the Southern Hemisphere are more severe. But the actual date varies throughout the year over a period of 21,000 years. In A.D. 1200 it took place on 21st December; in 9300 B.C. it was on 21st June. Naturally, the influence of the perihelion and the aphelion can become particularly great when the eccentricity of the orbit is most marked. Variations in all these factors can be worked out over the last few hundred thousand years. This is a tremendous extrapolation but in view of the precision of astronomical measurements and calculations, and the inexactitude of geological requirements, the accuracy obtained is probably sufficient. We can, therefore, calculate how much radiation was reaching the earth's surface at every season during that time. The annual mean has varied relatively little, but there have probably been times with relatively cool summers, when the simultaneous occurrence of slight tilt of the axis, great eccentricity of the orbit, and winter perihelions, gave rise to the conditions which, according to Köppen, Wegener, Spitaler, and others, favor the growth of extensive ice sheets. Cool summers are always linked with mild winters.

The oscillations in solar radiation differ at different latitudes. At present, because of the inclination of the axis, northern and southern hemispheres receive different amounts of radiation. So, too, do the poles and the equator.

At the upper limit of the atmosphere, a locality 5° from the equator receives 161 Kg./cal. in summer, 149 Kg./cal. in winter, while one at latitude 75° receives 132 Kg./cal. in summer, and only 7 Kg./cal. in winter.

Graphical representation of these calculated values yields the much debated curves (fig. 131), which have been drawn up to indicate radiation at

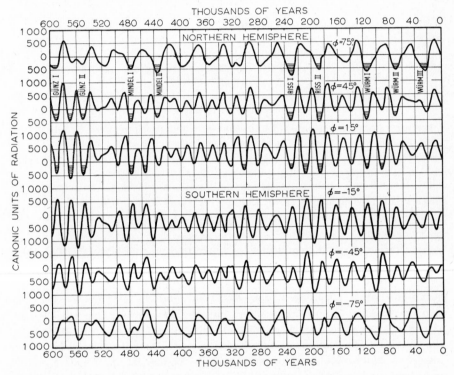

FIG. 131. SOLAR RADIATION CURVES AFTER MILANKOVITCH (1938) FOR THE NORTHERN HEMISPHERE AND SOUTHERN HEMISPHERE

(Lat. 15°, 45°, 75° N & S in summer.) Glacial phases according to Köppen, Soergel, Zeuner, etc. (From Köppen, 1940.) (Note that Emiliani has proposed a different correlation.)

different latitudes over the period of the last million years. The curves calculated by Milankovitch, and later improved by Woerkom (1953; fig. 132), are applied most frequently.

From the *radiation curves*, it appears that the temperature minima did not occur simultaneously in both hemispheres. They were not far separated in time, though, because the inclination of the earth's axis was of prime importance, and that affected both hemispheres in the same way.

Variation in radiation can be expressed in arbitrary units (canonic units). Milankovitch has also expressed it in terms of the depression or elevation of the snow line. Later, at W. Wundt's suggestion, he took into account

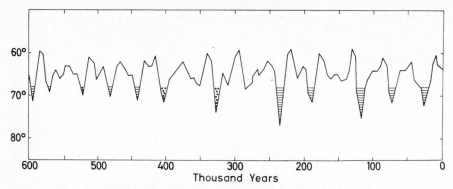

FIG. 132. IMPROVED SOLAR RADIATION CURVES AFTER WOERKOM, 1953, FOR THE PAST
600,000 YEARS AT LATITUDE 65° N

Ordinate = latitude equivalent. During the Great Interglacial (between "Mindel 2" and
"Riss 1"), there are minima, the greatest of which compare with the "Mindel" and "Riss"
glacial phases (after Woerkom, 1953).

secondary effects caused by changing albedo and the like. The variation in
solar radiation resulting from changes in the earth's orbit only initiates
climatic variations; other factors are set up which can greatly increase the
effect of the initial change.

The realization that the onset of glacial advances and retreats takes place
quite some time after the climate changes is also of great importance. This
can be compared with diurnal and seasonal temperatures which reach their
maximum effect after noon, and after the summer solstice, respectively.
Consequently, it is quite possible that the ice sheets are still melting
although a decrease in solar radiation has again set in. The subdivisions of
the Ice Ages are, therefore, influenced to a great extent by the length of
time over which radiation is increased or reduced; short periods of increased
radiation need not, by any means, be represented by interglacials. Accordingly, Soergel has transformed Milankovitch's radiation curves into a
"glaciation curve", which is of much less complex construction because
several small oscillations can be merged into one large one, to give, in theory,
an immediate picture of the course of the actual glaciations. Soergel has
given no precise basis for his glaciation curve. It should always be remembered that around the ice centers, Ice Ages are much more uniform, much
less subdivided, than in the marginal areas.

Equation with the Geological Subdivisions of the Ice Age

The detailed equation of radiation curves with Penck's geological subdivisions of the Pleistocene Ice Age was first undertaken by Köppen and
Wegener (1924). They recognized that several of the oscillations in the
radiation curves had to be grouped together to cover the same length of
time as Penck had suggested for each glacial and interglacial phase. This is

all the more striking, since Soergel (1925) and B. Eberl (1930) later erected a fine subdivision of the Quaternary Period based on river terraces in the Ilm-Middle Germany and the Iller-Lech areas respectively. Over and above Penck and Brückner's classic fourfold division, they postulated a bipartite division of the three earlier glacial phases, and a tripartite division of the last glacial phase; they also discovered pre-Günz glaciations, and believed that all these fine subdivisions could be recognized from radiation curves. It is, therefore, no wonder that these investigators and their pupils, particularly Zeuner (most recently in 1959), have accepted the use of astronomical curves as a completely justifiable method of geological chronology. Zeuner and Soergel give the following ages for the glacial phases: Wurm III, 22,100–25,000; Würm II, 72,000; Würm I, 115,000; Riss II, 187,000; Riss I, 230,000; Mindel II, 435,000; Mindel I, 476,000; Günz II, 550,000; Günz I, 590,000 B.P.

Critical Arguments Against Radiation Curves and their Geological Interpretation

Many objections can be raised; they are of differing importance, and some were recognized by Köppen and Wegener themselves.

(*a*) Radiation curves have been devised not only by Milankovitch and by von Woerkom, whose curves are largely similar, but also by Spitaler (1921, 1940), who has constructed curves which differ considerably, especially in amplitude. The difference arises because Spitaler divided the radiation received at any particular latitude by the diurnal arc while Milankovitch divided it by the diurnal and nocturnal arc. According to Wundt and others, Spitaler's technique is unsound.

(*b*) Why are there glacial phases in the Quaternary and not in the Tertiary, etc.? Radiation curves can be calculated for more than the last million years, and while their accuracy decreases with increasing age, minima must obviously have been present in pre-Quaternary times. In point of fact, the paleoclimatic interpretation of radiation curves requires some supplementary assumptions to be made; obviously it is only in some cases that the astronomically controlled minima acquire "the necessary echoing circumstances to enable true Ice Ages to appear" (W. Wundt). A certain "glacial readiness" (*Eiszeitbereitschaft*) must already be present.

Paleogeographic conditions have been looked upon as such a supplementary factor—particularly the deflection of the Gulf Stream by the Faroes-Iceland ridge, though opinions on the exact role of the Gulf Stream are very divided (see Chapters 22 and 23).

It is remarkable that in the last 600 million years, conditions such that changes in incident radiation could give rise to glacial phases, should have existed no more than twice—in the Pleistocene and possibly also in the Permo-Carboniferous.

Baczák has recently put forward an *astronomical* solution to this problem.

At present, the ascending nodes of all seven major planets, i.e. the points where their orbital planes intersect the earth's ecliptic, lie in the quadrant between 45° and 135°. This, however, is an abnormal state of affairs which, according to Baczåk, began some 600,000 years ago and will remain for the next 25 million years. Only during such periods is the obliquity of the ecliptic sufficient to enable glaciation to occur.

As with all astronomical theories, the geologist is not in a position to comment on its astronomical basis. Indeed, it can almost be said that neither are modern astronomers, for the classical tasks of calculation of orbits have been put aside while they deal with the quite different problems of astrophysics.

(c) According to the radiation curves, cool summers do not occur simultaneously in both hemispheres, so glacial phases must have alternated between the two. Geological observations contradict this, however, at least for the Last Glaciation. The uniform depression of the snow line in particular can probably only be interpreted as indicating that an Ice Age was a world-wide phenomenon.

Wundt, Meinardus, and others, assume that the time differences of the minima in each hemisphere have no particular significance. Glaciation probably originated almost entirely in the land-rich Northern Hemisphere. This ice gave rise to cooling, first of the tropics, and then of the Southern Hemisphere. After a few thousand years, a minimum therefore developed in the Southern Hemisphere while ice persisted in the Northern Hemisphere.

It is quite certain that eustatic variations of sea level (and hence marine terrace chronology) were controlled almost entirely by the ice of the Northern Hemisphere. We need only compare the present and former areal extent of ice in both hemispheres for this to become apparent:

Northern Hemisphere: maximum glaciated area 12.5 million sq. mls. (32 m. sq. km.); present area 0.9 million sq. mls. (2.3 m. sq. km.).

Southern Hemisphere: maximum glaciated area 5.2 million sq. mls. (13.3 m. sq. km.); present area 5.0 million sq. mls. (12.7 m. sq. km.) (figures after Flint).

(d) The correspondence between the geological subdivisions of the Ice Age and radiation curves is not so conclusive as Eberl, Soergel, and others have assumed, and have put forward as a particularly important argument in favor of a planetary hypothesis.

This applies not only to Milankovitch's "classic" curves, but also to an even greater extent to von Woerkom's improved curves (fig. 132). In that section of the curves representing the period of more than 250,000 years ago, there is no sort of agreement with the geological subdivisions devised by Soergel and others (Schwarzbach, 1954). For example, there are minima in the "Great Interglacial" more pronounced than those of the Günz or Mindel Glacial phases.

The best indication of the subjective nature of the assignment of the many minima of the radiation curves into different glacial phases is afforded by the fact that Emiliani and Wundt have recently proposed completely different interpretations. For example, they equate the Gunz Glaciation with the minima of 330,000 years ago, while Soergel *et al.* consider it to have occurred between 550,000 and 590,000 years ago. The allegedly striking agreement between geological subdivisions and radiation curves owes a great deal to the power of autosuggestion.

(*e*) Geological and astronomical absolute chronology are not in very good agreement either.

Zeuner has rightly said that Kay's dating may not be brought forward as an argument against radiation curves because it is based on inexact data. Nevertheless, comparison with precise varve chronology and with C^{14} dating is at least partly unfavorable. According to Soergel's interpretation, the Last Interglacial took place between 170,000 and 130,000 B.P.; from C^{14} measurements, half that age seems more probable.

The values obtained from radiation curves and from C^{14} dating of the period of the last 50,000 years are compared in Table 48. We must, of course,

TABLE 48

RADIATION CURVE—AND C^{14}—CHRONOLOGY OVER THE LAST 50,000 YEARS (Before Present)

	RADIATION CURVES	C^{14}
Last Climatic Optimum.	10,000	ca. 6000
Last Glacial phase	25,000	ca. 20,000
Last Interglacial	40,000–60,000	ca. 30,000–40,000

consider the possibility that climatic changes caused by fluctuations in solar radiation would have occurred quite some time after the fluctuations themselves. Granted this, we cannot deny certain agreement between the two time scales for this youngest part of the Quaternary Period.

(*f*) Postglacial climatic development shows no obvious relation to radiation curves. The postglacial Climatic Optimum may perhaps be equated with a maximum in the radiation curve for a delay of some thousands of years might be possible; but the extensive Younger Dryas Period cannot be explained in this way; it has no equivalent minimum in the radiation curve (Firbas; fig. 114).

(*g*) Even the meteorological assumptions may be disputed. Are cool summers—which in the radiation curves are automatically linked with milder winters—the essential requirement for the onset of Ice Ages?

Variation in the length of glaciers in historic times is of particular importance in this connection. The glacier retreat over the last few decades has been associated with an amelioration of winter temperatures (fig. 116), i.e. exactly the opposite of what might be expected (see A. Wagner, and also

Simpson's hypothesis). The Antarctic also deserves mention, for there too the meteorological requirements for advance and retreat of ice are obviously quite different (Meinardus, 1928).

Review of Radiation Curves

From all that has been said, it is apparent that the connection between radiation and glaciation is much more complex than Koppen, Wegener, and others have assumed. Even if it did exist, however, it is hard to believe that such relatively small oscillations in radiation as are shown in Milankovitch's curves could have influenced climates so fundamentally. Certainly, self-induced cooling can be of great importance, but only when many other factors are working in the same direction, and that is not the case here. Increased radiation in winter does not always favor glaciation, nor do the nodes of the curves for different latitudes correspond in amount or, sometimes, even in sense.

We must, therefore, remain doubtful of the climatological interpretation of radiation curves. The basis of these planetary hypotheses appears to be very insecure. Ice Ages are, of course, such complex phenomena that we can hardly pronounce definitely for or against planetary hypotheses by deductive methods; only direct and detailed comparison of geological and astronomical chronology of the Ice Age can yield really positive results. At the present time the amount of geological data is not yet sufficient to be conclusive; but meanwhile, it is probably more against than for.

APERIODIC ORBITAL VARIATIONS

It is possible to conceive of aperiodic as well as periodic variations in the earth's orbit. For example, the earth could once have rotated more quickly, or the axis could have been much more inclined than it is now. A case of theoretical interest would arise if the obliquity of the ecliptic were 35° because then, as Gripenberg pointed out in 1933, all latitudes would receive the same amount of solar energy, namely that at present received by lat. 36°. It would then be possible for a subtropical climate to prevail throughout the world; the tropic sun would stand high in the heavens in summer; and lower or below the horizon during the long, cool winters, i.e., conditions would favor coal formation.

Geological observations gainsay such extreme seasonal variations in climate; moreover, astronomers can find no criteria for such an inclination of the axis in the latter part of the earth's history. The same objection applies to the hypothesis that the earth's axis once stood vertical to give rise to a 12-hour day (Allard, 1948).

27

Extra-Terrestrial Hypotheses

ABSORPTION BY INTERSTELLAR MATTER

Clouds of fine dust (nebulae) screen certain parts of the heavens. F. Nölke, in 1909, was the first to assume that solar radiation would have been considerably reduced by passage through such interstellar matter, and that an Ice Age would thereby have arisen. He considered especially the nebula in Orion.

Mathematical investigation shows, however, that absorption is very small in the distance between the earth and the sun; a considerable cooling effect is thus improbable (see Krook, 1953).

According to Shapley and others, nebulae played the opposite role; they could activate the sun into giving out more radiation. (See next section but one.)

Satellite Rings

R. L. Ives (1940) proposed a similar, rather fantastic, hypothesis that assumes that solar radiation was reduced by matter outside the earth's atmosphere. Ives postulated that, during the Permian Period, there was a ring of tiny satellites round the earth, of the type that now form Saturn's rings. The shadow of this ring was sharply focussed on the equatorial area, and could have given rise to the circumequatorial Gondwana Glaciation. However, the Gondwana Glaciation was probably not at all circumequatorial, and furthermore, this hypothesis of satellite rings, which appeared for a short time at the end of the Carboniferous and disappeared again in the Permian—a sort of astronomical *deus ex machina* on a flying visit— does not explain other Ice Ages.

THE SUN AS A VARIABLE STAR

In the hypotheses already dealt with, the sun has been regarded as a star giving out a constant amount of radiation, which was altered only by secondary effects, or was differently distributed. But the sun has not remained eternally unchanged. In the course of time, the intensity of radiation may have varied uniformly or periodically, thereby greatly influencing the climate of the earth.

E. Dubois argued on behalf of such a view in 1893; he was thinking particularly of a slow cooling of the sun (he explained the Gondwana Glaciation as having been due to paleogeographic conditions).

In 1922, Huntington and Visher developed a "solar cyclonic hypothesis", whereby, at times of increased sunspot activity, the circulation in the earth's atmosphere increased; stormy weather caused greater precipitation and hence led to glaciation. Favorable paleogeographic conditions (continents with considerable relief) were also required.

Shapley (1921), Hoyle and Lyttleton (1939), Himpel (1947), and others, have all assumed that the nebulae already mentioned caused increased solar radiation, i.e., that the sun was a variable star for this reason. Interstellar matter would, therefore, cause primary changes in radiation, and not secondary changes as in Nölke's hypothesis.

In any event, variable solar radiation is regarded as a cause of climatic variation, though it is true that astronomers have no other sort of indication that solar radiation is subject to great fluctuations.

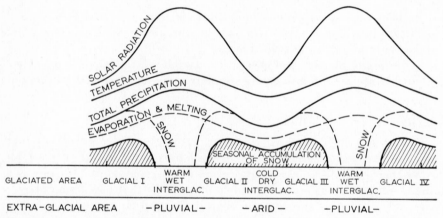

FIG. 133. G. C. SIMPSON'S GLACIAL THEORY

Simpson's Hypothesis

It was at first supposed that decreased solar radiation led to glaciation, but conditions are not so straightforward, and Sir George Simpson (1927) has shown that given Quaternary temperature conditions, *increased* radiation can also favor the growth of ice sheets. At the same time, he has attempted to give a simple explanation of the occurrence of multiple glaciations.

Figure 133 indicates the fundamentals of his hypothesis. Solar radiation rises from a minimum to a maximum, and then falls off once more. The curves for temperature, evaporation, and precipitation run in like manner, but the snowfall curve differs. At first it rises but soon falls as the temperature becomes too high. Accumulation of ice and snow therefore ceases during the phase of maximum radiation when there is a warm, wet interglacial.

As the amount of radiation decreases, this sequence is repeated in reverse order. When radiation is at a minimum, and this is important, there is likewise little accumulation of snow because precipitation is too low. Simpson equates this stage with a cool, dry interglacial. *One* oscillation in solar radiation thus corresponds to *two* fluctuations in the glaciers. Pluvials are caused in low latitudes at the time of greatest radiation and correspond not to a glacial phase, but to the warm, wet interglacials.

A. Wagner and others have considered whether Simpson's simple scheme would really satisfy the complex, interdependent processes of nature. For

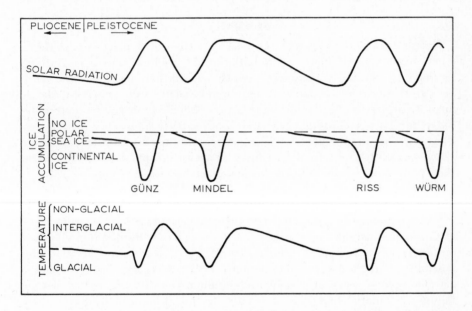

FIG. 134. MODIFICATION OF SIMPSON'S THEORY BY B. BELL (after B. Bell, 1953).

example, he has not considered the varying velocity of flow of ice. The most important objection, however, is a geological one; the interglacial climates did not correspond to Simpson's theoretical concept of them. According to him, solar radiation fluctuated twice in the Quaternary Period, and so gave rise to four glacial phases; the Great Mindel-Riss Interglacial should, like the present day, have been cool and dry; the Günz-Mindel, and Riss-Wurm interglacials warm and wet. Paleoclimatic evidence shows no such difference; in fact, it tends to show just the reverse.

Furthermore, the hypothesis demands that the glacial and pluvial phases should not coincide, yet what evidence there is suggests that they do. Also, there seem to have been as many pluvials as glacials, and not just two as there should have been.

Modification of Simpson's Hypothesis

One particularly weak point in Simpson's hypothesis is the "cool-dry" interglacial at the time of minimum solar radiation. This weakness would disappear if each glacial phase corresponded to one complete radiation rhythm. The problem has been thoroughly discussed by Willet, and most recently by B. Bell (1953) who supposes that a radiation minimum led, at least, to glaciation of the polar oceans. When radiation increases, it gives rise first of all to increased precipitation and growth of glaciers, i.e. to glaciation; finally, though, it becomes too high, and with melting of the glaciers, an interglacial or nonglacial phase results (fig. 134).

SUMMARY

Meteorologists concede that the basic principle of Simpson's hypothesis seems to be correct; increased radiation *could* produce growth of glaciers, provided the initial temperature were sufficiently low. On the other hand, geological observations make it improbable that there were two fundamentally different types of interglacial; the scheme probably fits better the difference between interglacials and interstadials. Simpson's assumption that the four major glacial phases correspond to two rhythms in solar radiation is, therefore, hard to believe. If such rhythms do cause Ice Ages, then there must be one rhythm to each glacial phase.

Whether increased or decreased radiation leads to glaciation is not of such primary interest to the geologist as to the meteorologist.

There remains the question, "Is the sun a variable star?" Measurements of the solar constant over the last few decades have afforded no indication of any great fluctuation in solar radiation, but that does not preclude the possibility that the sun is a long-period variable. A regular rhythm either of 250–300 million years, or possibly of 80 million years, can be considered for the major climatic changes of the earth's history (Chapter 20); one of a few tens or hundreds of thousands of years for the Pleistocene glacial phases. E. J. Öpik (1950), who has investigated such endogenic rhythms mathematically, suggests that fluctuation in radiation "could have been caused by the combination of nuclear reaction and gas diffusion" recurring over a period of 250 million years. Short-term variations, such as those in the Quaternary, cannot be deduced so simply by calculation.

An *aperiodic* course of events can also be considered. This would be caused by phenomena outside of the solar system, e.g. by nebulae increasing solar radiation (Hoyle and Lyttleton). It is unlikely that any definite proof of such hypotheses will appear, but it is also clear that they may not be rejected just because it is technically impossible to verify them.

Further reading: WEXLER, 1953.

28

Attempted Synthesis

Nothing can contribute more to peace of mind
than having no opinion whatsoever.
                    C. C. LICHTENBERG (1742-1799).

This much is certain; major climatic variations are extraordinarily complex phenomena, which are achieved through the workings of countless individual factors. It is, therefore, no wonder that not one of the many hypotheses which have been advanced offers a complete solution; in fact, it still appears almost impossible to solve the mystery of the Ice Ages. Geological data is still much too scanty for that, and we can only venture an attempt at a synthesis. The following observations may be regarded as fairly definite:

(1) Climates have remained fundamentally unchanged throughout the last thousand million years, except for relatively short-term "Ice Ages", one of which still exists at present.

(2) Climate is largely controlled by *geographic* conditions, which have altered continuously throughout the earth's history.

(3) The Quaternary Ice Age came *after* the Tertiary mountain building, the Gondwana Glaciation *after* the Upper Paleozoic mountain building.

(4) Varying geography cannot explain *all* climatic changes. Paleogeographic conditions in the Permo-Carboniferous and in the Pleistocene were not so fundamentally different from those of the preceding and succeeding epochs, for us to understand why Ice Ages should have originated just precisely at those times. Still less can geography account for the repeated succession of glacial and interglacial phases. The same stipulations probably apply to other less well-known cold phases.

(5) Radiation curves apparently do *not* suffice to explain the multiple glaciation of the Pleistocene Period.

(6) Polar wandering and continental drift have played no part in determining climatic conditions from Tertiary times onward, but numerous findings, especially in Paleozoic strata, suggest a different position for the pole at that time; this is in complete agreement with paleomagnetic results.

SOLAR-RELIEF HYPOTHESES

Many climatic developments can be explained on the basis of paleogeography, continental drift, etc., but it seems to me that one cannot dispense with variations in primary solar radiation. Penck was probably right to propose that "the Ice Age is exogenic in the truest sense of the word". I should imagine that two principal factors influenced climatic development simultaneously: varying solar radiation and changing geography.

When decreased radiation coincided with a favorable configuration and distribution of land and sea, there existed the basic requirements for extensive glaciation. This was the case in the Upper Paleozoic, and in the Pleistocene (particularly in the glacial phases). Geographic conditions favorable to the development of Ice Ages also existed at other times, and solar radiation must likewise have been decreased at other times, but where the two did not coincide, glaciation did not result.

R. F. Flint advocates a very similar interpretation with his Solar-Topographic Hypothesis. The ideas which I have expressed can also be referred to as a Solar-Relief Hypothesis.

Many lesser factors also influenced climate; these were responsible for small climatic changes. Individual stadials of the Quaternary Ice Age were probably dependent on such subordinate factors, but the major climatic divisions I would rather attribute to primary variations in solar radiation.

It seems to me that interpretation of the climatic history of earlier periods is not really possible without the additional assumption of polar wandering and continental drift. This applies not only to the Gondwana Glaciation, but also to the migration of the evaporite belt and the reef belt during the Paleozoic Era. Extensive shift of the continents, as proposed by Wegener, is not necessary; a moderate amount of drift would suffice to explain paleoclimatic findings. Overall movement of the earth's crust was probably more important than drift of individual continents.

29

Future Climatic Development: A Prospect

Don't worry the children about the cold,
just keep them warm. Burn everything
except Shakespeare.

Telegram from Mr. Antrobus at the approach of the
Ice age. T. Wilder, "The Skin of Our Teeth", 1942.

It is impossible to make any safe prognosis of the climatic developments of the future. This is not surprising, for we have not yet arrived at a proper diagnosis of the causes of climatic changes. Moreover, prophecy doesn't really belong in the realms of "paleo"-climatology; but it is, naturally, tempting to extrapolate the results derived from a study of paleoclimates, to predict future developments. After all, Thornton Wilder has dramatised the incident of an approaching Ice Age in his play, "The Skin of Our Teeth".

The climatic destiny of the earth is very closely related to the destiny of its source of heat, the sun, so the question is really a problem in astronomy. Many astronomers now assure us that the sun is no "burnt-out dwarf", as had been thought certain for several decades previously. It is not yet approaching extinction; rather the reverse, for in E. J. Öpik's opinion, its radiation should increase. Terrestrial temperatures would thereby eventually be raised to a point where life on earth would probably hardly be possible. This development will, however, proceed very slowly by our standards; so, despite it, Ice Ages may still be possible if conditions are otherwise favorable. Adherents of the "radiation curve" theory have expressed their views on this most definitely. W. Köppen said, for example, in 1931, "The reappearance of glacial phenomena, in the Northern Hemisphere, during the next 20,000 years or more, is out of the question according to astronomical data", and Milankovitch prophesied in his ingenious book "*Durch ferne Welten und Zeiten*" (1936) that in 26,000 years' time, Pomeranian, Mecklenburg, and Holstein wines will appear on the wine-lists of Berlin restaurants. Himpel points out that our solar system is heading toward the region of Lyra and Hercules, i.e., towards a region of the heavens where nebulae are less abundant than in the vicinity of Orion, Auriga, and Taurus, the area that we are just leaving.

However, the obvious fall in temperature since the postglacial Climatic Optimum is disquieting; from it we might deduce that we are living in an interglacial, and that a new glacial phase is approaching. C. E. P. Brooks' gloomy prediction may also be quoted here: "Some thousands of years hence, ice will again spread out from Norway and the Alps." Ewing and Donn (1956), too, see all the indications of an early return to glacial conditions, and R. W. Fairbridge (1960) concludes, from the variation in sea level, that the temperature in middle latitudes will fall by about 1° C over the next 500 years.

We are therefore faced with the choice between two opposed views; which will turn out to be correct remains to be seen. *Qui vivra verra.*

Man, himself, is already interfering with the course of climatic development through deforestation, production of CO_2, etc. Probably, in the foreseeable future, he will do so even more effectively (and possibly more disastrously—by causing, say, melting of the continental ice sheets). Then the fact that natural conditions would otherwise have favored the appearance of a new Ice Age will probably no longer hold any terrors for us— provided, of course, that there are any of us left to care.

Bibliography

"Sich gar nicht zu finden, drückt berühmte
Männer stärker, als sie sagen wollen".

JEAN PAUL RICHTER, *Dr. Katzenbergers Badereise*, 1809.

Only a selection of the older works is included; for further references see first
edition of this book.

Abbreviations used for frequently occurring periodicals

AJS	*American Journal of Science*, New Haven.
BAAPG	*Bull. Amer. Assoc. of Petrol. Geol.*, Tulsa.
BGSA	*Bull. Geol. Soc. Amer.*, New York.
BSGF	*Bull. Soc. Géol. France*, Paris.
Dokl	*Doklady Akad. Nauk U.S.S.R., Geol. Ser.*, Moscow.
EuG	*Eiszeitalter und Gegenwart*, Öhringen.
GFF	*Geol. För. Förhandl.*, Stockholm.
GM	*Geol. Mag.*, Cambridge.
GR	*Geol. Rundschau*, Stuttgart.
GS Bull	*Geol. Survey U.S.A., Bull.*, Washington.
GS ProfP	*Geol. Survey U.S.A., Prof. Paper*, Washington.
Izv	*Izvestia Akad. Nauk U.S.S.R., Geol. Ser.*, Moscow.
Izv Geogr. Ser.	*Izvestia Akad. Nauk U.S.S.R., Geogr. Ser.*, Moscow.
JG	*Journal of Geology*, Chicago.
JP	*Journal of Paleontology*, Tulsa.
NJAbh	*Neues Jahrbuch f. Geol. u. Pal., Abhandl.*, Stuttgart.
NJBB	*Neues Jahrbuch f. Geol. u. Pal., Beil.-Bd.*, Stuttgart.
NJMh	*Neues Jahrbuch f. Geol. u. Pal., Monatshefte*, Stuttgart.
QJGS	*Quart. Journ. Geol. Soc.*, London.
ZDGG	*Zeitschr. Deutsch. Geol. Ges.*, Hanover.

A

AARIO (L.), 1944.—Die spätglaziale Entwicklung der Vegetation und des Klimas
in Finnland. *GR*, 34.

ACKERMANN (E.), 1951.—Geröllton! *GR*, 39.

ADAMS (J. E.) and FRENZEL (H. N.), 1950.—Capitan barrier reef. Texas and New
Mexico. *JG*, 58.

ADIE (R. J.), 1952.—Representatives of the Gondwana System in the Falkland
Islands. *Congr. Géol. Int. 1952 Alger. Symp. Gondw.*

ADIE (R. J.), 1952.—Representatives of the Gondwana System in Antarctica.
Congr. Géol. Int. 1952. Alger. Symp. Gondw.

AHLMANN (H. W.), 1953.—*Glacier Variations and Climatic Fluctuations*. New York.

ALBRECHT (F.), 1947.—Die Aktionsgebiete des Wasser- u. Wärmehaushalts der
Erdoberfläche. *Z. Meteorol.*, 1.

ALFANO (G. B.), and FRIEDLANDER (I.).—*Die Geschichte des Vesuv.* Berlin.

ALISSOV (B. P.), 1954 —*Die Klimate der Erde.* Berlin.

ALISSOV (B. P.), DROSDOV (O. A.) and RUBINSTEIN (E. S.), 1956.—*Lehrbuch der Klimatologie.* Berlin.

ALLARD (H. A.), 1948.—Length of day in the climates of past geological eras. In: *Vernalization and Photoperiodism*, ed. A. E. Murneek and R. O. Whyte, Waltham.

ALMEIDA (F. F. M. DE), 1953.—Botucatú, a triassic desert of South America. *Congr. Géol. Int. 1952 Alger*, 7.

ALTEHENGER (A.), 1959.—Floristisch belegte Klimaschwankungen im mittel-europäischen Pliozän der Reuver-Stufe. *Palaeontogr.*, B, 106 (cf. *EuG*, 9, 1958).

ANDERSEN (S. T.), 1961.—Vegetation and its environment in Denmark in the Early Weichselian Glacial. *Danm. Geol. Unders.*, II, 75, Copenhagen.

ANDERSON (J. G. C.), 1954.—The Pre-Carboniferous rocks of the Slieve League promontory, Co. Donegal, *QJGS*, 109.

ANDERSON (R. C.), 1955.—Pebble lithology of the Marseilles till sheet in north-eastern Illinois, *JG*, 63.

ANDERSON (R. Y.) and KIRKLAND (D. W.), 1960.—Origin, varves, and cycles of Jurassic Todilto formation, New Mexico. *BAAPG*, 44.

ANDRÉANSKY (G.), 1959.—*Die Flora der sarmatischen Stufe in Ungarn.* Budapest.

ANDRÉE (K.), 1934.—Der Blitz als allgemein-geologischer Faktor und erdges-chichtliche Erscheinung. *Schrift. Phys.-ökon. Ges.* Königsberg, 68.

ANTEVS (E.), 1917.—Die Jahresringe der Holzgewächse und die Bedeutung derselben als klimatischer Indikator. *Progr. rei botan.* 5.

ANTEVS (E.), 1928.—Shell beds on the Skagerak. *GFF*, 50.

ANTEVS (E.), 1928.—The last glaciation. *Amer. Geogr. Soc., Res. Ser.*, 17.

ANTEVS (E.), 1954.—Climate of New Mexico during the Last Glacio-Pluvial. *JG*, 62.

ARBENZ (P.), 1923.—Blitzspuren vom Monte del Forno (3220 m) im Oberengadin. *Mitt. Naturforsch. Ges. Berne.*

ARCHANGELSKI (A. D.), 1927.—On the Black Sea sediments and their importance for the study of sedimentary rocks. *Bull. Soc. Nat. Moscow, Geol.*, 35.

ARELLANO (A. R. V.), 1953.—Barrilaco pedocal, a stratigraphic marker ca. 5000 B.C. and its climatic significance. *Congr. Geol. Int. 1952 Alger*, 7.

AREMBOVSKII (I. V.), 1954.—Fossil beavers in East Siberia. (Russian) *Trudy Irkutsk Univ.*, 6, 2.

ARKELL (W. J.), 1935.—On the nature, origin and climatic significance of the coral reefs in the vicinity of Oxford. *QJGS*, 91.

ARLDT (T.), 1922.—Handbuch der *Paläogeographie.* II. Leipzig.

ARRHENIUS (S.), 1896.—On the influence of carbonic acid in the air upon the temperature of the ground. *Phil. Mag.*, 41.

ASSMANN (E.), 1959.—Höhenbonität und wirkliche Ertragsleistung. *Forstwiss. Cbl.*, 78.

ATWOOD (W. W.), 1915.—Eocene glacial deposits in south-western Colorado. *GS ProfP*, 95 B.

ATWOOD (W. W.) and ATWOOD (W. R.), 1926.—Gunnison tillite of Eocene Age. *JG*, 34.

AUDOVA (A.), 1929.—Aussterben der mesozoischen Reptilien. I. II. *Paläobiol.*, 2.

AUER (V.), 1956.—The Pleistocene of Fuego-Patagonis. I. *Ann. Acad. Sci. Fenn.*, A, III, 45.

Avias (J.), 1952.—Sur la formation actuelle de gypse dans certains marais cotiers de la Nouvelle Calédonie. *Congr. Géol. Int. 1952 Alger, Rés.*

Avsjuk (G. A.), Markov (K. K.) and Shumskii (P. A.), 1956.—Cold Wastes in Antarctica. (Russian) *Izv. Geogr. Ser.*

Axelrod (D. I.), 1950.—Evolution of desert vegetation in western North America. *Publ. Carn. Inst.*, 590.

Axelrod (D. I.), 1956.—Mio-Pliocene floras from West-Central Nevada. *Publ. Univ. Calif. Geol. Sci.*, 33.

Axelrod (D. I.), 1958.—The Pliocene Verdi flora of Western Nevada. *Publ. Univ. Calif. Geol. Sci.*, 34.

B

Bacsák (G.), 1955.—Pliozän- und Pleistozänzeitalter im Licht der Himmelsmechanik. *Act. Geol.* Budapest, 3.

Bader (F. J. W.), 1960.—Die Coniferen der Tropen. *Decheniana*, 113.

Bagnold (R. A.), 1954.—*The Physics of Blown Sand and Desert Dunes*, London.

Bailey (E. B.), Collet (L. W.) and Field (R. M.), 1928.—Paleozoic submarine landslips near Quebec City. *JG*, 36.

Bailey (J. W.) and Sinnot (E. W.), 1915.—A botanical index of Cretaceous and Tertiary climates. *Sci.*, 41.

Bain (G. W.), 1956.—Concentration of brines and deposition of salts from sea water under frigid conditions. *AJS*, 254.

Bain (G. W.), 1958.—Possible Permian climatic zonation and its application. *AJS*, 256.

Bain (G. W.), 1960.—Climatic zones of the Paleozoic. *Int. Geol. Congr. 1960 Copenhagen, Rep.*, 12, Copenhagen.

Bajkovski (T. N.), 1953.—On the Neogene Flora of the Transcarpathian Area of the U.S.S.R. (Russian). *Trudy Lvov geol. Obsch.*, 2.

Bandy (O. L.), 1960.—The geologic significance of coiling ratios in the foraminifer Globigerina pachyderma. *JP*, 34.

Banks (M. R.), Loveday (J. L.) and Scott (D. L.).—Permian varves from Wyngard, Tasmania. *Pap. Proc. Roy. Soc. Tasm.*, 89.

Bardoschi (D.), 1957.—Geology of the Bauxite Deposits of Hungary. (Russian) *Izv.*

Barghoorn (E. S.), 1951.—Age and environment: a survey of North American Tertiary plant in relation to paleocology. *J. Pal.*, 25.

Barrows (W. L.), 1910.—A fulgurite from the Raritan Sands of New Columbia. *Columb. School of Mines. Quart. J.*, 31.

Barth (T. F. W.), 1956.—Geology and petrology of the Pribilof Islands, Alaska. *GS Bull.*, 1028–F.

Bateman (A. M.), 1950.—*Economic Mineral Deposits.* 2nd ed. Wiley, New York.

Becker (H. F.), 1960.—The Tertiary Mormon Creek flora from the upper Ruby River basin in SW Montana. *Palaeontogr.*, B, 107.

Bederke (E.), 1956.—Erdbild und Klima des Quartärs. *Congr. Int. Quat. 1953 Rome, Act.*, II, Rome.

Beetz (W.), 1927.—Über Glazialschichten an der Basis der Nama- und Konkipformation in der Namib. *NJBB*, 56, B.

Behrmann (W.), 1944.—Das Klima der Präglazialzeit auf der Erde. *GR*, 34.

BELIANKIN (D. S.) and PETROV (W. P.), 1950.—Petrology and Origin of the Askana Clays. (Russian) *Izv.*

BELL (B.), 1953.—Solar variation as an explication of climatic change. In: *Climatic Change*, Ed. H. Shapley.

BELL (H. S.), 1940.—Armored mud-balls—their origin, properties and role in sedimentation. *JG*, 48.

BELL (K. G.), 1948.—Geology of the Boston Metropolitan Area. Thesis, M.I.T., Cambridge (Mass.).

BENEO (E.), 1956.—Accumuli terziari da risedimentazione (Olistostroma) nell' Appennino centrale e frane sottomarine. Boll. Serv. Geol. Ital., 78.

BERG (L. S.), 1958.—*Die geographischen Zonen der Sowjetunion.* I. Leipzig.

BERGER (W.), 1952.—Neue Ergebnisse der Tertiärbotanik im Wiener Becken. *NJMh.*

BERNARD (E. A.), 1962.—Théorie astronomique des pluviaux et interpluviaux du Quaternaire africain. (Fluctuations séculaires du régime d'insolation des latitudes tropicales et leurs effets sur les régimes thermiques et pluviométriques.) *Mém. Acad. roy. Sci. d'Outre-Mer, Classe des Sci. nat. et méd.*, XII, 1, 232 pp., Brussels.

BERNARD (E. A.), 1962.—Le caractère tropical des paléoclimats à cycles conjoints de 11 et 21,000 ans et ses causes: migration des poles ou dérivé des continents. *Ibid.* XIII, 6, 60 pp., Brussels.

BERNARD (E. A.), 1962.—Théorie des oscillations annuelles et diurnes de la température à la surface des continents et des océans. Archiv. für Meteorologie, Geophysik und Bioklimatologie, Ser. A, Vol. 12, 4, pp. 502–543, Vienna.

BERNARD (E. A.), in preparation 1963.—Le rayonnement thermique des latitudes et la validation de la théorie astronomique des glaciations quaternaires.

BERNAUER (F.), 1915.—'Gekritzte Geschiebe' aus dem Diluvium von Heidelberg. *Jber. Oberrhein. Geol. Ver.*, 5.

BERRY (E. W.), 1930.—The past climate of the North Polar region. *Smith Misc. Coll.*, 82.

BERSIER (A.), 1936.—Un critère de durée dans l'Oligocène vaudois. *Bull. Soc. Vaud. Sci. Nat. Lausanne*, 59.

BESAIRIE (H.), 1952.—Les formations de Karroo à Madagascar. *Congr. Géol. Int. 1952 Alger, Symp. Gondw.*

BEURLEN (K.), 1938.—Die Bedeutung der organischen Entwicklung für die Erdgeschichte. *Nov. Act. Leop. Halle*, 5.

BEURLEN (K.), 1957.—Das Gondwana-Inlandeis in Südbrasilien. *GR*, 45.

BLACK (R. F.), 1954.—Permafrost—a review. *BGSA*, 65.

BLACKETT (P. M. S.), 1961.—Comparison of ancient climates with the ancient latitudes deduced from rock magnetic measurements. *Proc. Roy. Soc.*, A, 263.

BLACKETT (P. M. S.), CLEGG (J. A.) and STUBBS (P. H. S.), 1960.—An analysis of rock magnetic data. *Proc. Roy. Soc.*, A. 256.

BLACKWELDER (E.), 1926.—Pre-Cambrian geology of the Medicine Bow Mountains, *BGSA*, 37.

BLACKWELDER (E.), 1932.—An ancient glacial formation in Utah. *JG*, 40.

BLACKWELDER (E.), 1932.—Paleozoic glaciation in Alaska. *Sci.*, 76.

BLAKE (S. F.), 1953.—The Pleistocene fauna of Wailes Bluff and Landsleys Bluff, Maryland. *Smith Misc. Coll.*, 121.

BOETTGER (C. R.), 1954.—Die Molluskenfauna des Interglazials von Lehringen. *NJAbh.*, 100.

BOGOLEPOV (K. W.), 1955.—Stages in the Development of the Tertiary Flora of the Angara Region of the Yenisei Highlands. (Russian) *Dokl.*, 100.

BOGOLEPOV (K. W.) and POPOV (P. A.), 1955.—On the Age of the Bauxite in the Yenesei Mountains. (Russian) *Dokl.*, 100.

BÖHM V. BÖHMERSHEIM (A.), 1901.—Geschichte der Moränenkunde. *Abh. Geogr. Ges. Wien*, 3.

BOND (G.), 1950.—The Lower Carboniferous reef limestones of northern England. *JG*, 58.

BOND (G.), 1952.—Evidence of glaciation in the lower part of the Karroo System in Southern Rhodesia. *Trans. Geol. Soc. South Africa*, 55.

BORCHERT (H.), 1959.—*Ozeane Salzlagerstätten*. Berlin.

BOURDIER (F.), SITTLER (C.) and SITTLER-BECKER (J.), 1956.—Observations nouvelles relatives aux flores polliniques pliocènes et quaternaires du Bassin du Rhône. *Bull. Serv. Carte géol. Als. Lorr.*, 9.

BOUT (P.), 1951.—Sur la présence de quartz bipyramidés rhyolitiques du Mont-Dore dans les dépôts villafranchiens de Perrier. *C.R. Soc. géol. Fr.*

BOUT (P.), 1960.—*Le Villafranchien du Velay*. Le Puy.

BOUTAKOFF (N.), 1956.—Les massifs volcaniques du Kahusi et du Biega. *Mém. Inst. Géol. Louvain*, 9.

BOWEN (R. L.), 1958.—Late Paleozoic glaciation of eastern Australia. *BGSA*, 69.

BOWEN (R. N. C.), 1960.—Palaeotemperature analyses of Mesozoic Belemnoidea from Australia and New Guinea. *BGSA*, 71.

BOWEN (R. N. C.), 1961.—Palaeotemperature analyses of Mesozoic Belemnoidea from Germany and Poland. *JG*, 69, pp. 75–83.

BOWEN (R. N. C.), 1961.—Oxygen isotope palaeotemperature measurements on Cretaceous Belemnoidea from Europe, India and Japan. *JP*, 35.

BRADLEY (W. H.), 1929.—The varves and climate of the Green River Epoch. *GS ProfP*, 158–E.

BRADSHAW (J. S.), 1957.—Laboratory studies on the rate of growth of the foraminifer 'Streblus beccarii (Linné) var. tepida (Cushm.)'. *JP*, 31.

BRAITSCH (O.), 1962.—*Entstehung und Stoffbestand der Salzlagerstätten*. Springer Verlag, Berlin.

BRETZ (J. H.) and HORBERG (L.), 1949.—Caliche in south-eastern New Mexico. *JG*, 57.

BRINKMANN (R.), 1932.—Über fossile Inselberge. *Nachr. Ges. Wiss. Göttingen, Math.-phys. Kl.*

BRINKMANN (R.), 1932.—Über die Schichtung und ihre Bedingungen. *Fortschr. Geol. Pal.*, 11.

BRINKMANN (R.), 1959.—*Abriss der Geologie*. II. 8th ed. Stuttgart.

BROCH (H.), 1922.—Riffkorallen im Nordmeer einst und jetzt. *Naturw.*, 10.

BROCKAMP (B.), 1952.—Zur Frage der Vereisungszentren. *NJMh.*

BROECKER (W. S.), TUREKIAN (K. K.) and HEEZEN (B. C.), 1958.—The relation of deep sea sedimentation rates to variations in climate. *AJS*, 256.

BROOKS (C. E. P.), 1949.—*Climate through the Ages*. 2nd ed. London.

BROOKS (C. E. P.), 1949.—Post-glacial climatic changes in the light of recent glaciological research. *Geogr. Ann.*, 31.

BROWN (C. N.), 1956.—The origin of caliche on the north-eastern Llano Estacado, Texas. *JG*, 64.

BRÜCKNER (W.), 1955.—The mantle rock ('laterite') of the Gold Coast and its origin. *GR*, 43. (Cf. *Ecl. Geol. Helv.*, 50, 1957.)

BRUNNACKER (K.), 1957.—Die Geschichte der Böden im jüngeren Pleistozän in Bayern. *Geol. Bavar.*, 34.

BRYAN (M. S.), 1954.—Interglacial pollen spectra from Greenland. *Danm. Geol. Unders.*, II, 80.

BUBNOFF (S. v.), 1956.—*Einführung in die Erdgeschichte*. 3rd ed. Berlin.

BUCHER (W. H.), 1919.—On ripples and related sedimentary surface forms and their palaeogeographic interpretation. *AJS* (4), 47.

BÜDEL (J.), 1951.—Die Klimazonen des Eiszeitalters. *EuG*, 1.

BÜDEL (J.), 1959.—Periodische und episodische Solifluktion im Rahmen der klimatischen Solifluktionstypen. *Erdkd.*, 13.

BÜDEL (J.), 1960.—Die Gliederung der Würmkaltzeit. *Würzbg. Geogr. Arb.*, 8.

BÜLOW (K. v.), 1960.—Blitzröhren. *Kosmos*, 56.

BUTZER (K. W.), 1958.—Quaternary stratigraphy and climate in the Near East. *Bonner Geogr. Abh.*, 24.

C

CAHEN (L. S.) and LEPERSONNE (J.), 1951.—Esquisse de la géologie du Congo Belge. *Int. Geol. Congr. 1948 London, Rep.*, 14.

CAHEN (L. S.) and LEPERSONNE (J.), 1954.—Acquisitions nouvelles relatives aux terrains du soubassement du Congo Belge. *Congr. Géol. Int. 1952 Alger, C.R.*, 20.

CAILLEUX (A.), 1942.—Les actions periglaciaires en Europe. *Mém. Soc. géol. Fr.*, 21.

CAILLEUX (A.), 1950.—Paléoclimats et optimums physiologiques. *C.R. Séanc. Soc. Biogéogr.*, 230.

CAILLEUX (A.), 1954.—Les loess et limons éoliens de France. *Bull. Serv. Carte géol. Fr.*, 51.

CAILLEUX (A.) and TAYLOR (G.), 1954.—*Cryopédologie. Exp. Pol. Franç. Victor*, 1203, Paris.

CALDENIUS (C.), 1938.—Carboniferous varves, measured at Paterson, N.S. Wales. *GFF*, 60.

CAMPANA (B.) and WILSON (R. B.), 1955.—Tillites and related topography of South Australia. *Ecolog. Geol. Helv.*, 48.

CAMPBELL (K. S. W.), 1961.—Carboniferous fossils from the Kuttung rocks of New South Wales. *Palaeontology*, 4, pt. 3.

CASTER (K. E.), 1952.—Stratigraphic and paleontologic data relevant to the problem of Afro-American ligation during the Paleozoic and Mesozoic. *Bull. Amer. Mus. Nat. Hist.*, 99.

CECIONI (G.), 1957.—Cretaceous flysch and molasse in Departamento Ultima, Esperanza, Magallanes Province, Chile. *BAAPG*, 41.

CECIONI (G.), 1958.—Preuves en faveur d'une glaciation néojurassique en Patagonie. *BSGF*, IV, 8.

CHAMBERLIN (T. C.), 1899.—An attempt to frame a working hypothesis of the cause of glacial periods on an atmospheric basis. *JG*, 7.

CHANEY (E. W.), 1940.—Tertiary forests and continental history. *BSGA*, 51.

CHANEY (R. W.) and SANBORN (E. I.).—The Goshen flora of West Central Oregon. *Publ. Carn. Inst.*, 439.

CHAPMAN (F.), 1929.—Obsidian buttons: an Australian riddle. In: *Open-air Studies in Australia*, London.

CHARLESWORTH (J. K.), 1957.—*The Quaternary Era with Special Reference to its Glaciation*. 2 vols. London.

CHESTERS (K. J. M.), 1957.—The Miocene flora of Rusinga Island, Lake Victoria, *Palaeontogr.*, (B) 101.

CHEVALIER (J. P.), 1956.—Le récif Miocène de Langudoc. *BSGF* (6) 6.

CHEVALIER (J. P.), 1957.—Les formations récifales Miocènes de la Catalogne Espagnole. *BSGF* (6) 7.

CLARK (J.), 1962.—Field interpretation of red beds. *BGSA*, 73, pp. 423–428.

CLARKE (J. M.), 1917.—Strand and undertow markings of upper Devonian time as indication of the prevailing climate. *Bull. N. York State Mus.*, 196.

CLOUD (P. E.), 1955.—Physical limits of glauconite formation. *BAAPG*, 39.

CLOUD (P. E.), 1959.—Paleoecology—retrospect and prospect. *JP*, 33.

COLBERT (E. H.), 1953.—The record of climatic change as revealed by vertebrate paleoecology. In: *Climatic Change*, Ed. H. Shapley.

COLEMAN (A. P.), 1926.—*Ice Ages, Recent and Ancient*. London.

COLLISON (D. W.) and RUNCORN (S. K.), 1960.—Polar wandering and continental drift: evidence from paleomagnetic observations in the United States. *BSGA*, 71.

CONRAD (V.), 1936.—Die klimatologischen Elemente in ihrer Abhängigkeit von terrestrischen Einflüssen. In: Köppen-Geiger, *Hdb. Klimat.*, I, B.

COX (A.) and DOELL (R. R.), 1960.—Review on palaeomagnetism. *BGSA*, 71.

CRAIG (B. C.) and FYLES (J. G.), 1960.—Pleistocene geology of Arctic Canada. In: *Geology of the Arctic* (Ed. G. O. Raasch), I, Toronto.

CRANDELL (D. R.) and WALDRON (H. H.), 1956.—A recent volcanic mudflow of exceptional dimensions from the Mr. Rainier, Washington. *AJS*, 254.

CRANWELL (L. M.) and POST (L. v.), 1936.—Post-Pleistocene pollen diagrams from the southern hemisphere. *I. Geogr. Ann.*, 18.

CRARY (A. P.), 1962.—The Antarctic. *Scientific American*, Vol. 207, No. 3, pp. 60–73.

CROLL (J.), 1875.—*Climates and Time in their Geological Relations*. London (4th ed. 1890).

CROUZEL (F.), 1957.—Le miocène continental du Bassin d'Aquitaine. *Bull. Serv. Carte géol. Fr.*, 248.

CROWELL (J. C.), 1957.—Origin of pebbly mudstones. *BGSA*, 68.

CUMINGS (E. R.), 1932.—Reefs or bioherms? *BGSA*, 43.

CZECZOTT (H.), 1951.—The middle-Miocene flora of Zalesce near Wisnowice. *Act. geol. Pol.*, 2.

D

DAILY (B.), 1956.—The Cambrian in South Australia. *Congr. Geol. Int. 1956 Mexico, Symp. Cambr.*, II.

DALY (R. A.), 1934.—*The Changing World of the Ice Age*. New Haven.

DANGEARD (L.), 1953.—Les 'varves' lacustres de Selune. *C.R. Soc. géol. Fr.*

Dars (R.) and Sougy (J.), 1958.—La stratigraphie du 'Cambro-Ordovicien' de L'Ouest africain. *Colloq. int. Centre nat. Rech. sci. Paris*, 76.

David (T. W. E.) and Browne (W. R.), 1950.—*The Geology of the Commonwealth of Australia.* 3 vols., London.

Davis (J.), 1946.—The peat deposits of Florida. *Florida Geol. Surv. Bull.*, 30.

Deecke (W.), 1930.—Jahreszeitliche Spuren in der geologischen Stratigraphie. *Ber. Freibg. Nat. Ges.*, 30.

Deevey (E. S.), 1951.—Late-glacial and postglacial pollen diagrams from Maine. *AJS*, 249.

Deevey (E. S.), 1953.—Paleolimnology and climate. In: *Climatic Change,* Ed. H. Shapley.

Deevey (E. S.) and Flint (R. F.), 1957.—The postglacial Hypsithermal interval. *Sci.*, 125.

Degerböl (M.) and Krog (H.), 1951.—Den europaeiske Sumpskildpadde (Emys orbicularis) i Danmark. *Danm. geol. Unders.*, II, 78.

Dewall (H. R. v.), 1929.—Geologisch-biologische Studie über die Kieselgurlager der Lüneburger Heide. *Jb. Preuss. Geol. L.A.*, 49, II.

Dicke (R. H.), 1962.—The earth and cosmology. *Sci*, 138, pp. 653–664.

Dietrich (G.), 1957.—*Meereskunde.* Berlin.

Dillon (L. S.), 1956.—Wisconsin climate and life zones in North America. *Sci.*, 123.

Dimbleby (G. W.), 1952.—Pleistocene ice wedge in north-east Yorkshire. *J. Soil Sci.*, 3.

Dittmer (E.), 1941.—Das nordfriesische Eem. *Kieler Meeresforsch.*

Dolianiti (E.), 1955.—Frutos de Nipa no Paleoceno de Pernambuco, Brasil. *Dep. Nac. Prod. Min., Bol.*, 158.

Dorf (E.), 1933.—Pliocene floras of California. *Publ. Carn. Inst. Wash.*, 412

Dorf (E.), 1955.—Plants and the geologic time scale. *Geol. Soc. Amer.*, Spec. Pap., 62.

Dorf (E.), 1959.—Climatic changes of the past and present. *Contr. Mus. Pal. Michigan*, 13.

Dorman (F. H.) and Gill (E. D.), 1959.—Oxygen isotope palaeotemperature measurements on Australian fossils. *Proc. Roy. Soc. Victoria*, 71, Melbourne.

Dott (R. H.), 1961.—Squantum 'tillite', Massachusetts. *BGSA*, 72, pp. 1289–1303.

Dubief (J.), 1956.—Note sur l'évolution du climat saharien au cours des derniers millénaires. *Congr. Int. Quat. 1953 Rome, Act.*, II.

Dubois (E.), 1893.—*Die Klimate der geologischen Vergangenheit und ihre Beziehungen zur Entwicklungsgeschichte der Sonne.* Leipzig.

Ducker (A.), 1954.—Die Periglazial-Erscheinungen im holsteinischen Pleistozän. *Gött. Geogr. Abh.*, 16.

Dunbar (C. O.), 1959.—*Historical Geology.* 2nd ed. New York.

Dunbar (C. O.) and Rodgers (J.), 1957.—*Principles of Stratigraphy.* New York.

Dunham (K. C.), 1953.—Red coloration in desert formations of Permian and Triassic age in Britain. *Int. Geol. Congr. 1952 Alger, C.R.*, 7.

Durham (J. W.), 1950.—Cenozoic marine climates of the Pacific coast. *BGSA*, 61.

Durham (J. W.), 1952.—Early Tertiary marine faunas and continental drift. *AJS*, 250.

Durham (J. W.), 1959.—Palaeoclimates. *Phys. Chem. Earth*, 3.

Dusén (P.), 1908.—Die tertiäre Flora der Seymourinsel. *Wiss. Erg. Schwed. Südpolarexp.* (1901–03).

Du Toit (A. L.), 1937.—*Our Wandering Continents*. Edinburgh.

Du Toit (A. L.), 1954.—*The Geology of South Africa*. 3rd ed. Ed. S. H. Haughton. Edinburgh.

E

Eardley (A. J.) and Gvosdetzky (V.), 1960.—Analysis of Pleistocene core from Great Salt Lake. *BGSA*, 71.

Eberl (B.), 1930.—*Die Eiszeitenfolge im nördlichen Alpenvorland*. Augsburg.

Ebert (H.), 1957.—Beitrag zur Gliederung des Präkambriums in Minas Gerais. *GR*, 45.

Eckardt (W. R.), 1921.—Die Paläoklimatologie, ihre Methoden und ihre Anwendungen auf die Paläobiologie. *Hdb. biol. Arbeitsmeth.*, X, 3.

Edwards (W. N.), 1936.—The flora of the London clay. *Proc. Geol. Assoc.*, 47.

Eidmann (H.), 1942.—Zur Ökologie der Tierwelt des afrikanischen Regenwaldes. *Beitr. Kolonialforsch.*, 2.

Einarsson (T.), 1961.—Pollenanalytische Untersuchungen zur spät- und postglazialen Klimageschichte Islands. *Sonderveröffentl. Geol. Inst. Köln*, 6.

Elwell (R. W. D.), 1955.—The lithology and structure of a boulder-bed in the Dalradian of Mayo, Ireland. *QSGS*, 111.

Emery (K. O.), 1941.—Transportation of rock particles by sea-mammals. *J. Sed. Petrol.*, 11.

Emiliani (C.), 1955.—Pleistocene temperatures. *JG*, 63.

Emiliani (C.), 1956.—Oligocene and Miocene temperatures of the equatorial and subtropical Atlantic Ocean. *JG*, 64.

Emiliani (C.), 1958.—Paleotemperatures analysis of core 280 and Pleistocene correlations. *JG*, 66.

Emiliani (C.) and Epstein (S.), 1953.—Temperature variations in the Lower Pleistocene of southern California. *JG*, 61.

Emiliani (C.) and Geiss (J.), 1959.—On glaciations and their causes. *GR*, 46.

Engelhardt (W.), 1962.—Neuere Erdgebnisse der Tonmineralien forschung. *Geol. Rund.*, 51, pp. 457–477.

Enquist (F.), 1916.—Der Einfluss des Windes auf die Verteilung der Gletscher. *Bull. Geol. Inst. Uppsala*, 14.

Erdtmann (G.), 1937.—Pollen grains recovered from the atmosphere over the Atlantic. *Medd. Göteb. Bot. Trädj.* 12.

Erhart (H.), 1956.—La genèse des sols en tant que phénomène géologique. Paris.

Ericson (D. B.), 1959.—Coiling direction of Globigerina pachyderma as a climatic index. *Sci.*, 130.

Ericson (D. B.), Broecker (W. S.), Kulp (J. L.) and Wollin (G.), 1956.—Late Pleistocene climates and deep-sea sediments. *Sci.*, 124.

Eristavi, (M.S.), 1955.—Lower Cretaceous Fauna of Georgia. (Russian) Monogr. *Geol. Min. Akad. Nauk Grus. U.S.S.R.*, 6.

Ewing (M.), and Donn (W. L.), 1958.—A theory of Ice Ages. *Sci.*, 123, 1958 and 127, 1958.

Eyles (V. A.), 1952.—The composition and origin of the Antrim laterites and bauxites. *Mem. Geol. Surv., Gov. N. Ireland*.

F

FAIRBRIDGE (R. W.), 1947.—Possible causes of intraformational disturbances in the Carboniferous varve rocks of Australia. *J. Proc. Roy. Soc. New South Wales*, 81, 1947.

FAIRBRIDGE (R. W.), 1950.—Recent and Pleistocene coral reefs of Australia. *JG*, 58.

FAIRBRIDGE (R. W.), 1953.—*Australian Stratigraphy*. 2nd ed. Nedlands.

FAIRBRIDGE (R. W.), 1958.—Dating the latest movements of the Quaternary sea level. *Trans. New York Acad. Sci.*, II, 20.

FAIRBRIDGE (R. W.) and TEICHERT (C.), 1953.—Soil horizons and marine bands in the coastal limestones of Western Australia. *J. Proc. Roy. Soc. New South Wales*, 86.

FELL (H. B.), 1956.—Tertiary sea temperatures in Australia and New Zealand, from the evidence of fossil echinoderms. *Int. Zool. Congr. 1953 Copenhagen, Proc.*

FENTON (C. L.) and FENTON (M. A.), 1957.—Paleoecology of the Precambrian of North-western North America. *Mem. Geol. Soc. Amer.*, 67.

FIALA (F.) and SVOBODA (J.), 1956.—The problem of the Subcambrian and of the Subcambrian glaciation in Zelezne Hory. *Sborn. Ustr. Ust. Geol.*, 22.

FIEGE (F.), 1939.—Die Zyklische Sedimentation in der Salzfazies des deutschen Zechsteins und die Grossfluthypothese. *Zbl. Min. etc.*, B.

FILZER (P.), 1948.—Ein Beitrag zur ökologischen Anatomie von Rhynia. *Biol. Zbl.*, 67.

FINK (J.), 1956.—Zur Korrelation der Terrassen und Lösse in Österreich. *EuG*, 7.

FIRBAS (F.), 1949 and 1952.—*Spät- und nacheiszeitliche Waldgeschichte Mitteleuropas nördlich der Alpen*. I. II. Jena.

FIRBAS (F.), 1951.—Die quartäre Vegetationsentwicklung zwischen den Alpen und der Nord- und Ostsee. *Erdkunde*, 5.

FISCHER (E.), 1950.—Pflanzenabdrücke aus dem alttertiär von Mosel b. Zwickau. *Abh. Geol. LA Berlin*, 221.

FISCHER (W.), 1927.—Blitzröhren aus den miozänen Glassanden von Guteborn bei Ruhland. *NJBB*, 56, A (cf. *Abh. Nat. Ges. Görlitz*, 30, 3, 1929).

FIWEG (M. P.), 1954.—On the duration of sedimentation of salt-beds. (Russian) *Trudy Vses. nauch-issl. Inst. Gal.*, 29.

FLEMING (C. A.), 1956.—Quaternary geochronology in New Zealand. *Congr. Int. Quat., 1953 Rome, Act.*, II.

FLEMING (R. H.), 1957.—General features of the ocean. *Mem. Geol. Soc. Amer.*, 67.

FLINT (R. F.), 1957.—*Glacial and Pleistocene Geology*. New York.

FLINT (R. F.), 1959.—Pleistocene climates in eastern and southern Africa. *BGSA*, 70.

FLINT (R. F.) and GALE (W. E.), 1958.—Stratigraphy and radiocarbon dates at Searles Lake, California. *AJS*, 256.

FLOHN (H.), 1952.—Algemeine atmosphärische Zirkulation und Paläoklimatologie. *GR*, 40.

FLOHN (H.), 1959.—Kontinental-Verschiebungen, Polwanderungen und Vorzeitklimate im Lichte paläomagnetischer Massbergebnisse. *Nat. Rdsch.*, 12.

FONT-ALBA (M.) and CLOSAS (J. M.), 1960.—A bauxite deposit in the Paleozoic of Leon, Spain. *Econ. Geol.*, 55.

FORMAN (McL. J.) and SCHLANGER (S. O.), 1957.—Tertiary reef and associated Limestone facies from Louisiana and Guam. *JG*, 65.

FÖYN (S.), 1937.—The Eo-Cambrian series of the Tana district, Northern Norway. *Norsk Geol. Tidskr.*, 17.

FRÄNKEL (J. J.), 1955.—Water-faceted pebbles from Isipingo Beach. Natal, South Africa. *JG*, 63.

FRÄNKL (E.), 1953.—Geologische Untersuchungen in Ost-Andrées Land. Medd. Grönld., 113, 4.

FRENZEL (B.), 1960.—Die Vegetations- und Landschaftszonen Nordeurasiens während der letzten Eiszeit und während der postglazialen Wärmezeit. I. *Akad. Wiss. Lit. Mainz, Abh. Math.-Nat. Kl.*, 1959, 13 (cf. *Erdkd.*, 9, 1955, and with C. Troll, *EuG*, 2, 1952).

FREYBERG (B. v.), 1957.—Bilder vom Bergrutsch bei Ebermannstadt vom 18–19 Februar 1957, *Geol. Bl. NO-Bay.*, 7.

FRISTRUP (B.), 1953.—High arctic deserts. *Congr. géol. int. 1952 Alger, C.R.*, 7.

FRYE (J. C.) and LEONARD (A. B.), 1957.—Ecological interpretations of Pliocene and Pleistocene stratigraphy in the Great Plains region. *AJS*, 255.

FUCHS (V. E.) and PATTERSON (T. T.), 1947.—The relation of volcanicity and orogeny to climatic change. *GM*, 84.

FURON (R.), 1950.—Les problèmes de paléoclimatologie et de paléobiologie posés par la géologie de l'Arctide. *C.R. Séanc. Soc. Biogéogr.*, 230.

G

GAERTNER (H. R. v.), 1943.—Bemerkungen über den Tillit von Bigganjarga am Varangerfjord. *GR*, 34, 1943.

GAGEL (C.), 1923.—Das Klima der Diluvialzeit. *ZDGG*, 75, *Mber.*

GALLIHER (E. W.), 1935.—Geology of glauconite. *BAAPG*, 19.

GALLWITZ (H.), 1949.—Eiskeile und glaziale Sedimentation. *Geologica*, 2.

GAMS (H.), 1954.—Neue Beiträge zur Vegetations- und Klimageschichte der nord- u. mitteleuropäischen Interglaziale. *Experientia*, 10.

GEER (G. DE), 1940.—Geochronologia Suecia principles. *Kg. Svensk Vet.* Akad. Hd., 18 (6).

GENIESER (K.), 1955.—Ehemalige Elbeläufe in der Lausitz. *Geol.*, 4.

GENTILLI (J.), 1948.—Present-day volcanicity and climatic change. *GM*, 85.

GENTILLI (J.), 1958.—*A Geography of Climate*. Perth.

GERASSIMOV (I. P.) and MARKOV (K. K.), 1954.—Die Paläogeographie der USSR im Eiszeitalter. *Congr. géol. int. 1952, Alger, C.R.*, 15.

GERTH (H.), 1925.—Die Bedeutung der tertiären Riffkorallenfauna des malayischen Archipels für die Entwicklung der lebenden Riff-Fauna. *Verh. Geol. Mijnb. Gen., Geol. Ser.*, 8.

GERTH (H.), 1952.—Das Klima des Permzeitalters. *GR*, 40.

GERTH (H.), 1957.—Das Vorkommen von permokarbonischen Fusulinenkalken im westpatoginischen Archipel und seine paläogeographische und paläoklimatologische Bedeutung. *ZDGG*, 109.

GEVERS (T. W.), 1933.—Zur Kenntnis des Chuos-Tillits in Südwestafrika. *CblMin.* etc. B.

GEVERS (T. W.) and BEETZ (W.), 1937.—Pre-Dwyka glacial periods in southern Africa. *Int. Geol. Congr. 1936 Moscow, Abstr.*

GIESENHAGEN (K.), 1925–26.—Kieselgur als Zeitmass für eine Interglazialzeit. *Z. Gletscherkd.*, 14.

GILBERT (G. K.), 1890.—Lake Bonneville. *U.S. Geol. Surv. Mon.*, 1.

GILES (A. W.), 1930.—Peat as a climatic indicator. *BGSA*, 41.

GILL (E. D.), 1956.—Current Quaternary studies in Victoria, Australia. *Congr. Int. Quat. 1953, Rome, Act.*, II.

GLAESSNER (M. F.) and PARKIN (L. W.), 1958.—*The Geology of South Australia.* Melbourne.

GLEN (J. W.), DONNER (J. J.) and WEST (R. G.), 1957.—On the mechanism by which stones in till become orientated. *AJS*, 255.

GODWIN (H.), 1956.—*The History of British Flora.* Cambridge.

GOLD (T.), 1955.—Instability of the earth's axis of rotation. *Nature*, 175.

GORDON (M.), TRACEY (J. I.) and ELLIS (M. W.), 1958.—Geology of the Arkansas bauxite region. *GS ProfP*, 299.

GOTHAN (W.), 1924.—Paläobiologische Betrachtungen über die fossile Pflanzenwelt. *Fortschr. Geol. Pal.*, 8.

GOTHAN (W.) and WEYLAND (H.), 1954.—*Lehrbuch der Paläobotanik.* Berlin.

GRAHMANN (R.), 1932.—Der Löss in Europa. *Mitt. Ges. Erdkd. Leipzig*, 51.

GRAHMANN (R.), 1937.—Form und Entwässerung des nordeuropäischen Inlandeises. *Mitt. Ges. Erdkd. Leipzig*, 54.

GRAINDOR (M.-J.), 1957.—Le Briovérien dans le nord-est du Massif Armoricain. *Mém. Carte Géol. Fr.*, 1957.

GRAUL (H.), 1959.—Der Verlauf des glazial-eustatischen Meeresspiegel-Anstieges, berechnet an Hand von C–14–Datierungen. *Dtsch. Geographentag Berlin.*

GRIFFIN (G. M.), 1962.—Regional clay mineral facies—products of weathering intensity and current distribution in the north-eastern Gulf of Mexico. *Bull. Geol. Soc. Amer.*, 73, pp. 737–768.

GRIGORIEV (V. N.) and SEMICHATOV (M. A.), 1958.—On the question of the age of 'tillites' in the northern part of the Yenisei Mountains. (Russian) *Izv.*

GRIPENBERG (W. S.), 1933.—Über eine theoretisch mögliche Art der Paläothermie. *Ark. Kemi* etc., 11, A.

GRIPP (K.), 1924.—Über die äussere Grenze der letzten Vereisung in NW-Deutschland. *Mitt. geogr. Ges. Hamburg*, 36.

GRIPP (K.), 1929.—Glaziologische und geologische Ergebnisse der Hamburger Spitzbergen-Expedition 1927. *Abh. Nat. Ver. Hamburg*, 22.

GRIPP (K.), 1958.—Rezente und fossile Flachmeer-Absätze, petrologisch betrachtet und gedeutet. *GR*, 47.

GRISTCHENKO (M. N.) and GLUSTCHENKO (E. I.), 1956.—Flora of the Kinelj Beds near Shiguli on the Volga. (Russian) *Dokl.*, 106.

GROMOV (V. I.) *et al.*, 1960.—Stratigraphy of the Quaternary (Anthropogene) Deposits of Asiatic Russia, and their Correlation with Europe. (Russian) *Trudy Geol. Inst. Akad. Nauk USSR*, 26.

GROMOV (W. I.), KRASNOV (I. I.) and NIKIFOROVA (K. W.), 1959.—Grundprinzipien der stratigraphischen Gliederung des Quartärs. *Ber. Geol. Ges. DDR*, 4.

GROSS (H.), 1958.—Die bisherigen Ergebnisse von C[14]-Messungen und paläo-

lithischen Untersuchungen für die Gliederung und Chronologie des Jungpleis-
tozäns in Mitteleuropa. *EuG*, 9.

GRUND (H.), 1928.—Beiträge zum Studium fossiler Holzkohlenbildungen,
besonders in Braunkohlenlagerstätten. *Jb. Preuss. Geol. L.A.*, 49, I.

GUNTER (G.), 1957.—Temperature. *Mem. Geol. Soc. Amer.*, 67.

GUSSOW (W. C.), 1956.—Late Keweenawan or early Cambrian glaciation in
Upper Michigan? *BGSA*, 67.

H

HADDING (A.), 1950.—Silurian reefs of Gotland. *JG*, 58.

HALL (W. E.), 1957 and 1959.—Genesis of 'Haymond boulder beds', Marathon
Basin, West Texas. *BAAPG*, 41, 1957 and 43, 1959.

HAMILTON (E. L.), 1956.—Sunken islands of the Mid-Pacific mountains. *Mem.
Geol. Soc. Amer.*, 64.

HAMMEN (T. V. D.), 1957.—Climatic periodicity and evolution of South American
Maestrichtian and Tertiary floras. *Bol. Geol.*, 5, 2.

HAMMEN (T. V. D.) and GONZALEZ (E.), 1960.—Holocene and late Glacial climate
and vegetation of Paramo de Palacio. *Geol. en Mijnb.*, 39.

HANDLIRSCH (A.), 1910.—Die Bedeutung der fossilen Insekten für die Geologie.
Mitt. Geol. Ges. Wien, 3.

HANN (J. V.) and KNOCH (K.), 1932.—*Handbuch der Klimatologie.* 4th ed. Stuttgart.

HANSEN (H. P.), 1948.—Postglazial forests of the Glacier National Park region.
Ecology, 29.

HANSEN (S.), 1940.—Varvity in Danish and Scanian Late-Glacial deposits. *Danm.
Geol. Unders.*, II.

HANTKE (R.), 1954.—Die fossile Flora der obermiozänen Oehningen-Fundstelle
Schrozburg. *Denkschr. Schweiz. Nat. Ges.*, 80.

HÄNTZSCHEL (W.), 1935.—Rezente Eiskristalle in meerischen Sedimenten und
fossile Eiskristall-Spuren. *Senckenbergiana*, 17.

HANZAWA (S.), 1950.—Tertiary paleogeography of North Japan. *Short Pap.,
Inst. Geol. Tohoku Univ. Sendai*, 2.

HARKIN (D. A.), McKINLAY (A. C. M.) and SPENCE (J.), 1954.—The Karroo
System of Tanganyika. *Congr. Geol. Int. 1952 Alger, C.R.*, 21.

HARLAND (W. B.), 1960.—The development of Hekla Hoek rocks in Spitzbergen.
Int. Geol. Congr. 1960 Copenhagen, Rep., 19.

HARRASSOWITZ (H. L. F.), 1926.—Laterit. *Fortschr. Geol. Pal.*, IV, 14.

HARRIS (S. E.), 1943.—Friction cracks and the direction of glacial movement.
JG, 51.

HARRIS (T. M.), 1958.—Forest fire in the Mesozoic. *J. Ecol.*, 46.

HAUGHTON (S. H.) and MARTIN (H.), 1956.—The Nama system in South and SW
Africa. *Congr. Geol. Int. 1956 Mexico, Symp. Cambr.*, I.

HAUPT (H.), 1950.—Die Käfer (Coleopteren) aus der eozänen Braunkohle des
Geiseltals. *Geologica*, 6.

HEER (O.), 1855–59.—*Flora tertiaria Helvetiae.* I–III. Winterthur.

HEER (O.), 1868–83.—*Flora fossilis arctica.* I–VII.

HEIM (ALB.), 1919–23.—*Geologie der Schweiz.* I–II. Leipzig.

HEIM (ALB.), 1932.—*Bergsturz und Menschenleben.* Zürich.

HEIM (ARN.), 1924.—Über submarine Sedimentation und chemische Sedimente. *GR*, 15.

HEIM (ARN.), 1951.—On the glaciation of South America as related to tectonics. *Ecl. Geol. Helv.*, 44.

HERMES (K.), 1955.—Die Lage der oberen Waldgrenze in den Gebirgen der Erde und ihr Abstand zur Schneegrenze. *Köln. Geogr. Arb.*, 5.

HESSE (R.), 1924.—*Tiergeographic auf ökologischer Grundlage.* Jena.

HIBBARD (C. W.), 1955.—The Jinglebob interglacial (Sangamon?) fauna from Kansas and its climatic significance. *Contr. Mus. Pal. Mich.*, 12, 10.

HIGGINS (C. G.), 1956.—Formation of small ventifacts. *JG*, 64.

HILL (D.), 1957.—The sequence and distribution of Upper Paleozoic coral faunas. *Aust, J. Sci.*, 19.

HILL (D.), 1959.—Sakmarian geography. *GR*, 47.

HIMPEL (K.), 1947.—Ein Beitrag zum Eiszeitproblem. *Z. Naturf.*, 2, a.

HINTZE (E.), 1934.—Biostratonomische Betrachtungen zur Karte eines umgebrochenen miozänen Braunkohlenwaldes im Tagebau 'Vergissmeinnicht'. *Braunk.*, 33.

HÖGBOM (B.), 1914.—Über die geologische Bedeutung des Frostes. *Bull. Geol. Inst. Uppsala*, 12.

HOLLICK (A.), 1936.—The Tertiary floras of Alaska. *GS ProfP*, 182.

HOLMES (C. D.), 1960.—Evolution of till-stone shapes, Central New York. *BGSA*, 71.

HOLMES (C. D.) and COLTON (R. B.), 1960.—Patterned ground near Dundas, Greenland. *Medd. Grönld.*, 158.

HOLMSEN (P.), 1957.—The Eocambrian beds below the Hyolithus-zone between Carajavrre and Caskias, Western Finmark. *Norg. Geol. Unders.*, 200.

HOLTEDAHL (O.), 1960.—Geology of Norway. *Norg. Geol. Unders.*, 208.

HOLTEDAHL (O.), FÖYN (S.) and REITAN (P. H.), 1960.—Aspects of the geology of northern Norway. *Int. Geol. Congr. 1960 Copenhagen, Guide A 3.*

HOLZ (H. W.), 1960.—Geologie der Höhlen von Ründeroth und Wiehl. *Decheniana*, 113.

HOPKINS (D. M.), 1959.—Cenozoic history of the Bering land bridge. *Sci.*, 129.

HOPKINS (D. M.) and KARLSTROM (T. N. V.), 1955.—Permafrost and ground water in Alaska. *GS ProfP*, 264.

HOPKINS (D. M.), MACNEIL (F. S.) and LEOPOLD (E. B.), 1960.—The coastal plain at Nome, Alaska: a late Cenozoic type section of the Bering Strait region. *Int. Geol. Congr. 1960 Copenhagen, Rep.*, 4.

HORNSTEIN (F. F.), 1902.—Eine Reihe von Belegmaterialien zur Geologie der Umgebung von Kassel. *ZDGG*, 54.

HOSHIAI (M.) and KOBAYASHI (K.), 1957.—A theoretical discussion on the so-called 'snow-line', with reference to the temperature during the last Glacial Age in Japan. *Jap. J. Geol. Geogr.*, 28.

HOUGH (J. L.), 1950.—Pleistocene lithology of Antarctic ocean-bottom sediments. *JG*, 58.

HOUPÉ (P.), 1958.—Essai de corrélation de quelques formations cambriennes et infracambriennes. *Colloq. int. Centre nat. rech. sci. Paris*, 76.

HOUTEN (F. B. v.), 1948.—Origin of red-banded early Cainozoic deposits in Rocky Mountains region. *BAAPG*, 32, 1948.

Houten (F. B. v.), 1957.—Appraisal of Ridgway and Gunnison 'tillites' in south-western Colorado. *BGSA*, 68.

Hoyle (F.) and Lyttleton (R. A.), 1939.—The effect of interstellar matter on climatic variation. *Proc. Cambridge Phil. Soc.*, 35.

Huber (B.), 1948.—Die Jahresringe der Bäume als Hilfsmittel der Klimatologie und Chronologie. *Naturw.*, 35.

Huber (B.), 1960.—Dendrochronologie. *GR*, 49.

Humphrey (W. E.), 1955.—Permian glaciation in northern Mexico? *BGSA*, 66.

Hunt (C. B.) and Sokoleff (V. P.), 1950.—Pre-Wisconsin soil in the Rocky Mountain region, a progress report. *GS ProfP.*, 221–G.

Huntington (E.) and Visher (S. S.), 1922.—*Climatic Changes, their Nature and Cause*. New Haven.

Hyde (J. E.), 1911.—The ripples of the Bedford and Beren formations of Central and Southern Ohio. *JG*, 19.

Hyyppä (E.), 1942.—Über das spätglaziale Klima in Finnland. *GR*, 32.

I

Illies (H.), 1949.—Die Lithogenese des Untereozäns in Nordwestdeutschland. *Mitt. Geol. Staatsinst. Hamburg*, 18.

Illies (H.), 1960.—Geologie der Gegend von Valdivia (Chile). *NJAbh.*, 111.

Irving (E.), 1960.—Palaeomagnetic pole positions. I. *Geophys. T.*, 3.

Iversen (J.), 1936.—Sekundärer Pollen als Fehlerquelle. *Danm. Geol. Unders.*, IV, 2.

Iversen (J.), 1960.—Problems of the early Post-Glacial forest development in Denmark. *Danm. Geol. Unders.*, IV, 4. 3.

Ives (R. L.), 1940.—An astronomical hypothesis to explain Permian glaciation. *J. Franklin Inst.*, 230.

Ives (R. L.), 1946.—Desert ripples. *AJS*, 244.

Ives (R. L.), 1948.—An early report of ancient lakes in the Bonneville Basin. *JG*, 56.

Ives (R. L.), 1950.—Glaciation in Little Cottonwood Canyon. *Utah Sci. Monthly*, 71.

J

Jacob (H.), 1956.—Untersuchungen über die Beziehung zwischen dem petrographischen Aufbau von Weichbraunkohlen und der Brikettierbarkeit. *Freib. Forsch. H.*, A 45.

Jacob (K.), 1955.—Jurassic plants from the Saighan Series of Northern Afghanistan and their palaeo-climatological and palaeo-geographical significance. *Pal. Ind.*, 33.

Jakubovskaya (T. A.), 1955.—Sarmatian flora in the Moldau region. (Russian) *Trudy Bot. Inst. Ak. Nauk USSR*, 11.

James (H. L.), 1958.—Stratigraphy of Pre-Keweenawan rocks in parts of Northern Michigan. *GS ProfP*, 314–C.

Johnsson (G.), 1959.—True and false ice-wedges in Southern Sweden. *Geogr. Ann.*, 41.

Johnston (W. A.), 1922.—The character of the stratification of the sediments in the recent delta of Fraser River. *JG*, 30.

JOLEAUD (L.), 1939.—*Atlas de Paléobiographie*. Paris.

JONSSON (J.), 1954.—Outline of the geology of the Hornarfjordur region. *Geogr. Ann.*, 36.

JUDSON (S.), 1946.—Late glacial chronology on Adak. *JG*, 54.

JÜNGST (H.), 1934.—Zur geologischen Bedeutung der Synärese. *GR*, 25.

JÜNGST (H.), 1938.—Paläogeographische Auswertung der Kreuzschichtung. *Geol. Meere u. Binneng.*, 2.

JUNNER (N. R.), 1954.—Notes on the classification of the Pre-Cambrian of West Africa. *Congr. Géol. Inst. 1952 Alger, C.R.*, 20.

JUX (U.), 1956.—Über Alter und Entstehung von Decksand und Löss, Dünen und Windschliffen an den Randhöhen des Bergischen Landes östlich von Köln. *NJAbh.*, 104.

JUX (U.), 1960.—Die devonischen Riffe im Rheinischen Schiefergebirge. *NJAbh.*, 110.

JUX (U.) and ROSENBAUER (K. A.), 1959.—Zum Vorkommen von Cetaceen-Resten in jungpleistozänen Flussablagerungen der Niederrheinischen Bucht. *NJAbh.*, 108.

K

KAISER (E.), 1927.—Über Fanglomerate, besonders im Ebrobecken. *Sitz. ber. Bay. Akad. Wiss., Math.-nat. Kl.*

KAISER (K.), 1956.—Geologische Untersuchungen über die Hauptterrasse in der Niederrheinischen Bucht. *Sonderveröff. Geol. Inst. Köln*, 1.

KAISER (K.), 1958.—Die Talasymmetrien des Erftbeckens als Zeugen des jungpleistozänen Periglazialklimas. *Decheniana*, 111.

KAISER (K.), 1958.—Wirkungen des pleistozänen Bodenfrostes in den Sedimenten der Niederrheinischen Bucht. *EuG*, 9.

KAISER (K.), 1960.—Klimazeugen des periglazialen Dauerfrostbodens in Mittel- und Westeuropa. *EuG*, 11.

KAISER (R. F.), 1962.—Composition and origin of glacial till, Mexico and Kasoag quadrangles, New York. *J. Sed. Petrol.*, 32, pp. 502–513.

KATZ (H. R.), 1954.—Einige Bemerkungen zur Lithologie und Stratigraphie der Tillitprofile im Gebiet des Kaiser-Franz-Joseph-Fjords, Ostgrönland. *Medd. Grönld.*, 72.

KAUTSKY (G.), 1949.—Eokambrische Tillitvorkommen in Norbotten, Schweden. *GFF*, 71.

KAY (G. F.), 1931.—Classification and duration of the Pleistocene period. *BGSA*, 42.

KEGEL (W.), 1957.—Das Paranaiba-Becken. *GR*, 45.

KEILHACK (K.), 1929.—Der Glassand von Hohenbocka. *Abh. Nat. Ges. Görlitz*, 30, 3.

KENDREW (W. G.), 1957.—*Climatology*. 2nd ed. Oxford.

KERNER-MARILAUN (F.), 1930.—*Paläoklimatologie*. Berlin.

KERSEN (J. F. v.), 1956.—Bauxite deposits in Suriname and Demerara. *Leidse Geol. Med.*, 21.

KESSLER (P.), 1925.—*Das eiszeitliche Klima und seine geologischen Wirkungen im nicht vereisten Gebiet*. Stuttgart.

KHAN (M. H.), 1950.—Note on the depth and temperature of the Gault sea as indicated by foraminifera. *GM*, 87.

KINDLE (E. M.), 1930.—Sedimentation in a glacial lake. *JG*, 38.

KING (L. C.), 1958.—Basic palaeogeography of Gondwanaland during the late Palaeozoic and Mesozoic eras. *QJGS*, 114.

KING (P. B.), 1938.—Geology of the Marathon region, Texas. *GS ProfP*, 187.

KIRCHHEIMER (F.), 1929.—Zur Biologie des fossilen Laubblattes. Träufelspitzige Regenblätter in miozanen Tertiärfloren. *Biol. Cbl.*, 49.

KIRCHHEIMER (F.), 1937.—*Grundzüge einer Pflanzenkunde der deutschen Braunkohlen.* Halle.

KIRCHHEIMER (F.), 1957.—*Die Laubgewächse der Braunkohlenzeit.* Halle.

KIRK (E.), 1918.—Paleozoic glaciation in south-eastern Alaska. *AJS*, 46.

KLEBELSBERG (R. v.), 1948.—*Handbuch der Gletscherkunde und Glazialgeologie.* I. II. Vienna.

KLOTZ (G.), 1955.—Die wichtigsten Etappen der Vegetationsentwicklung auf dem Boden der USSR vom Beginn des Mesozoikums bis zum Ausgang des Tertiärs nach Ergebnissen der Sporen- und Pollenanalyse. *Wiss. Z. Univ. Halle*, 5.

KLOTZ (G.) and NEYSTADT (M. I.), 1955.—Die Vegetationsgeschichte der USSR im Holozän nach Ergebnissen der Pollenanalyse. *Wiss. Z. Univ. Halle*, 4.

KLUMPP (B.) and WETZEL (W.), 1950.—Über mesozoische und alttertiäre Treibhölzer Norddeutschlands. *Schrift. Nat. Ver. Schleswig-Holst.*, 24.

KLUTE (F.), 1928.—Die Bedeutung der Depression der Schneegrenze für eiszeitliche Probleme. *Z. Gletsch.*, 16.

KLUTE (F.), 1951.—Das Klima Europas während des Maximums der Weichsel-Würmeiszeit und die Anderungen bis zur Jetztzeit. *Erdk.*, 5.

KLUTE (F.) and KRASSER (L.), 1940.—Über Wüstenlackbildung im Hochgebirge. *Peterm. Geogr. Mitt.*, 86.

KNETSCH (G.), 1954.—Allgemein-geologische Beobachtungen aus Ägypten. *NJAbh*, 99.

KOBAYASHI (T.), 1942.—On the climatic bearing of the Mesozoic floras in eastern Asia. *Jap. J. Geol. Geogr.*, 18.

KOBAYASHI (T.), 1956.—A palaeo-meteorological interpretation to the occurrence of the Argonautinae in Province Kayo, Central Japan. *Jap. J. Geol. Geogr.*, 27.

KOENIGSWALD (H. R. v.), 1930.—Die Klimaänderung im Jungtertiär Mitteleuropas und ihre Ursachen. *Z. Geschiebef.*, 6.

KOMAROV (A. G.), 1960.—Polar wandering during the earth's history. (Russian) *Priroda.*

KÖPPEN (W.), 1914.—Lufttemperatur, Sonnenflecken und Vulkanausbrüche. *Met. Z.*, 31.

KÖPPEN (W.), 1931.—*Grundriss der Klimakunde.* Berlin.

KÖPPEN (W.) and WEGENER (A.), 1924.—*Die Klimate der geologischen Vorzeit.* Berlin. (Supplement by W. Köppen 1940.)

KORN (H.), 1938.—Schichtung und absolute Zeit. *NJBB*, 74, A.

KORNFELD (J. A.), 1952.—Deep-seated lower Permian reefs of West Texas basin, U.S.A. *Congr. Géol. Int. 1952 Alger, Rés.*

KOSSOVICH (N. L.), 1935.—On the Difference in Structure of the North and South Sides of Conifer Trunks. (Russian) *Bot. Zh.*, 20.

KRAMER (W. B.), 1933.—Boulders from Bengalia. *JG*, 41.

KRAMES (K.), 1956.—Stubbenuntersuchungen im Braunkohlentagebau der Grube Berrenrath. *Braunkohle*, 8.

KRASOVSKI (W. I.) and SHKLOVSKI (I. S.), 1957.—Influence of Supernovae on Terrestrial Evolution. (Russian) *Dokl.*, 116.

KRÄUSEL (R.), 1929.—Fossile Pflanzen aus dem Tertiär von Süd-Sumatra. *Verh. Geol. Mijnb. Gen. Niederl., Geol. Ser.*, 9.

KREJCI-GRAF (K.), 1927.—Zur Kritik von Vereisungsanzeichen. *Senckenbergiana*, 9.

KRENKEL (E.), 1925–38.—*Geologie Afrikas*. I. II. III. Berlin.

KRIGE (L. J.), 1929.—Magmatic cycles, continental drift and ice ages. *Proc. Geol. Soc. S. Afr.* 32.

KRIVSOV (A. I.), 1955.—New data on the stratigraphy of the lower Carboniferous deposits on the eastern margin of the Baltic Shield. (Russian) *Inform. Sborn. Vses. naut.-issl. Geol. Inst.*

KROOK (M.), 1953.—Interstellar matter and the solar constant. In: *Climatic Change*, Ed. H. Shapley.

KROTOV (B. P.), 1958.—Climatic control of present deposits of iron and aluminium. (Russian) *Dokl.*, 121.

KROTOV (B. P.) and SOTOVA (T. I.), 1956.—Distribution of the Bauxite Deposits of the Urals. (Russian) *Dokl.*, 108.

KRUMBEIN (W. C.) and SLOSS (L. L.), 1951.—*Stratigraphy and Sedimentation*. San Francisco.

KRYNINE (P. D.), 1935.—Arkose deposits in the humid tropics. *AJS*, (5) 29.

KRYNINE (P. D.), 1949.—The origin of red beds. *Trans. New York Acad. Sci.*, II, 2.

KUBIENA (W. L.), 1953.—*Bestimmungsbuch und Systematik der Böden Europas*. Stuttgart.

KUENEN (P. H.), 1947.—Water-faceted boulders. *AJS*, 245.

KUENEN (P. H.), 1956.—Problematic origin of the Naples Rocks around Ithaca. *N.Y. Geol. Mijnb.*, 18.

KUENEN (P. H.) and SANDERS (J. E.), 1956.—Sedimentation phenomena in Kulm and Flözleeres graywackes, Sauerland and Oberharz, Germany. *AJS*, 254.

KUGLER (H. G.) and SAUNDERS (J. B.), 1959.—Occurrence of armored mud-balls in Trinidad, West Indies. *JG*, 67.

KULLING (O.), 1951.—The Caledonian mountain range. *Sver. Geol. Unders.*, Ca., 37.

KULLING (O.), 1951.—Traces of the Varanger Ice Age in the Caledonides of Norrbotten. *Sver. Geol. Unders.*, C, 503.

KULP (J. L.), 1953.—Climatic changes and radioisotope dating. In: *Climatic Change*, Ed. H. Shapley.

KULP (J. L.), 1960.—The geological time scale. *Int. Geol. Congr. 1960, Copenhagen, Rep.*, 3.

KURDYUKOV (K. W.), 1957.—Transport of boulders by ice in inland lakes. (Russian) *Priroda*, 46.

KURTZ (V. E.), MCNAIR (A. H.) and WALES (D. B.), 1952.—Stratigraphy of the Dundas Harbour area, Devon Island, Arctic Archipelago. *AJS*, 250.

L

LACROIX (A.), 1936.—Les fulgurites du Sahara. *C.R. Acad. Sci. Colon.*, 25.

LACROIX (A.), 1942.—Nouvelles observations sur les fulgurites du Sahara. *Bull. Serv. Mines Afr. Occ. Fr.*, 6.

LADD (H. S.), TRACEY (J. I.), WELLS (J. W.) and EMERY (K. O.), 1950.—Organic growth and sedimentation on an atoll. *JG*, 58.

LA FORGE (L.), 1932.—Geology of the Boston area. *Mass. GS Bull.*, 839.

LAITIKARI (A.), 1942.—Hauptzüge der Erzforschung in Finnland. *GR*, 32.

LAMB (H. H.), 1961.—Fundamentals of climate. In: *Descriptive Palaeoclimatology*, Ed. A. E. M. Nairn, New York.

LAPPARENT, DE (A. F.), 1962.—Footprints of dinosaur in the Lower Cretaceous of Vestspitzbergen. *Svalbard. Norsk Polarinstitutt, Arbok*, 1960, pp. 14–21.

LASAREFF (P.), 1929.—Sur un méthode permettant de démontrer la dépendance des courants océaniques des vents alizés. *Beitr. Geophys.*, 21.

LAVROV (V. V.), 1955.—Periods of Tertiary coal formation in Kazakstan. (Russian) *Dokl.*, 100.

LECOMPTE (M.), 1958.—Les récifs paléozoique s en Belgique. *GR*, 47 (cf. *Mém. Inst. Géol. Louvain*, 10, 1936 and *Bull. Mus. Roy. Hist. Nat. Belg.*, 14, 1938).

LE DANOIS (E.), 1950.—*Le rythme des climats dans l'histoire de la terre et de l'humanité*. Paris.

LEE (J. S.), 1937.—Sinian glaciation of China. *Int. Geol. Congr. 1937, Moscow, Abstr.*

LEFFINGWELL (K.), 1915.—Ground-ice wedges the dominant form of ground-ice on the north coast of Alaska. *JG*, 23 (cf. *GS ProfP*, 109, 1919).

LEINZ (V.), 1938.—Petrographische und geologische Beobachtungen an den Sedimenten der permokarbonischen Vereisungen Südbrasiliens. *NJBB*, B, 79.

LEVET (M. N.), 1950.—Summary of Russian papers on upper Paleozoic reefs. *JG*, 58.

LIESE (W.) and DADSWELL (H. E.), 1959.—Über den Einfluss der Himmelsrichtung auf die Länge von Holzfasern und Tracheiden. *Holz als Roh- und Werkstoff*, 17.

LINCK (O.), 1946.—Die sogenannten Steinsalz-Pseudomorphosen als Kristall-Relikte. *Abh. Senck. Nat. Ges.*, 470.

LINDROTH (C. H.), 1957.—*The Faunal Connections between Europe and North America*. New York.

LIVINGSTONE (D. A.), 1957.—Pollen analysis of a valley fill near Umiat, Alaska. *AJS*, 255.

LIVINGSTONE (D. A.), 1959.—Theory of the Ice Ages. *Sci.*, 129.

LONG (W. E.), 1959.—Preliminary report of the geology of the central range of the Horlock Mountains, Antarctica. *USNC-IGY Antarct. Glac. data, Rep. 2*, VII.

LONG (W. E.), 1961.—Permo-Carboniferous glaciation in Antarctica. *Geol. Soc. Amer., Abstr.*

LOTZE (F.), 1949.—Das Alter der Dünen bei Mantinghausen an der oberen Lippe. *Nat. u. Heimat*, 9.

LOTZE (F.), 1957.—*Steinsalz und Kalisalze*. I. 2nd ed. Berlin, 1957.

LOUIS (H.), 1929.—Die Form der norddeutschen Bogendünen. *Z. Geomorph.*, 4.

Louis (H.), 1944.—Die Spuren eiszeitlicher Vergletscherung in Anatolien. *GR*, 34.

Louis (H.), 1960.—*Geomorphologie*. Berlin.

Lowenstam (H. A.), 1950 and 1957.—Niagaran reefs of the Great Lakes area. *JG*, 58, 1950 and *Mem. Geol. Soc. Amer.*, 67, 1957.

Lowenstam (H. A.) and Epstein (S.), 1954.—Palaeotemperatures of the Post-Apta in Cretaceous as determined by the oxygen isotope method. *JG*, 62.

Lozek (V.), 1955.—Mollusken des tschechoslowakischen Quartärs. *Rozpr. Ust. ust. geol.*, 17.

Lüdi (W.), 1953.—Die Pflanzenwelt des Eiszeitalters im nördlichen Vorland der Schweizer Alpen. *Veröff. Geobot. Inst. Rübel Zürich*, 27.

Lull (R. S.), 1948.—*Organic Evolution*. New York.

Lundquist (G.), 1948.—Blockens orientering; olika jordarter. *Sver. Geol. Unders.*, C, 497.

Lungershausen (G. F.), 1957.—Periodic climatic variation and major glaciations during the earth's history. (Russian) *Sov. Geol.*

Lungershausen (G. F.), 1958.—Loess and its probable analogues in Pre-Quaternary deposits of the USSR. (Russian) *Sov. Geol.*

Lungershausen (G. F.), 1960.—Traces of glaciations in the Late Pre-Cambrian of south Siberia and the Urals. (Russian) *Int. Geol. Kongr. XXI, Dokl. Sov. Geol.*

Lyell (C.), 1851.—On fossil rainmarks of the Recent, Triassic and Carboniferous Periods. *QJGS*, 7.

Lyell (C.), 1875.—*Principles of Geology*. 12th ed. London (1st ed. 1830–33).

Lysgaard (L.), 1949.—Recent climatic fluctuations. *Folia Geogr. Danica*, 5, Copenhagen.

M

Ma (T. Y. H.), 1934.—On the seasonal change of growth in a reef coral, *Favia speciosa*. *Proc. Imp. Acad. Jap.*, 10.

Ma (T. Y. H.), 1937.—On the seasonal growth in paleozoic tetracorals and the climate during the Devonian period. *Paleont. Sinica*, B, II, 3. (cf. *Research on the Past Climate and Continental Drift*, Taipeh, 1956–57 and *Int. Geol. Congr. 1960 Copenhagen, Rep.*, 12).

Maack (R.), 1957.—Über Vereisungsperioden und Vereisungsspuren in Brasilien. *GR*, 45 (cf. Int. Geol. Congr. 1952 and 1960).

Maarleveld (G. C.) and Toorn (J. C. v. d.), 1955.—Pseudo-sölle in Noord-Neederland. *Tijdskr. Kon. Ned. Aard. Gen.*, 72.

Mabesoone (J. M.), 1959.—Tertiary and Quaternary sedimentation in a part of the Duero basin. *Leidse Geol. Med.*, 24.

Macfadyen (W. A.), 1950.—Sandy gypsum crystals from Berbera, British Somaliland. *GM*, 87.

MacGinitie (H. D.), 1958.—Climate since the Late Cretaceous. In: *Zoogeography*, Ed. C. L. Hubbs (*Amer. Ass. Adv. Sci. Publ.*, 51).

Machatschek (F.), 1944.—Diluviale Hebung und eiszeitliche Schneegrenzen-depression. *GR*, 34.

Mädler (K.), 1939.—Die pliozäne Flora von Frankfurt am Main. *Abh. Senck. Nat. Ges.*, 446.

MÄGDEFRAU (K.), 1956.—*Paläobiologie der Pflanzen.* 3rd ed. Jena.

MAHABALE (T. S.), 1954.—Ferns and palms as indicators of climate and paleoclimate. *Palaeobot.*, 3.

MALZAHN (E.), 1957.—Devonisches Glazial im State Piaui, Brasilien. *Beih. Geol. Jb.*, 25.

MANLEY (G.), 1949.—The extent of the fluctuations shown during the 'instrumental' period in relation to post-glacial events in NW-Europe. *Quart. J. Roy. Met. Soc.*, 75.

MANTLE (H. G.), 1927.—On a faceted quartzite pebble from a coal seam at Ashby-de-la-Zouch. *GM*, 64.

MARK (W. D.), 1932.—Fossil impressions of ice crystals in Lake Bonneville beds. *JG*, 40.

MARKOV (K. K.), 1960.—*Paleogeography.* (Russian) 2nd ed. Moscow.

MARKOV (K. K.) and POPOV (A. J.), 1959.—*The Ice Age in European Russia and in Siberia.* (Russian) Moscow.

MARR (J. E.), 1928.—A possible chronometric scale for the graptolite-bearing strata. *Palaeobiolog.*, 1.

MARTIN (H.), 1953.—Notes on the Dwyka succession and on some pre-Dwyka valleys in South West Africa. *Trans. Geol. Soc. S. Afr.*, 56.

MARTIN (H.) and SCHALK (K.), 1959.—Gletscherschliffe an der Wand eines U-Tales im nördlichen Kaokofeld, SW Afrika. *GR*, 46.

MATTHEW (W. D.), 1939.—Climate and evolution. *New York Acad. Sci., Spec. Publ.*, 1.

MAWSON (D.), 1949.—Sturtian tillite of Mt. Jacob and Mt. Warren Hastings North Flinders Ranges. *Trans. Roy. Soc. S. Austr.*, 72.

MAWSON (D.), 1949.—The Late Precambrian ice-age and glacial record of the Bibliando Dome. *J. Proc. Roy. Soc. New South Wales*, 82.

MAYNC (W.), 1942.—Stratigraphie und Faziesverhältnisse der oberpermischen Ablagerungen Ostgrönlands. *Medd. Grönld.*, 115.

MAYR (F.), 1953.—Durch Tange verfrachtete Gerölle bei Solnhofen und anderwärts. *Geol. Bl. NO-Bay.*, 3.

McKEE (E. D.), 1945.—Small-scale structures in the Coconino sandstone of northern Arizona. *JG*, 53 (cf. *AJS*, 228, 1934).

McKEE (E. D.), 1954.—Stratigraphy and history of the Moenkopi formation of Triassic age. *Mem. Geol. Soc. Amer.*, 61.

McKEE (E. D.), 1959.—Storm sediments on a Pacific atoll. *J. Sed. Petrol.*, 29.

MEINARDUS (W.), 1928.—Der Wasserhaushalt der Antarktis. *Nachr. Ges. Wiss. Göttingen. Math.-phys. Kl.*

MEINARDUS (W.), 1944.—Zum Kanon der Erdbestrahlung. *GR*, 34.

MEINECKE (F.), 1910.—Das Liegend des Kupferschiefers. *Jb. Preuss. Geol. L.A.*, 31, II.

MENCHER (E.), 1938.—The salinity of the ocean in relation to water vapor in the atmosphere and the level of the sea. *JG*, 46.

MERTENS (R.), 1958.—Eine lebende Tuatera oder Brückenechse. *Nat. u. Volk*, 88.

MESHVILK (A. A.), 1956.—Molasse in the Lena Delta. (Russian) *Dokl.*, 108.

MIKI (S.), 1956.—Remains of *Pinus koraiensis* and associated remains in Japan. *Bot. Mag.*, 89.

MIKI (S.), HUZITA (K.) and KOKAWA (S.), 1957.—On the occurrence of many broad-leafed evergreen tree remains in the Pleistocene bed of Uegahara, Nish. City, Japan. *Proc. Jap. Acad.*, 33.

MILANKOVITCH (M.), 1930.—Mathematische Klimalehre und astronomische Theorie der Klimaschwankungen. *Hdb. Klimat.*, I, A (cf. *Hdb. Geophys.*, IX, 1938).

MILANKOVITCH (M.), 1941.—Kanon der Erdbestrahlung. *Kgl. Serb. Akad.* Belgrade.

MILANOVSKI (E. E.), 1960.—On traces of Late Pliocene glaciation in the Central Caucasus Mountains. (Russian) *Dokl.*, 130.

MILLER (A. A.), 1961.—*Climatology.* New York.

MILLER (D. J.), 1953.—Late Cenozoic marine glacial sediments and marine terraces of Middleton Island, Alaska. *JG*, 61.

MILORADOVITCH (B.), 1935.—Die obersilurischen glazial-marinen Ablagerungen von Nowaja Zemlja. *Cbl. Min.* etc., B.

MINDER (L.), 1938.—Der Zürichsee als Eutrophierungsphänomen. *Geol. Meere Binnengew.*, 2.

MISAR (Z.), 1960.—Eine Bemerkung zur Stellung der archäischen Warwite in der Umgebung von Tempere in Finnland. *NJMh.*, 1.

MISCH (P.), HAZZARD (J. C.) and TURNER (F. E.), 1957.—Precambrian tillite schists in the southern Deep Creek Range, Western Utah. *(Abstr.) BGSA*, 68.

MISCH (P.) and OLES (K. F.), 1957.—Interpretation of Ouachita Mountains of Oklahoma. *BAAPG*, 41.

MISTARDIS (G.), 1953.—Sur le caractère plus ou moins désertique d'une partie de l'Egéide méridionale durant quelques périodes du pliocène et du quaternaire. *Congr. Géol. Int. 1952 Alger, C.R.*, 17.

MOFFIT (F. H.), 1954.—Geology of the eastern part of the Alaska Range and adjacent area. *GS Bull.*, 989–D.

MOHR (E. C. J.) and BAREN (F. A. v.), 1954.—*Tropical Soils.* The Hague.

MOHR (H.), 1950.—Vorläufiger Bericht über die Auffindung vorquartärer Vereisungsspuren am Ostabhang des Wechsels. *Anz. math.-nat. Kl., Österr. Akad. Wiss.*, 87.

MOORE (G. W.), 1956.—Aragonite speleotherms as indicators of paleotemperature. *AJS*, 254.

MOORE (R. C.), 1934.—The origin and age of the boulder-bearing Johns Valley shale in the Ouachita Mountains of Arkansas and Oklahoma. *AJS*, (5) 27.

MOORE (R. C.), 1958.—*Introduction to Historical Geology.* 2nd ed. New York.

MORTENSEN (H.), 1927.—Der Formenschatz der nordchilenischen Wüste. *Abh. Ges. Wiss. Göttingen, Math.-phys. Kl.*, (11) 12.

MORTENSEN (H.), 1952.—Heutiger Firnruckgang und Eiszeitklima. *Erdkd.*, 6.

MORTENSEN (H.), 1957.—Temperaturgradient und Eiszeitklima am Beispiel der pleistozänen Schneegrenzdepression in den Rand- und Subtropen. *Z. Geomorph.*, 1.

MOSKVITIN (A. J.), 1954.—Quaternary stratigraphy of the USSR. (Russian) *Izv.*

MOSKVITIN (A. J.), 1958.—Pliocene deposits in the central Volga district and the question of their possible extension into the Lower Pleistocene. (Russian) *Trudy Geol. Inst. Akad. Nauk USSR*, 12.

MOUTA (F.), 1952.—Le système du Karroo de l'Angola. *Congr. Géol. Int. 1952 Alger, Symp. Gondw.*

Movius (H. L.), 1956.—Late Pleistocene conditions and Palaeolithic settlement in Soviet Central Asia and Western Siberia. *Congr. Int. Quat. 1953 Rome, Act.* II.

Mühlberg (M.), 1943.—Temperaturmessungen in der Bohrung Tuggen. *Ecl. geol. Helv.*, 36.

Müller (F.), 1959.—Beobachtungen über Pingos. *Medd. Grönld.*, 153.

Müller (G.), 1958.—Untersuchungen über die Querschnittformen der Baumschäfte. *Forstw. Cbl.*, 77.

Muller (S. W.), 1936.—Triassic coral reefs in Nevada. *AJS*, 31.

Mülleried (F. K. G.), 1952.—Erosion éolienne dans la région tropicale du Mexique. *Congr. Géol. Int. 1952 Alger, Rés.*

Murr (J.), 1926.—Neue Übersicht über die Flora der Höttinger Breccie. *Jb. Geol. B.A. Wien*, 76.

Murray (R. C.), 1955.—Late Keweenawan or early Cambrian glaciation in Upper Michigan. *BGSA*, 66.

Murray (R. C.), 1956.—Late Keweenawan or early Cambrian ice shove in Upper Michigan—a reply. *BGSA*, 67.

N

Nairn (A. E. M.), 1960.—Paleomagnetic results from Europe. *JG*, 68.

Nairn (A. E. M.), 1961.—(Ed.) *Descriptive Palaeoclimatology*. London.

Najdin (D. P.), Tejs (R. W.) and Tchupachin (M. S.), 1956.—Determination of climatic conditions in parts of the USSR during the Upper Cretaceous using isotope palaeothermometry. (Russian) *Geochim.*

Nathorst (A. G.), 1911.—Fossil floras of the arctic regions as evidence of geologic climates. *GM*, V, 8. (cf. *Congr. Géol. Int. 1910 Stockholm*).

Nehring (A.), 1890.—*Über Tundren und Steppen der Jetzt und Vorzeit mit besonderer Berücksichtigung ihrer Fauna*. Berlin.

Neumayr (M.), 1883.—Über klimatische Zonen während der Jura- und Kreidezeit. *Denkschr. Akad. Wiss. Wien, Math.-nat. Kl.*, 47.

Newell (N. D.), Rigby (J. K.), Fischer (A. G.), Whiteman (A. J.), Hickox (J. E.) and Bradley (J. S.), 1953.—*The Permian Reef Complex of the Guadeloupe Mountains Region, Texas and New Mexico*. San Francisco.

Neystadt (M. I.), 1957.—*Vegetational History of the USSR during the Holocene from the Results of Pollen Analyses*. (Russian) Moscow (cf. Klotz).

Nichols (R. L.), 1960.—Geomorphology of Marguerite Bay area, Palmer Peninsula, Antarctica. *BGSA*, 71.

Nickles (M.), 1951.—Notice géologique de l'Afrique équatoriale française et du Cameroun. *Int. Geol. Congr. 1948 London, Rep.*

Nikiforova (K. W.) and Alexeyeva (L. I.), 1959.—On the Tertiary-Quaternary boundary on the basis of the mammalian fauna. (Russian) *Trudy Geol. Inst. Akad. Nauk, USSR.*

Noakes (L. C.), 1956.—Upper Proterozoic and Sub-Cambrian rocks in Australia. *Congr. Geol. Int. 1956 Mexico, Symp. Cambr.*, II.

Nölke (F.), 1928.—Das Klima der geologischen Vorzeit. *Peterm. Geogr. Mitt.*, 74.

Norin (E.), 1941.—The Tarim Basin and its border regions. *Reg. Geol. d. Erde*, 2, IV b.

O

OERTEL (G.), 1952.—A structural investigation of the porphyritic basalts of Arthur's Seat, Edinburgh. *Trans. Edin. Geol. Soc.*, 14, III.

OLSON (E. C.), 1962.—Late Permian terrestrial vertebrates, U.S.A. and U.S.S.R. *Trans. Amer. Phil. Soc.*, n.s., 52, pt. 2, pp. 1–224.

OPDYKE (N. D.) and RUNCORN (S. K.), 1960.—Wind direction in the western United States in the late Paleozoic. *BGSA*, 71.

ÖPIK (A. A.), 1956.—Cambrian palaeogeography of Australia. *Congr. Geol. Int. 1956 Mexico, Symp. Cambr.*, II.

ÖPIK (E. J.), 1950.—Secular changes of stellar structure and the Ice Ages. *Monthly Not. Roy. Astr. Soc.*, 110.

ÖPIK (E. J.), 1957.—Ice Ages. In: D. R. Bates, *The Planet Earth*. London.

ORTON (J. H.), 1923.—On the significance of 'rings' on the shells of *Cardium* and other molluscs. *Nature*, 112.

OSBORNE (F. F.), 1956.—Geology near Quebec City. *Nat. Canad.*, 83.

OVERBECK (F.), MUNNICH (K. O.), ALETSEE (L.) and AVERDIEK (F. R.), 1957.— Das Alter des 'Grenzhorizontes' norddeutscher Hochmoore nach Radiokarbon-Datierungen. *Flora*, 145.

OVEY (C. D.), 1950.—On the interpretation of climatic variations as revealed by a study of samples from an equatorial Atlantic deep-sea core. *Centenary Proc. Roy. Met. Soc.*

OWEN (H. B.), 1954.—Bauxite in Australia. *Commonwealth Aust., Dept. Nat. Develop., Bur. Min. Res., Bull.*, 24.

P

PARKINSON (D.), 1957.—Lower Carboniferous reefs of Northern England. *BAAPG*, 41.

PATALEYEV (A. V.), 1955.—Ice Wedges in Soils. (Russian) *Priroda*, 44.

PEABODY (F. E.), 1957.—Annual growth zones in bone of Lower Permian verte-brates. *BGSA*, 68.

PENCK (A.), 1936.—Das Klima der Eiszeit. *Verh. III. Int. Quartär-Konf. Wien.*

PENCK (A.), 1938.—Die Strahlungskurve und die geologische Zeitrechnung. *Z. Ges. Erdkd. Berlin.*

PENCK (A.), 1938.—Säugetierfauna und Paläolithikum des jüngeren Pleistozän in Mitteleuropa. *Abh. Preuss. Akad. Wiss., Phys.-math. Kl.*

PENCK (A.) and BRÜCKNER (E.), 1901–09.—*Die Alpen im Eiszeitalter.* 3 vols. Leipzig.

PEPPER (J. F.), WITT (W. DE) and DEMAREST (D. F.), 1954.—Geology of the Bedford Shale and Berea Sandstone in the Appalachian basin. *GS ProfP*, 259.

PETTIJOHN (F. J.), 1949.—*Sedimentary Rocks.* New York.

PETTIJOHN (F. J.), 1962.—Dimensional fabric and ice flow, Precambrian (Huron-ian) glaciation. *Sci.*, 135, p. 442.

PETTY (J. J.), 1936.—The origin and occurrence of fulgurites in the Atlantic coastal plain. *AJS*, 31.

PÉWÉ (T.), 1960.—Glacial history of the McMurdo Sound region, Antarctica. *Int. Geol. Congr. 1960 Copenhagen, Rep.*, 4.

PÉWÉ (T.), 1960.—Multiple glaciation in the McMurdo Sound region, Antarctica. *JG*, 68.

PFANNENSTIEL (M.), 1929.—Spuren von Eiskristallen im oberbadischen Wellen-
kalk. *NJBB*, 61, B.

PFANNENSTIEL (M.), 1944.—Die diluvialen Entwicklungsstadien und die Urges-
chichte von Dardanellen, Marmarameer und Bosporus. *GR*, 34.

PHILIPPI (E.), 1910.—Über einige paläoklimatologische Probleme. *NJBB*, 29, B.

PIA (J. v.), 1942.—Übersicht über die fossilen Kalkalgen und die geologischen
Ergebnisse ihrer Untersuchung. *Mitt. alp. geol. Ver.*, 33.

PILGRIM (L.), 1904.—Versuch einer rechnerischen Behandlung des Eiszeitalters.
Jber. Ver. vaterl. Nat. Württ., 60.

PILKEY (O. H.) and HOWER (J.), 1960.—The effect of environment on the concentration of skeletal magnesium and strontium in *Dendraster*. *JG*, 68.

PLASS (G. N.), 1956.—The carbon dioxide theory of climatic change. *Tellus*, 8.

PLUMLEY (W. J.) and GRAVES (R. W.), 1953.—Virgilian reefs of the Sacramento
mountains, New Mexico. *JG*, 61.

POOLE (F. G.), 1957.—Palaeo-wind directions in late Paleozoic and early Mesozoic
time on the Colorado plateau as determined by cross-strata. (*Abstr.*) *BGSA*,
68.

POPOV (J. N.), 1956.—Discovery of fossilized animals in permanently frozen
ground. (Russian) *Priroda*, 45.

PORTMANN (J. P.), 1956.—Les méthodes d'étude pétrographique des dépôts
glaciaires. *GR*, 45.

POSER (H.), 1947.—Auftautiefe und Frostzerrung im Boden Mitteleuropas
während der Würm-Eiszeit. *Naturwiss.*, 34.

POSER (H.), 1948.—Boden und Klimaverhältnisse in Mittel- und Westeuropa
während der Würm-Eiszeit. *Erdkd.*, 2.

POSER (H.), 1951.—Die nördliche Lössgrenze in Mitteleuropa. *EuG*, 1.

POTONIÉ (H.), 1920.—*Die Entstehung der Steinkohle*. 6th ed. Berlin.

POTONIÉ (R.), 1928.—Spuren von Wald- und Moorbränden in Vergangenheit und
Gegenwart. *Jb. Preuss. Geol. L.A.*, 49, II.

POTONIÉ (R.), 1953.—Zur Paläobiologie der karbonischen Pflanzenwelt. *Naturwiss.*,
40.

POTZGER (J. E.) and THARP (B. C.), 1947.—Pollen profile from a Texas bog. *Ecol.*,
28.

POULSEN (C.), 1930.—Contribution to the stratigraphy of the Cambro-Ordovician
of East Greenland. *Medd. Grönld.*, 74. (cf. *Congr. Geol. Int. Mexico, Symp.
Cambr., 1956, and Coll. int. Paris, 1958*).

PRICE (W. A.), 1962.—Stages of oxidation coloration in dune and barrier sands
with age. *Bull. Geol. Soc. Amer.*, 73, pp. 1281–1284.

PURI (G. S.), 1949.—The family Lauraceae in the Pleistocene of India. *Quart. J.
Geol. Min. Met. Soc. India*, 21.

R

RAMSAY (W.), 1910.—Orogenesis und Klima. *Overs. Finska Vet. Soc. Förh.*, 52, A.
(cf. *GM*, 61, 1924).

RANGE (P.), 1923.—Über das spätglaziale Klima. *ZDGG*, 75.

RANGE (P.), 1936.—Über die kambrische Eiszeit. *ZDGG*, 88.

RATHJENS (C.), 1954.—Das Problem der Gliederung des Eiszeitalters in physisch-
geographischer Sicht. *Münch. Geogr. H.*, 6.

RAUP (D. M.), 1958.—The relation between water temperature and morphology in Dendraster. *JG*, 66.

REDINI (R.), 1934.—Raffigurazzioni prodotte da cristalli di ghiaccio. *Riv. It. Pal.*, 40.

REECE (A.), 1958.—Discussion on L. C. King. *QJGS*, 114.

REGEL (C. v.), 1957.—Die Klimaänderung der Gegenwart in ihrer Beziehung zur Landschaft. *Dalp-Taschenb.*, 335.

REICHE (P.), 1938.—An analysis of cross-lamination: The Coconino Sandstone. *JG*, 46.

REID (E. M.) and CHANDLER (M. E. J.), 1933.—*The London Clay Flora*. London.

REINECK (H. E.), 1955.—Marken, Spuren und Fährten in den Waderner Schichten bei Martinstein (Nahe). *NJAbh.*, 101.

REMY (H.), 1958.—Zur Flora und Fauna der Villafranca-Schichten von Villaroya. *EuG*, 9.

RENSCH (B.), 1952.—Klima und Artbildung. *GR*, 40.

REUNING (E.) and MARTIN (H.), 1957.—Die Prä-Karroo-Landschaft, die Karroo-Sedimente und Karroo-Eruptivgesteine des südlichen Kaokofeldes in SW-Afrika. *NJb. Min., Abh.*, 91.

REVELLE (R.) and FAIRBRIDGE (R. W.), 1957.—Carbonates and carbon dioxide. *Mem. Geol. Soc. Amer.*, 67.

RICHMOND (G. M.), 1949.—Stone nets, stone stripes and soil stripes in the Wind River Mountains, Wyoming. *JG*, 57.

RICHTER (K.), 1932.—Die Bewegungsrichtung des Inlandeises, rekonstruiert aus den Kritzen und Längsachsen der Geschiebe. *Z. Geschiebef.*, 8.

RICHTER (R.), 1954.—Marken von Schaumblasen als Kennmal des Auftauch-Bereiches im Hunsrückschiefer-Meer. *Senckenb. leth.*, 35.

RICHTER (W.), SCHNEIDER (H.) and WAGNER (R.), 1951.—Die saaleeiszeitliche Stauchzone von Itterbeck-Uelsen. *ZDGG*, 102 (1950).

RICHTER-BERNBURG (G.), 1941.—Paläogeographische und tektonische Stellung des Richelsdorfer Gebirges im Hessischen Raum. *Jb. Reichsst. Bod.*, 61 (1940).

RICHTER-BERNBURG (G.), 1955.—Über salinare Sedimentation. *ZDGG*, 105 (1953) (cf. *Naturw.*, 37, 1950 and *GR*, 49, 1960).

RIGG (G. B.) and GOULD (H. R.), 1957.—Age of Glacier Peak eruption and chronology of postglacial peat deposits in Washington. *AJS*, 255.

ROBINSON (G. W.), 1949.—*Soils*, 3rd. ed. London.

ROD (E.), 1960.—Geologic reconnaissance of upper Yapacani river, Bolivia. *BAAPG*, 44.

RODGERS (J.), 1957.—The distribution of marine carbonate sediments: a review. In: Regional Aspects of Carbonate Deposition. *Soc. Econ. Pal. Min., Spec. Publ.*, 5.

ROEMER (F.), 1852.—*Die Kreidebildungen von Texas*. Bonn.

ROMER (A. S.), 1961.—Palaeozoological evidence of climate. (1) Vertebrates. In: *Descriptive Palaeoclimatology*. New York.

RONOV (A. B.) and KHEIN (P. E.), 1956.—World Wide Permian Stages. (Russian) *Sov. Geol.*

ROOTS (E. F.), 1953.—Preliminary note on the geology of western Dronning Maud Land. *Norsk Geol. Tidskr.*, 32.

ROSENDAHL (C. O.), 1948.—A contribution to the knowledge of the Pleistocene flora of Minnesota. *Ecol.*, 29.

ROSHOLT (J. N.), EMILIANI (C.), GEISS (J.), KOCZY (F. F.) and WANGERSKY (P. J.), 1961.—Absolute dating of deep-sea cores by the Pa^{231}/Th^{230} method. *JG*, 69.

RUCHIN (L. B.), 1958.—*Grundzüge der Lithologie*. Berlin.

RUEDEMANN (R.), 1939.—Climates of the past in North America. In: *Geology of North America*, Ed. R. Ruedemann and R. Balk, Berlin.

RUHE (R. V.), 1952.—Topographic discontinuities of the Des Moines Lobe. *AJS*, 250.

RUHE (R. V.), GOMEZ (R. S.) and CADY (R. C.), 1961.—Paleosols of Bermuda. *BGSA*, 72.

RUNCORN (S. K.), 1956.—Magnetization of rocks. In: *Hdb. d. Physik*, Ed. S. Flügge, 47.

RUNCORN (S. K.), 1959.—On the Permian climatic zonation and paleomagnetism. *AJS*, 257.

RUNCORN (S. K.), 1962.—Climatic change through geological time in the light of the palaeomagnetic evidence for polar wandering and continental drift. *Quart. J. Roy. Met. Soc.*, Vol. 87, No. 373.

RUTTE (E.), 1958.—Kalkkrusten in Spanien. *NJAbh.*, 106.

RUTTEN (M. G.), 1958.—Detailuntersuchungen an gotländischen Riffen. *GR*, 47.

S

SAKS (V. N.), BELOV (N. A.) and LAPINA (N. N.), 1955.—Modern views on the geology of Antarctica. (Russian) *Priroda*, 44.

SALMI (M.), 1948.—The Hekla ashfalls in Finland. *C.R. Soc. géol. Finld.*, 21.

SALOMON-CALVI (W.), 1931.—Epeirophorese. *III. Sitz. Ber. Heidelb. Akad. Wiss.*

SALOMON-CALVI (W.), 1933.—*Die permokarbonischen Eiszeiten*. Leipzig.

SANBORN (E. I.), 1937.—The Comstock flora of West Central Oregon. *Publ. Carn. Inst. Wash.*, 465.

SANDBERG (C. G. S.), 1940.—*Ist die Annahme von Eiszeiten berechtigt?* Leiden 1937, 2nd Part 1940.

SATO (T.), 1960.—A propos des courants océaniques froids prouvés par l'existence des ammonites d'origine arctique dans le Jurassique japonais. *Int. Geol. Congr. 1960 Copenhagen, Rep.*, 12.

SAURAMO (M.), 1929.—The Quaternary geology of Finland. *Bull. Com. géol. Finld.*, 86.

SAURAMO (M.), 1958.—Die Geschichte des Ostsee. *Ann. Acad. Sci. Fenn.*, A, III, 51.

SAYLES (R. W.), 1914.—The Squantum tillite. *Bull. Mus. Comp. Zool. Cambr.*, 56, 2.

SAYLES (R. W.), 1919.—Seasonal deposition in aqueo-glacial sediments. *Mem. Mus. Comp. Zool. Cambr.*, 47.

SAYLES (R. W.), 1931.—Bermuda during the Ice Age. *Proc. Amer. Acad. Sci. Arts*, 66.

SCHAFER (J. P.), 1949.—Some periglacial features in central Montana. *JG*, 57.

SCHENK (E.), 1955.—Die Mechanik der periglazialen Strukturböden. *Abh. Hess. L.A. Bodenf.*, 13. (cf. *EuG*, 5, 1955).

SCHILDER (F. X.), 1941.—Verwandtschaft und Verbreitung der Cypraeacea. *Arch. Mollusk. kd.*, 73.

Schindehütte (G.), 1907.—Die Tertiärflora des Basalttuffes vom Eichelskopf. *Abh. Preuss. Geol. L.A.* 54.

Schindewolf (O. H.), 1951.—Glaziale Erscheinungen im Oberdevon von Menorca. *Akad. Wiss. Lit. Mainz, Abh. Math.-nat.* Kl.

Schindewolf (O. H.), 1954.—Über die Faunenwend vom Paläozoikum zum Mesozoikum. *ZDGG*, 105 (1953).

Schindewolf (O. H.) and Seilacher (A.), 1955.—Beiträge zur Kenntnis des Kambriums in der Salt Range. *Akad. Wiss. Lit. Mainz, Abh. Math.-nat.* Kl.

Schloemer-Jäger (A.), 1958.—Alttertiäre Pflanzen aus Flözen der Brögger-Halbinsel Spitzbergens. *Palaeontogr.*, B, 104 (cf. *Pal. Z.*, 30, 1956).

Schmidt (J. W.), 1954.—Tektonisch entstandend gekritzte Geschiebe. *NJMh.*

Schmucker (U.), 1959.—Gesteinsmagnetische Untersuchungen an permischen Nahe-Eruptiven. *GR*, 48.

Schneiderhöhn (H.), 1962.—*Erzlagerstätten*. 4th ed. Stuttgart.

Schoeller (H.), 1945.—Le Quaternaire de la Saoura et du Grand Erg Occidental. *Trav. Inst. Rech. Sahar.*, 3.

Schott (W.), 1938.—Stratigraphie rezenter Tiefseesedimente auf Grund der Foraminiferenfauna. *GR*, 29.

Schove (D. J.), Nairn (A. E. M.) and Opdyke (N. D.), 1958.—The climatic geography of the Permian. *Geogr. Ann.*, 40.

Schrepfer (H.), 1933.—Inselberge in Lappland und Neufundland. *GR*, 24.

Schuchert (C.), 1914.—Climates of geologic time. *Publ. Carn. Inst. Wash.*, 192.

Schuchert (C.), 1927.—Winters in the upper Devonian of New York and Acadia. *AJS*, 13 and 14.

Schuchert (C.), 1928.—Review of the late Paleozoic formations and faunas, with special reference to the Ice-Age of middle Permian time. *BGSA*, 39.

Schüller (A.) and Ying (S. H.), 1959.—Das Sinian-System in China. *Geologie*, 8.

Schulman (E.), 1956.—*Dendroclimatic Changes in Semi-arid America*. Tucson.

Schwarzbach (M.), 1940.—Das diluviale Klima während des Höchstandes einer Vereisung. *ZDGG*, 92.

Schwarzbach (M.), 1942.—Bionomie, Klima und Sedimentationsgeschwindigkeit im oberschlesischen Karbon. *ZDGG*, 94.

Schwarzbach (M.), 1946.—Klima und Klimagürtel im Alttertiär. *Naturw.*, 33.

Schwarzbach (M.), 1949.—Fossile Korallenriffe und Wegeners Drifthypothese. *Naturw.*, 36.

Schwarzbach (M.), 1949.—Zur Entstehung der Steinsalz-Pseudomorphosen. *Nat. u. Volk*, 30.

Schwarzbach (M.), 1952.—Aus der Klimageschichte des Rheinlandes. *GR*, 40.

Schwarzbach (M.), 1952.—Ein Pseudo-Eiskeil aus den Albaner Bergen bei Rom. *GR*, 40.

Schwarzbach (M.), 1953.—Das Alter der Wüste Sahara. *NJMh.*

Schwarzbach (M.), 1953.—Orogenesen und Eiszeiten. *Naturw.*, 40.

Schwarzbach (M.), 1954.—Eine Neuberechnung von Milankovitchs Strahlungskurve. *NJMh.*

Schwarzbach (M.), 1955.—Allgemeiner Überblick der Klimageschichte Islands. *NJMh.*

Schwarzbach (M.), 1958.—Die 'Tillite' von Menorca und das Problem devonischer Vereisungen. *Sonderveröff. Geol. Inst. Köln*, 3.

SCHWARZBACH (M.), 1960.—Der 'Squantum-Tillit' bei Boston als Beispiel für die Problematik paläoklimatologischer Zeitmarken. *GR*, 49.

SCHWARZBACH (M.), 1960.—Die Eiszeit-Hypothese von Ewing u. Donn, *ZDGG*, 112.

SCHWARZBACH (M.) and PFLUG (H. D.), 1956.—Das Klima des jüngeren Tertiärs in Island. *NJAbh.*, 104.

SCHWINNER (R.), 1936.—*Lehrbuch der Physikalischen Geologie*. I. Berlin.

SCOTT (H. W.), 1938.—Eocene glaciation in SW Montana. *JG*, 46.

SEARS (P. B.) and CLISBY (K. H.), 1955.—Pleistocene climate in Mexico. *BGSA*, 66.

SEIBOLD (E.), 1958.—Jahreslagen in Sedimenten der mittleren Adria. *GR*, 47.

SELLING (O. H.), 1948.—On the Late Quaternary History of the Hawaiian Vegetation. Honolulu, (cf. *Svensk Bot. Tidskr.*, 45).

SELZER (G.), 1936.—Diluviale Lösskeile und Lösskeilnetze aus der Umgebung Göttings. *GR*, 27.

SEMPER (M.), 1896.—Das paläothermale Problem, speziell die klimatischen Verhaltnisse des Eozans in Europa und im Polargebiet. *ZDGG*, 48 (and 51, 1899).

SEWARD (A. C.), 1931.—*Plant Life through the Ages*. Cambridge.

SHAPLEY (H.) (Ed.), 1953.—*Climatic Change*. Cambridge (Mass.).

SHARP (R. P.), 1948.—Early Tertiary fanglomerate, Big Horn Mountains, Wyoming. *JG*, 56.

SHARP (R. P.), 1959.—Pleistocene ventifacts east of the Big Horn Mountains, Wyoming. *JG*, 57.

SHATSKI (N. S.), 1954.—Zonal and Bipolar Distribution of the Upper Cretaceous and Eocene Glauconitic Formations. (Russian) *Bull. Mosc. Obsh. Isyp. Prir., Geol.*, 29.

SHATSKI (N. S.), 1958.—Les relations du Cambrien avec le Protérozoique. *Colloq. int. Centre nat. Rech. sci. Paris*, 76.

SHEPARD (F. P.), 1922.—Possible Silurian tillite in south-eastern British Columbia. *JG*, 30.

SHERLOCK (R. L.), 1947.—*The Permo-Triassic Formations*. London.

SHEYNMAN (J. M.), 1954.—Upper Palaeozoic and Mesozoic climatic zones of east Asia. (Russian) *Bull. Mosc. Obsh. Isyp. Prir., Geol.*, 29.

SHOKALSKAYA (S. I.), 1953.—*Die Böden Afrikas*. Berlin.

SHOTTON (F. W.), 1956.—Some aspects of the New Red desert in Britain. *Liverp. and Manch. Geol. I.*, 1.V.

SHOTTON (F. W.), 1960.—Large-scale patterned ground in the valley of the Worcestershire Avon. *GM*, 97.

SIMPSON (G. C.), 1929-30.—Past climates. *Mem. Manch. Lit. Phil. Soc.*, 74 (cf. *Roy. Soc. Edin.*, 50, 1929-30, *Ann. Rep. Smith Inst. for 1938* and *Proc. Linn. Soc. London*, 152, 1940).

SMITH (E. S. C.), 1928.—A possible tillite from northern Maine. *AJS*, (5) 15.

SMITH (H. T. U.), 1948.—Giant glacial grooves in NW Canada. *AJS*, 246.

SMITH (H. T. U.), 1949.—Physical effects of Pleistocene climate changes in non-glaciated areas. *BGSA*, 60.

SMITH LA MOTTE (R.), 1936.—The upper Cedarville Flora of NW Nevada and adjacent California. *Publ. Carn. Inst. Wash.*, 455.

SOERGEL (W.), 1921.—*Die Ursachen der diluvialen Aufschotterung und Erosion.* Berlin.

SOERGEL (W.), 1925.—Die Gliederung und absolute Zeitrechnung des Eiszeitalters. *Fortschr. Geol. Pal.,* IV, 13.

SOERGEL (W.), 1928.—Apodiden aus dem Chirotherium-Sandstein. *Pal. Z.,* 10.

SOERGEL (W.), 1932.—Diluviale Frostspalten im Deckschichtenprofil von Ehringsdorf. *Fortschr. Geol. Pal.,* XI.

SOERGEL (W.), 1937.—*Die Vereisungskurve.* Berlin.

SOERGEL (W.), 1939.—Das diluviale System. *Fortschr. Geo. Pal.,* XII, 39.

SOERGEL (W.), 1942.—Die eiszeitliche Temperaturminderung in Mitteleuropa. *Jber. Mitt. Oberrhein. Geol. Ver.,* 31.

SOKOLOV (B. S.), 1958.—Le problème de la limite inférieure du Paléozoïque et les dépôts les plus anciens sur les plates-formes antésiniennes de l'Eurasie. *Colloq. int. Centre nat. Rech. sci. Paris,* 76.

SOLGER (F.), 1918.—Studien über nordostdeutsche Inland-Dünen. *Forsch. Dtsch. Landes- u. Volkskd.,* 19, 1.

SPITALER (R.), 1940.—Die Bestrahlung der Erde durch die Sonne und die Temperaturverhältnisse in der quartären Eiszeit. *Abh. Dtsch. Ges. Wiss. Prag, Math.-nat. Abt.,* 3.

SPJELDNES (N.), 1961.—Ordovician Climatic Zones. *Norsk Geol. Tidskr.,* 41.

STAESCHE (K.), 1954.—Sumpfschildkröten (*Emys orbicularis*) aus dem diluvialen Sauerwasserkalk von Cannstatt. *Jber. Mitt. oberrhein. geol. Ver.,* 36.

STAFFORD (P. T.), 1959.—Geology of part of the Horseshoe Atoll in Scurry and Kent Counties, Texas. *GS ProfP,* 315–A.

STAMP (L. D.), 1925.—Seasonal rhythms in the Tertiary sediments of Burma. *GM,* 62.

STEARNS (C. E.), 1942.—A fossil marmot from New Mexico and its climatic significance. *AJS,* 240.

STEARNS (C. E.), 1943.—The Galisteo formation of north-central New Mexico. *JG,* 51.

STECHOV (E.), 1954.—Zur Frage nach der Ursache des grossen Sterbens am Ende der Kreidezeit. *NJMh.,* 1954.

STEHLI (F. C.), 1957.—Possible Permian climatic zonation and its implications. *AJS,* 255 (reply 256, 1958 and 27, 1959).

STOKES (W. L.), 1955.—Another look at the Ice Age. *Sci.,* 122.

STOMMEL (H.), 1958.—*The Gulf Stream.* Berkeley.

STRAKA (H.), 1960.—Literaturübersicht über Moore und Torfablagerungen aus tropischen Gebieten. *Erdkd.,* 14.

STRAKHOV (N. M.), 1960.—Types of climatic zones in the Post-Proterozoic, and their geological significance. (Russian) *Izv.*

STRAKHOV (N. M.), ZALMANSON (Y. S.) and GLAGOLEVA (M. A.), 1962.—Upper Palaeozoic climatic regions in north-western Eurasia. *Int. Geol. Rev.,* Vol. 4, 4.

STRIGEL (A.), 1929.—Das deutsche Buntsandsteinbecken. *Verh. nat.-med. Ver.* Heidelberg, 16.

STROMER (E.), 1933.—Über Wüsten und Urwüsten nebst Bemerkungen über Aktualismus. *ZDGG,* 85.

STROMER (E.), 1939.—Kritische Bemerkungen. I. Der Wüstenfisch *Ceratodus* und seine meso- und känozoischen Verwandten. *NJBB,* 80, B.

STUBBLEFIELD (C. J.), 1960.—Sessile marine organisms and their significance in Pre-Mesozoic strata. *QJGS*, 116.

STUTZER (O.), 1923.—*Kohle*. Berlin.

SUKATCHEV (W. N.), 1954.—On the association of dwarf birch and *Brasenia* in interglacial deposits. (Russian) *Dokl.*, 94.

SUMMERS (H. S.), 1923.—The geology of the Bacchus Marsh and Coimadai district. *Proc. Pan-Pacif. Sci. Congr.*, 2.

SUTTON (J.) and WATSON (J.), 1954.—Ice-boulders in the Macduff group of the Dalradian of Banffshire. *GM*, 91.

SZAFER (W.), 1946–47.—The Pliocene flora of Kroszienko in Poland. I. II. *Pol. Akad. Um. Rozpr. Wydz.* III.

SZAFER (W.), 1954.—Pliocene flora from the vicinity of Czorsztyn and its relationship to the Pleistocene. *Inst. Geol., Prace*, 11.

T

TABER (S.), 1943.—Perennially frozen ground in Alaska: its origin and history. *BGSA*, 54.

TABER (S.), 1943.—Quartz crystals with clay and fluid inclusions. *JG*, 58.

TALJAARD (M. S.), 1939.—Note on the occurrence of faceted pebbles as products of streamflow. *Trans. Geol. Soc. S. Afr.*, 42.

TAYLOR (G.), 1940.—Antarctica. *Regionale Geologie der Erde*. Vol. 1, Sect. 8, Akademische Verlagsgesellschaft, Leipzig.

TCHURAKOV (A. N.), 1932.—Traces of Proterozoic glaciation in the southern part of Central Siberia. *BGSA*, 43.

TEICHERT (C.), 1947.—Stratigraphy of Western Australia. *BAAPG*, 31 (cf. *J. Proc. Roy. Soc. New South Wales*, 80, 1947).

TEICHERT (C.), 1958.—Cold- and deep-water coral banks. *BAAPG*, 42.

TEICHERT (C.), 1958.—Some biostratigraphical concepts. *BGSA*, 69.

TEICHMÜLLER (M.) and SCHONEFELD (W.), 1955.—Ein verkieselter Karbontorf im Namur C von Kupferdreh. *Geol. Jb.*, 71.

TEJS (R. W.), TCHUPACHIN (M. S.) and NAJDIN (D. P.), 1957.—Determination of paleotemperatures by oxygen-isotope measurements of calcite shells of some cretaceous fossils from the Crimea. (Russian) *Geochim.*

TERMIER (H.) and TERMIER (G.), 1952.—*Histoire géologique de la biosphère*. Paris.

TEUMER (T.), 1929.—Problem der Braunkohlengeologie und des Braunkohlenbergbaus. *Abh. Nat. Ges. Görlitz*, 30, 3 (cf. *Jb. Hall. Verbd.*, 3, 1922).

THENIUS (E.), 1952.—Welsreste aus dem Unterpliozän des Wiener Beckens. *NJMh.*

THENIUS (E.), 1955.—Zur Entwicklung der jungtertiären Säugetierfauna des Wiener Beckens. *Pal. Z.*, 29.

THEODOROVICH (G. I.), 1941.—Migration of Upper Paleozoic reefs in South Bashkira. *C.R. Acad. Sci. USSR*, 32.

THOMPSON (T. G.) and NELSON (K. H.), 1956.—Concentration of brines and deposition of salts from sea-water under frigid conditions. *AJS*, 254.

THORARINSSON (S.), 1944.—Tephrochronological studies in Iceland. *Geogr. Ann.*, 26.

THORARINSSON (S.), 1954.—The tephra-fall from Hekla on March 29th, 1947. *Soc. Sci. Isl.*

THORARINSSON (S.), 1958.—The Öraefajökull eruption of 1362. *Act. Nat. Isl.*, II, 2.

THORNBURY (W. D.), 1940.—Weathered zones and glacial chronology in Southern Indiana. *JG*, 48.

TICHVINSKAYA (E. I.), 1956.—Triassic glacial deposits in the north of the Russian platform. (Russian) *Trudy Vses. Sov. Rasr. unf. Schem. Strat. Mesos. Otl. Russ. Platf.*

TONGIORGI (E.) and TREVISAN (L.), 1942.—Un falso postulato di paleoclimatologia de Quaternario: la corrispondenza tra periodi glaciali e periodi pluviali. *Atti Soc. Tosc. Sci. Nat.*, 51.

TRAVES (D. M.), 1956.—Upper Proterozoic and Cambrian geology in N.W. Australia. *Congr. Geol. Int. 1956 Mexico, Symp. Cambr.*, II.

TRICART (J. L. F.), 1956.—Cartes des phénomènes périglaciaires quaternaires en France. *Mém. Carte Géol. Fr.*

TROELSEN (J. C.), 1956.—The Cambrian of North Greenland and Ellesmere Island. *Congr. Geol. Inst. 1956 Mexico, Symp. Cambr.*, I.

TROLL (C.), 1944.—Strukturböden, Solifluktion und Frostklimate der Erde. *GR*, 34.

TROLL (C.), 1948.—Der subnivale oder periglaziale Zyklus der Denudation. *Erdkd.*, 2.

TUMANSKAYA (O. G.), 1955.—On the Permian Reefs of Tethys. (Russian) *Bull. Mosc. Obsh. Isyp. Prir. Geol.*, 30.

TUSHINSKI (G. K.), 1958.—Post-volcanic glaciation of Elbruz and its dynamics. (Russian) In: *Inform. Geophys. Year 2, Elbruz Exped. Mosc. Geophys. Inst.*

TWENHOFEL (W.), 1950.—*Treatise on Sedimentation*. 2nd ed. New York.

U

UDDEN (J. A.), 1918.—Fossil ice crystals. *Univ. Texas Bull.*, 1821.

UDDEN (J. A.), 1924.—Laminated anhydrite in Texas. *BGSA*, 35.

ULLRICH (H.), 1956.—Fossile Sumpfschildkröten (*Emys orbicularis*) aus dem Diluvialtravertin von Weimar-Ehringsdorf-Taubach und Tonna. *Geologie*, 5.

ULRICH (E. O.), 1927.—Fossiliferous boulders in the Ouachita 'Caney' shale. *Bull. Okla. Geol. Surv.*, 45.

UMBGROVE (J. H. F.), 1947.—*The Pulse of the Earth*. 2nd ed. The Hague.

UREY (H. C.), LOWENSTAM (H. A.), EPSTEIN (S.) and McKINNEY (C. R.), 1951.—Measurement of paleotemperatures and temperatures of the upper Cretaceous of England, Denmark, and the south-eastern United States. *BGSA*, 62.

V

VACHRAMEYEV (V. A.), 1957.—Development of botanical provinces in Eurasia during the Palaeozoic and Mesozoic. (Russian) *Izv.*

VALENTINE (J. W.) and MEADE (R. F.), 1961.—Californian Pleistocene paleo-temperature. *Univ. Calif. Publ. Geol. Sci.*, 40, Berkeley and Los Angeles.

VALENTINE (J. W.) and MEADE (R. F.), 1962.—Isotopic and zoogeographic palaeotemperatures of the Californian and Pleistocene Mollusca. *Science*, 132, pp. 810–811.

VALETON (I.), 1957.—Lateritische Verwitterungsböden zur Zeit der jungkimmerischen Gebirgsbildung im nördlichen Harzvorland. *Geol. Jb.*, 73.

VASIKOVSKI (A. P.), 1954.—Remains of walnut (*Juglans cinerea*) and *Metasequoia disticha* in the Upper Pleistocene of the western part of the Kamchatka Peninsula. (Russian) *Kolyma.*

VAUGHAN (T. W.), 1919.—An account of the American Tertiary, Pleistocene and recent coral reefs. *Bull. U.S. Nat. Mus.*, 103.

VENZO (S.), 1952.—Geomorphologische Aufnahme des Pleistozäns im Bergamasker Gebiet und in der östlichen Brianza. *GR*, 40.

VENZO (S.), 1953.—Stadi della glaciazione del 'Donau' sotto al Günz nella serie lacustre di Leffe. *Geol. Bavar.*, 19.

VENZO (S.), 1955.—Le attuali conoscenze sul Pleistocene Lombardo con particulare riguardo al Bergamasco. *Atti Soc. It. Sci. Nat.*, 94, II.

VERZILIN (N. N.), 1956.—On the Lithology of the interglacial deposits in the southern part of the Kola Peninsula. (Russian) *Vestn. Leningr. Univ. Ser. Geol.*, 11.

VIETE (G.), 1960.—Zur Entstehung der glazigene Lagerungsstörungen unter besonderer Berücksichtigung der Flözformationen im mitteldeutschen Raum. *Freibg. Forschungsh.*, C, 78.

VISHER (S. S.), 1945.—Climatic maps of geologic interest. *BGSA*, 56.

VLERK (I. M. VAN) and FLORSCHÜTZ (F.), 1953.—The palaeontological base of the subdivision of the Pleistocene in the Netherlands. *Verh. Kon. Ned. Akad. Wet., Afd. Nat.*, (1), XX, 2.

VOIGT (E.), 1934.—Die Fische aus der mitteleozänen Braunkohle des Geiseltals. *Nov. act. Leop. Halle*, 2.

VOIGT (E.), 1939.—Die jährliche Klimakurve des mitteldeutschen Eozäns. *ZDGG*, 91.

VORONOVA (M. L.), 1954.—Data on the petrography of salt-bearing successions in the Lower Cambrian, Siberia. (Russian) *Trudy Vses. nautsch.-issl. Inst. Gal.*, 29.

VZNUZDAEV (S. T.), 1953.—New data on the Sarmatian Reef limestones in Moldavia. (Russian) *Dokl.*, 90.

W

WAGNER (A.), 1940.—*Klimaänderungen und Klimaschwankungen.* Brunswick.

WAHRHAFTIG (C.) and COX (A.), 1959.—Rock glaciers in the Alaska Range. *BGSA*, 70.

WALTER (K.), 1931.—Über ein Vorkommen von geschrammter Landoberfläche aus dem Gondwanaglazial. *Cbl. Min. etc.*, B.

WALTHER (J.), 1894.—*Lithogenesis der Gegenwart.* Jena.

WALTHER (J.), 1924.—*Das Gesetz der Wüstenbildung.* 4th ed. Leipzig.

WANG (Y. L.), 1955.—The Sinian tillite and its stratigraphical significance. *Act. Geol. Sin.*, 35, 4.

WANLESS (H. R.), 1960.—Evidence of multiple late Paleozoic glaciation in Australia. *Int. Geol. Congr. 1960 Copenhagen, Rep.*, 12.

WANLESS (H. R.) and SHEPARD (F. P.), 1936.—Sea level and climatic changes related to late Paleozoic cycles. *BGSA*, 47.

WASHBURN (A. L.), 1956.—Classification of patterned ground and review of suggested origins. *BGSA*, 67.

WATERSCHOOT VAN DER GRACHT (W. A. I. M.), 1931.—The pre-Carboniferous exotic boulders in the so-called 'Caney-shale' in the north-western front of the Ouachita Mountains of Oklahoma. *JG*, 39 (cf. *BAAPG*, 20, 1936).

WEGENER (A.), 1936.—*Die Entstehung der Kontinente und Ozeane.* 5th ed. Brunswick.

WEGMANN (E.), 1951.—Subkambrische Tillite in der hercynischen Faltungszone. *GR*, 39.

WEILER (W.), 1942.—Die Otolithen des rheinischen und nordwestdeutschen Tertiärs. *Abh. R.A. Bodenf.*, 206.

WEISSE (J. G. DE), 1948.—Les bauxites de l'Europe centrale. *Thesis*, Lausanne.

WELLER (J. M.), 1957.—Paleoecology of the Pennsylvanian period in Illinois and adjacent states. *Mem. Geol. Soc. Amer.*, 67.

WELLS (A. J.), 1960.—Cyclic sedimentation: a review. *GM*, 97.

WELLS (J. W.), 1957.—Coral reefs. *Mem. Geol. Soc. Amer.*, 67.

WELTEN (M.), 1944.—Pollenanalytische, stratigraphische und geochronologische Untersuchungen aus dem Faulenseemoos bei Spiez. *Veröff. Geobot. Inst. Rübel*, 21.

WERTH (E.), 1925.—Die pflanzenführenden Diluvialablagerungen der thüringisch-sächsischen Bucht. *Ber. Deutsch. Bot. Ges.* 43.

WETZEL (W.), 1940.—Betrachtungen zur Sedimentpetrographie und Altersstellung der Visingsö-Formation. *Cbl. Min.* etc., B.

WEXLER (H.), 1953.—Radiation balance of the Earth as a factor in climatic change. In: *Climatic Change*, Ed. H. Shapley.

WEYL (R.), 1952.—Geologische Auswirkungen zweier Unwetterkatastrophen des Jahres 1951. *NJMh.*

WHEELER (H. E.) and MURRAY (H. H.), 1957.—Base level control patterns in cyclothemic sedimentation. *BAAPG*, 41.

WHITEHOUSE (F. W.), 1940.—Studies in the late geological history of Queensland. *Univ. Queenld., Pap., Dep. Geol.*, 2, 1.

WIEBOLS (J. H.), 1955.—A suggested glacial origin for the Witwatersrand conglomerates. *Trans. Geol. Soc. S. Afr.*, 58.

WIEDMANN (S.), 1923.—Was there Pennsylvanian-Permian glaciation in the Arbuckle and Wichita Mountains in Oklahoma? *JG*, 31.

WIELAND (G. R.), 1942.—Too hot for the dinosaur! *Sci.*, 96.

WILHELMY (H.), 1957.—Eiszeit und Eiszeitklima in den feuchttropischen Anden. In: *Geomorph. Studien* (Machatschek-Festschr.).

WILLARD (B.), 1935.—Devonian ice in Pennsylvania. *JG*, 43.

WILLER (A.) and SCHUBERT (C.), 1952.—Steinverfrachtung durch Meeresalgen. *Decheniana*, 105–106.

WILLETT (H. C.), 1951.—Extrapolation of sunspot-climate relationships. *J. Met.*, 8.

WILLETT (H. C.), 1953.—Atmospheric and oceanic circulation as factors in glacial-interglacial changes of climate. In: *Climatic Change*, Ed. H. Shapley.

WILSER (J.), 1931.—*Lichtreaktionen in der fossilen Tierwelt.* Berlin.

WINTERER (E. L.) and MURPHY (M. A.), 1960.—Silurian reef complex and associated facies, Central Nevada. *JG*, 68.

WISEMAN (J. D. H.), 1959.—The relation between paleotemperature and carbonate in an equatorial Atlantic pilot core. *JG*, 67.

WISSMANN (H. v.), 1938.—Über Lössbildung und Wurmeiszeit in China. *Geogr. Z.*, 44.

WISSMANN (H. v.), 1959.—Die heutige Vergletscherung und Schneegrenze in Hochasien. *Akad. Wiss. Lit. Mainz, Abh. Math.-nat. Kl.*, 14.

WOERKOM (A. J. J. v.), 1953.—The astronomical theory of climate change. In: *Climatic Change*, Ed. H. Shapley.

WOIKOFF (A.), 1895.—Geologische Klimate. *Perm. Geogr. Mitt.*, 41.

WOLBACH (J.), 1953.—The insufficiency of geographical causes of climatic change. In: *Climatic Change*, Ed. H. Shapley.

WOLDSTEDT (P.), 1954 and 1958.—*Das Eiszeitalter.* 2nd ed. Stuttgart, 1954 (Vol. 1), 1958 (Vol. 2).

WOLFE (P. E.), 1956.—Pleistocene-periglacial frost-thaw phenomena in New Jersey. *Trans. New York Acad. Sci.*, 2, 18.

WOODBURN (M. O.), 1959.—A fossil alligator from the lower Pliocene of Oklahoma and its climatic significance. *Mich. Acad. Sci.*, 44.

WOODRING (W. P.), 1957.—Marine Pleistocene of California. *Mem. Geol. Soc. Amer.*, 67.

WOODWORTH (J. B.), 1912.—Geological expedition to Brazil and Chile. *Bull. Mus. Comp. Zool. Camb.*, 56.

WORTMANN (H.), 1956.—Ein erstes sicheres Vorkommen von periglazialem Steinnetzboden im norddeutschen Flachland. *EuG*, 7.

WRIGHT (H. E., jr.), 1961.—Late Pleistocene climate in Europe—a review. *BGSA*, 72.

WRIGHT (W. B.), 1937.—*The Quaternary Ice Age.* 2nd ed. London.

WUNDT (W.), 1944.—Die Mitwirkung der Erdbahnelemente bei der Entstehung der Eiszeiten. *GR*, 34.

WUNDT (W.), 1955.—Pluvialzeiten und Feuchtzeiten. *Peterm. Geogr. Mitt.*

WUNDT (W.), 1958–59.—Die Pencksche Eiszeitgliederung und die Strahlungskurve. *Quartär*, 10–11.

Y

YABE (H.) and SUGIYAMA (T.), 1932.—Reef corals found in the Japanese seas. *Sci. Rep. Tohoku Imp. Univ.*, II (cf. J. Pal, 9, 1935).

YAKOVLEFF (N. N.), 1922.—Der Klimawechsel als Hauptfaktor der Veränderung der Organisemenwelt. *Nat. Wochenschr.*, 37.

YALKOVSKI (R.), 1957.—The relationship between paleotemperature and carbonate content in a deep-sea core. *JG*, 65.

YONGE (C. M.), 1951.—Die Gestalt der Korallenriffe. *Endeavour*. [In English also: The form of coral reefs. *Endeavour*, 10, p. 136.]

Z

ZABIROV (R. D.), 1955.—*Glaciation of the Pamirs.* (Russian) Moscow.

ZAGWIJN (W. H.), 1960.—Aspects of the Pliocene and early Pleistocene vegetation in the Netherlands. *Med. Geol. Sticht.*, C, III, 1, 5.

ZAHN (G. W. v.), 1929.—Wüstenrinden am Rande der Gletscher. *Chem. d. Erde*, 4.

ZAKLINSKAYA (E. D.), 1953.—Outline of the development of the Neozoic flora of the south of European Russia on the basis of spore and pollen analyses. (Russian) *Dokl.* (2), 89.

ZÁRUBA (Q.), 1943.—Periglaziale Erscheinungen in der Umgebung von Prag. *Mitt. Tschech. Akad. Wiss.*

ZÁRUBA (Q.), 1956.—Pleistocene outcrops in the sand pits at Lysolaje near Prague. *Anthropoz.*, 5 (1955).

ZEIL (W.), 1958.—Sedimentation in der Magallanes-Geosynklinale mit besonderer Berücksichtigung des Flysch. *GR*, 47.

ZEKKEL (J. D.), 1941.—Importance of reefs in the stratigraphy of the Kazuanian stage. (Russian) *C.R. Acad. Sci. USSR*, 32.

ZELLER (E. J.) and PEARN (W. C.), 1960.—Determination of past Antarctic climate by thermoluminescence of rocks. *Trans. Am. Geophys. Union*, 41.

ZEUNER (F. E.), 1932.—Die Nervatur der Blätter von Oeningen und ihre methodische Auswertung für das Klimaproblem. *Cbl. Min.* etc., B.

ZEUNER (F. E.), 1934.—Das Klima des Eisvorlandes in den Glazialzeiten. *NJBB*, 72, B.

ZEUNER (F. E.), 1934.—Die Beziehungen zwischen Schädelform und Lebinsweise bei den rezenten und fossilen Nashörnern. *Ber. Naturf. Ges. Freiburg*, 34.

ZEUNER (F. E.), 1959.—*The Pleistocene Period*. 2nd ed. London.

ZIEGLER (P. A.), 1959.—Frühpaläzoische Tillite im östlichen Yukon Territorium (Kanada). *Eclog. Geol. Helvet.*, 52.

TABLE FOR CONVERSION OF °FAHRENHEIT TO °CELSIUS (CENTIGRADE)

"Ich bin der Graf von Réaumur und hass euch wie
die Schande! Dient nur dem Celsio für und für, ihr
Apostatenbande!" Im Winkel König Fahrenheit hat
still sein Mus gegessen. "Ach Gott, sie war doch
schön, die Zeit, da man nach mir gemessen!"

CHRISTIAN MORGENSTERN

1°F = 0·56°C		1°C = 1·8°F	
Fahrenheit	**Celsius**	**Celsius**	**Fahrenheit**
−20	−28·9	−30	−22
−15	−26·1	−25	−13
−10	−23·3	−20	− 4
− 5	−20·6	−15	− 5
0	−17·8	−10	14
5	−15·0	− 5	23
10	−12·2	0	32
15	− 9·4	5	41
20	− 6·7	10	50
25	− 3·0	15	59
30	− 1·1	20	68
35	1·7	25	77
40	4·4	30	86
45	7·2	35	95
50	10·0	40	104
55	12·8		
60	15·6		
65	18·3		
70	21·1		
75	23·9		
80	26·7		
85	29·4		
90	32·2		
95	35·0		
100	37·8		

Author Index

*A photograph appears of authors whose names are marked ***

Place and Subject Index

Subjects in illustrations are marked *